D1457486

# METALLOGRAPHY – A PRACTICAL TOOL FOR CORRELATING THE STRUCTURE AND PROPERTIES OF MATERIALS

A symposium
presented at the
Seventy-sixth Annual Meeting
AMERICAN SOCIETY FOR
TESTING AND MATERIALS
Philadelphia, Pa., 25-26 June 1973

ASTM SPECIAL TECHNICAL PUBLICATION 557
Halle Abrams and G. N. Maniar, symposium cochairmen

List price $24.25

04-557000-28

 AMERICAN SOCIETY FOR TESTING AND MATERIALS
1916 Race Street, Philadelphia, Pa. 19103

NOTE

The Society is not responsible, as a body,
for the statements and opinions
advanced in this publication.

Printed in Tallahassee, Fla.
July 1974

# Foreword

The symposium on Metallography—A Practical Tool for Correlating the Structure and Properties of Materials, was given at the Seventy-sixth Annual Meeting of the American Society for Testing and Materials held in Philadelphia, Pa., 25-26 June 1973. Committee E-4 on Metallography sponsored the symposium. Halle Abrams, Bethlehem Steel Corporation, and G. N. Maniar, Carpenter Technology Corporation, presided as symposium cochairmen.

# Related
# ASTM Publications

Electron Beam Microanalysis, STP 506 (1972),
$3.75 (04-506000-28)

Stereology and Quantitative Metallography,
STP 504 (1972), $9.75 (04-504000-28)

Manual on Electron Metallography, STP 547 (1973),
$5.25 (04-547000-28)

# Contents

# Introduction

In the last several years the characterization of materials by metallographic techniques has been paralleled by a remarkable improvement in material capabilities. The ability to measure and characterize those material parameters that provide improved mechanical and physical properties has led directly to the development of new and better materials. Well known metallographic techniques such as hot-stage microscopy, transmission electron microscopy (TEM), and X-ray analysis, as well as the more recent techniques of scanning electron microscopy (SEM) and automatic quantitative metallography have provided the means to measure, characterize, statistically interpret, and, finally, predict the properties of materials.

The successful correlation of the structure and properties of materials, whether on a theoretical or empirical level, has been one of the primary forces in the current materials revolution. Accordingly, the objective of this symposium was to present both review and original papers that demonstrated, on a practical level, the application of an expanded range of metallographic techniques to the measurement, characterization, statistical interpretation, and prediction of the behavior of materials.

The papers presented have been prepared by authorities in their fields and include almost all phases of modern metallographic techniques. The opening session dealt with electron optical metallography covering the areas of electron microprobe analysis, SEM, and high voltage and conventional electron metallography. The second session covered hot-stage microscopy, microhardness techniques, and the new laser techniques of evaluating metallographic structures. The final session included a complete review of the techniques and applications of X-ray metallography and two application papers in the field of superalloys.

This special technical publication includes all the papers presented at the symposium, with the exception of the SEM and microhardness papers, which are not included due to publication deadlines.

Professor Weissman's paper is an excellent and concise summary of the X-ray metallographic techniques that he and his colleagues have developed to a high degree of sophistication over the past several years. In his paper, he describes various applications where combination X-ray methods are used to correlate lattice defects with structure-sensitive properties. In particular, his description of the use of X-ray Pendellösung fringes to analyze the distribution of microplastic and elastic strains in crack propagation would be of special interest to researchers working with low dislocation-density materials. In contrast to the more specialized techniques discussed by Weissman, Zwell's paper deals with practical applications of the more common X-ray metallographic techniques such as phase identification, residual-stress analysis, and texture determinations. The author demonstrates the usefulness of these techniques in failure analysis as well as in the development of new alloys.

In their paper, Bramfitt *et al.,* summarize the experimental techniques used in hot-stage light microscopy and the application of these techniques to the study of ferrous transformations. The paper provides a description of all the transformations occurring in low-alloy steels and includes an excellent bibliography. Of particular merit is the authors' work on the austenite to pearlite transformation emphasizing the advantage of *in situ* measurements on a single specimen to determine pearlite-nodule growth rates and transformation kinetics. Another innovative technique in light microscopy is described by Schaefer *et al.* Their paper discusses the basic concepts involved in the analysis of metallographic structures using optical transforms, holography, and other coherent-light methods. For the materials scientists, the most useful applications of holography employ interferometry to study transient events that occur at unpredictable locations, for example, the solidification of transparent analogs of metals.

The following three papers relate to the use of electron optics for characterizing and correlating the structure and properties of materials. In his paper, Professor Goldstein discusses the resolution and types of information that can be obtained from the various X-ray, secondary electron, and backscattered electron signals measured in the electron microprobe. The paper demonstrates the versatility of the microprobe as a metallurgical tool in the characterization of phases, diffusion studies, trace-element analysis, and quantitative metallography. The paper also contains an up-to-date and extensive bibliography. The review paper by Wells and Capenos describes applications of TEM in materials research. In covering selective papers from the literature, the authors provide several practical examples of the role of TEM in the study and understanding of materials system. The scope of applications of electron metallography has been expanded considerably with the advent of high-voltage instruments capable of operating at 1 MeV or more. In the area of high voltage electron metallography, the contributions of Szirmae and Fisher are well known, and their present paper presents a broad review of their work and a look toward the future of high voltage electron metallography (HVEM).

The paper by Muzyka and Maniar demonstrates the application of various metallography methods in optimizing properties of superalloys on the basis of a microstructural approach. The authors illustrate the value of microstructural studies in conjunction with phase relationships in improving hot working, heat-treat response, and the property optimization of iron and iron-nickel base superalloys. The contribution of analytical chemistry in support of microstructure studies is exemplified by Kriege's paper on phase separation as a technique for the characterization of superalloys. Although the paper deals with superalloys, the technique is equally applicable to other material systems.

These introductory comments on the papers contained in this volume illustrate the significant role that metallography plays in the development and characterization of materials. It was our objective in organizing this symposium to show, through both original studies and state-of-the-art reviews, how the metallographic disciplines within the scope of Committee E-4 on Metallography validate the premise that metallography is a practical tool for correlating the structure and properties of materials. We hope that this publication has contributed to the achievement of our objective. The American Society for Testing and Materials (ASTM) and the program chairmen wish to thank the authors for their excellent contributions to the symposium and this volume.

*Halle Abrams*

Homer Research Laboratories,
Bethlehem Steel Corp.,
Bethlehem, Pa. 18015; symposium
cochairman.

*Gunvant N. Maniar*

Manager, Research and
Development Center,
Carpenter Technology Corp.,
Reading, Pa. 19603; symposium
cochairman.

*Sigmund Weissmann*[1]

# Structure-Sensitive Properties of Materials Disclosed by a Combination of X-Ray Topography, X-Ray Diffraction Analysis, and Electron Microscopy Methods

**REFERENCE:** Weissmann, Sigmund, "Structure-Sensitive Properties of Materials Disclosed by a Combination of X-Ray Topography, X-Ray Diffraction Analysis, and Electron Microscopy Methods," *Metallography—A Practical Tool for Correlating the Structure and Properties of Materials, ASTM STP 557,* American Society for Testing and Materials, 1974, pp. 4–22.

**ABSTRACT:** To establish a significant correlation between lattice defects and structure-sensitive properties it is frequently desirable to combine various methods of structural analysis which provide supplementary information and have a synergistic effect on the course of study. Such combination methods have been developed in this laboratory. They comprise: (*a*) selected area X-ray topography, (*b*) X-ray line profile analysis, (*c*) anomalous X-ray transmission topography, (*d*) X-ray double-crystal diffractometry, (*e*) analysis of plastic and elastic strain distribution by disturbance of X-ray pendellösung fringes (PF), (*f*) transmission electron microscopy (TEM) of dislocation structure in selected areas of the specimen, and (*g*) scanning electron microscopy (SEM) of the specimen. Examples of the application of these combination methods are presented that include the tensile and compressive deformation of beryllium crystals, the deformation and fracture of germanium and silicon crystals, and the elucidation of the distribution of microplastic and elastic strains in crack propagation.

**KEY WORDS:** X-ray analysis, transmission, scanning, electron microscopy, deformation, fractures (materials), germanium, silicon, beryllium, plastic deformation, elastic properties

Many important properties of materials are structure-sensitive, and often a relatively small number of lattice defects have a disproportionately large effect on the properties. Of particular interest from scientific and technological viewpoints alike are the mechanical properties. To establish a significant correlation between lattice defects and mechanical properties it is frequently desirable to combine various methods of structural analysis which provide supplementary information and have a synergistic effect on the course of study. Such combination methods have been developed in the author's laboratory over a span of nearly two decades in response to challenging problems in materials science. Although some component parts of structural analysis have been treated individually in previous publications, an attempt will be made in this paper, spurred by new developments, to synthesize them all into powerful combination methods. Particular emphasis will be placed on these new developments and on the synergistic interplay of the component techniques. Exam-

---

[1] Professor, Materials Research Laboratory, College of Engineering, Rutgers University, New Brunswick, N.J. 08903.

ples will be presented which are relevant to problems of deformation and fracture of materials and which may serve to demonstrate the general usefulness of these methods. Since the principal aim of this paper is to show how the component techniques of the combination methods complement each other and to demonstrate what overall results one may expect, the reader will be frequently referred to previous publications for detailed technical information.

## Combination Method Based on X-Ray Divergent Beam Techniques

About two decades ago the study of lattice defects of single crystals was virtually confined to academic investigations only, but, starting with the development of transistor materials and spurred in recent years by the increased interest in ferroelectric, piezoelectric, and magnetic device materials, such studies have become also increasingly important to applied technology.

The X-ray diffraction method using a divergent beam as the X-ray source is well suited to provide the basis for a quantitative strain analysis of single crystals [1][2] and to offer a visualization of the defect structure by X-ray topography and by transmission electron microscopy (TEM).

The divergent beam method utilizes a long, horizontal X-ray tube, shown schematically in Fig. 1. An electron beam originating from an electron gun is

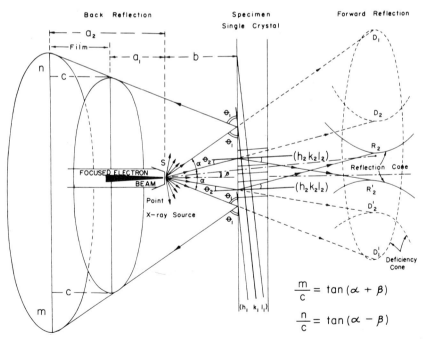

$$\frac{m}{c} = \tan(\alpha + \beta)$$

$$\frac{n}{c} = \tan(\alpha - \beta)$$

FIG. 1—*Schematic representation of the generation of pseudo-Kossel pattern by the divergent beam method.*

[2] The italic numbers in brackets refer to the list of references appended to this paper.

focused by means of an electromagnetic lens onto the tip of the vacuum-tight tube closed by a thin metal foil. Since the metal foil is bombarded by the electron beam, it functions as an X-ray target. By operating the tube at a suitable voltage, an X-ray beam composed mainly of characteristic radiation emerges from the tip of the tube, exhibiting a divergence of nearly 180 deg of arc. At the point of emergence the beam size is about 10 $\mu$m in diameter. When this beam impinges on the specimen, which is placed close to the tip of the tube, diffraction patterns of the characteristic spectrum in transmission, as well as in back reflection, may be recorded (Fig. 1). Since the X-ray source is located outside of the specimen, the conic patterns thus obtained are referred to frequently as pseudo-Kossel patterns to distinguish them from the true Kossel patterns, which are obtained by generating the X-ray source inside the crystal.

The method offers the unique advantage that various ($hkl$) planes, even sets of planes of a form, which satisfy the Bragg condition for reflection of the impinging divergent beam, will be recorded as separate reflections without the necessity of rotating the crystal. As shown in Fig. 1, the diffraction cones intersect the film in ellipse-like figures in the back-reflection region, while in transmission two types of patterns are obtained, namely, the diffraction conic and the deficiency conic patterns. Both types of the transmission pattern emanate from the same irradiated small crystal volume transversed by the beam.

It is the combined application of the back-reflection and transmission arrangement in the divergent beam method which jointly with TEM forms the basis of the first combination method of structural analysis to be discussed presently.

### Contribution of the Back-Reflection Patterns to Precision Measurements of Interplanar Spacings [2]

The back-reflection pseudo-Kossel pattern forms the principal basis for precision measurements of the interplanar spacings of the crystal. Since the exposure times of the back-reflection pattern are very short, varying from seconds to a few minutes depending on the diffracting power of the material, the elliptical pattern can be repeated several times by varying, with the aid of precision spacers, the film positions in a controlled manner. It will be seen from Fig. 1 that if the consecutive film position is $c$, the slopes $m_1$ and $m_2$ can be determined from the relationship

$$m_1 = \overline{m}/c = \tan(\alpha + \beta) \tag{1}$$

$$m_2 = \overline{n}/c = \tan(\alpha - \beta) \tag{2}$$

where $\alpha$ is the semiapex angle of the incident X-ray cone equal to $\pi/2 - \theta$, $\theta$ being the Bragg angle, and $\beta$ is the angle subtended by the normal of the reflecting ($hkl$) plane and the axis of the X-ray tube.

Using a multiple exposure technique such as that shown in Fig. 2, the slope parameters $m_1$ and $m_2$ of the diffracted rays are obtained by a method of

FIG. 2–*Multiple exposure back-reflection divergent beam photograph of beryllium-oxygen. (Courtesy of Dr. D.K. Smith, Pennsylvania State University.)*

least squares. The simultaneous solution of Eqs 1 and 2 yields $\alpha$ and hence the corresponding Bragg angle $\theta$. Subsequent substitution in the Bragg equation yields the corresponding $d$ value of the interplanar spacing. A computer program was written to expedite the repeated computation of $d$ spacings. The input to this program was: film coordinates $Y_i$, which are the intersections of the major axis with the ellipse, such as points $P$ and $R$ in Fig. 1; spacing coordinates $X_i$, which represent the distance of the film from a fixed origin $O$; film shrinkage factor and wavelength used. The output was: $d$ spacings and their corresponding standard errors [2].

## Computation of Stress-Strain Configuration of Strained Crystal; Applications and Limitations

The output of $d$-spacing computations of the various ($hkl$) reflections may now be used for the computation of a complete stress-strain analysis of the crystal [1,3]. If the crystal contains homogeneous, residual strains, then the changes in the interatomic spacings $\Delta d_{hkl}$ induced by the strains are manifested sensitively by changes in the parameters of the ellipses and hence in the observed $d$ spacings. If the strained crystal is sampled from many different directions, a collection of $\Delta d/d$ values is obtained which characterizes the strain distribution. The strain analysis which was developed recognizes the $\Delta d/d$ values to represent elements of an average strain tensor and by measuring more than six independent $(hkl)$ reflections the normal matrix equation is constructed and the average tensor $<T>$ determined. The principal strains $\epsilon_{111}$, $\epsilon_{222}$, $\epsilon_{333}$ are obtained as the eigen values of the matrix solution. A computer program was written which uses as its input data the collection of $\Delta d/d$ values, and supplies as output data the normal principal strains $\epsilon_{111}$, $\epsilon_{222}$, $\epsilon_{333}$ and their crystallographic directions [1]. If the elastic constants of the crystal are known, the complete stress-strain configuration is obtained [3,4]. Thus, the maximum magnitude and the direction of the shearing strain on a given set of crystallographic planes are obtained, and the set of crystallographic planes on which the maximum value of the shearing maxima occurs can also be determined.

The stress-strain analysis based on the back-reflection divergent beam method has been successfully performed for cases where the strain inhomogeneities in the crystal were very small compared to the residual, homogeneous elastic strains. Examples can be found in:

($a$) strain configuration of precipitation-hardened aluminum-copper crystals where the Guinier-Preston zones of the semicoherent $\theta\,'$ precipitates exert large, overall homogeneous strains in the matrix [1],

($b$) strains induced in the cubic matrix of copper-gold crystals by order transformation to tetragonal copper-gold I [3],

($c$) strains induced in oxidized $\alpha$-titanium crystals by the ordering of oxygen atoms [6], and

($d$) strain distribution generated during the early stages of neutron-irradiated quartz crystals [5].

It has been shown that the stress-strain analysis is not applicable to mechanically deformed crystals because the plastic strain inhomogeneities, caused by the induced dislocation structure, are large and vary from area to area [7]. Consequently, a representative sampling of the strain distribution cannot be obtained if the $\Delta d/d$ values are being gathered from the back-reflection divergent beam pattern. Local strain inhomogeneities caused by mechanical deformation can be determined, however, with the aid of divergent beam patterns taken in transmission and the basis of such analysis will be presently described.

**X-Ray Line Profile Analysis. Selected Area X-Ray Topography Based on Transmission Patterns [8-11]**

It may be seen with the aid of Fig. 1 that in transmission the reflection cones (also referred to as diffraction cones), as well as the deficiency cones, emanate from the same irradiated small crystal volume. If the crystal is thick and of low absorption, namely, beryllium, the diffraction conics will have a large width, as shown in Fig. 3, since each point along the path of the

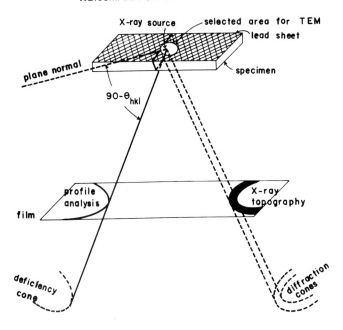

FIG. 3–*Schematic diagram illustrating the origin of deficiency and diffraction conics from the selected area of the specimen.*

incident beam passing through the crystal functions as a vertex of a diffraction cone. Strain inhomogeneities caused by dislocations will be spread out over the diffraction conics and, therefore, it is the diffraction conics which are being used to obtain X-ray topographs. In contrast to the diffraction conics, the deficiency conics are sharp, since the vertex of the absorption cone is the X-ray point source. Consequently, the sharp lines of the deficiency conics are being used for the analysis of the X-ray line profiles.

Before imaging the defect structure by X-ray topography, the divergent incident beam has to be transformed into a nearly parallel beam. This is accomplished by translating the specimen away from the X-ray source. The translation must be performed along the region of interest in the deficiency pattern, for only then are the identical diffraction conditions maintained. The technique of specimen translation, using a wire grid to preserve the area of interest and employing an aperture to convert the divergent beam into a parallel beam, has been described in detail [8]. Regions of special interest for analysis of the deficiency pattern are the intersections of several (hkl) lines. Such intersections pertain to a conic section which is common to the corresponding intersecting (hkl) planes. If the crystal is subjected to deformation, the line profiles will be sensitively changed. Microdensitometric measurements of the profiles carried out in the immediate vicinity of the intersection of the deficiency pattern may yield valuable information concerning the anisotropic deformation behavior of the crystal. Such information was obtained from compressive and tensile deformation of beryllium [9,10]. The corresponding topographs are obtained from the imaging of the intersection in the diffraction pattern and constitute the basis of selected area X-ray topography. Such topography affords a visualization of the defect structure of the crystal area pertaining to the corresponding line profile analysis.

To establish a correlation between the defect structure analyzed by the X-ray method and that disclosed by TEM, a thin lead sheet with a hole 1 mm in diameter is attached to the entrance surface of the specimen, as shown in Fig. 3. TEM foils are prepared after the completion of the X-ray selected area studies by cutting a 2.5-mm disk centered around the hole [10].

The X-ray transmission method applied to the study of compressive deformation of beryllium crystals showed that inhomogeneous lattice rotation and basal plane bending resulted from the interaction of basal slip dislocations with columnar subgrain boundaries, a development that leads to bend plane splitting [12]. Correlation to TEM studies showed that the formation of cell walls and subgrain boundaries resulted from the interaction of slip dislocations with ingrown dislocations lying on the basal plane [8].

## Lattice Distortions and Fracture in Brittle Crystals Disclosed by Anomalous Transmission of X-Rays (Borrmann Effect)

When brittle crystals are subjected to mechanical deformation they form microplastic regions which confine large regions of locked-in elastic strains. These strains find ultimate relief either in brittle fracture, as recent deformation studies of silicon have shown [13], or they may develop microcracks, as in low-temperature deformation of tungsten and germanium crystals [14]. Such highly localized lattice defects can be disclosed sensitively by applying the technique of anomalous transmission (AT) of X-rays (Borrmann effect), which is based on the dynamical interaction of X-rays inside of nearly perfect crystals [15-17]. The observation of AT is indicative of a high degree of lattice perfection (dislocation density $< 10^5$ cm$^{-2}$). If any atoms are displaced from their normal nodes, for example, as a result of the strain field of a dislocation, discontinuities of the anomalously intense lines will be observed on the film. The critical conditions for AT are being destroyed and normal absorption has set in.

Using the experimental arrangement schematically shown in Fig. 4, the X-ray divergent beam method can be effectively employed for the study of lattice defects in thick, elastically strained crystals. It offers the advantage that it never "loses sight" of the elastically strained lattice planes, for if the Bragg angles are slightly changed, some rays of the divergent beam will still be in reflecting position and an AT pattern will still be recorded. Furthermore, compared to the parallel beam method, the exposure times for obtaining AT patterns are five to ten times shorter. Figure 5 shows an AT pattern of a germanium crystal with the specimen kept stationary. If now the synchronized specimen and film translation is employed as shown in Fig. 4, one obtains a topographic mapping of the lattice perfection of the crystal. Thus, if adjacent

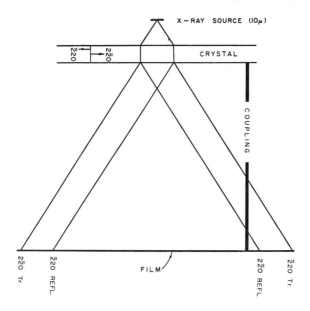

FIG. 4—*Experimental arrangement for obtaining AT patterns by the divergent beam method.*

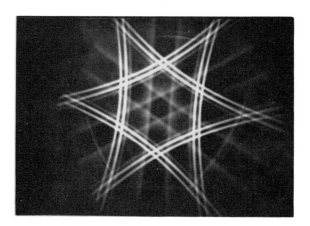

FIG. 5—*AT divergent beam pattern of unstrained germanium.*

areas exhibit such a high degree of lattice perfection that AT patterns can be obtained, the pattern of Fig. 5 will continuously broaden, as the specimen surface is traversed by the beam, and an AT pattern such as that shown in Fig. 6a is obtained. When the crystal, placed between the knife edges of the bending fixture, as shown in Fig. 8, was elastically bent short of fracture, the AT pattern shown in Fig. 6b was changed significantly. In agreement with the

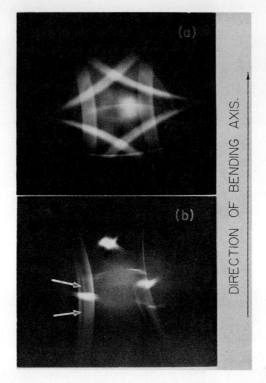

FIG. 6−*AT of germanium, scanned area 5.5 × 1.75 mm²; (a) undeformed, (b) bent, ε = 0.5 percent. Note nonreflecting area.*

theory of Penning and Polder [*18*], the reflections pertaining to the crystallographic planes, either parallel or perpendicular to the direction of the bending axis (DBA), remained unaltered in extent and intensity, while those pertaining to planes inclined at oblique angles to the DBA were considerably shortened. Focusing our attention now on the unaltered reflections parallel to DBA, it will be observed that certain areas in Fig. 6*b* indicated by arrows exhibited an absence of AT when the crystal was scanned. However, upon releasing the bending moment, the diffraction pattern assumed its original appearance of equal-sized segments and intensity as displayed in Fig. 6*a*.

The nonreflecting areas of Fig. 6*b*, indicating localized lattice defects in the crystal, could not be caused by the generation of glissile dislocations, since these constitute irreversible plastic sites and the observed effect was shown to be perfectly reversible. To elucidate the nature of the defect structure responsible for the absence of AT on bending, the crystal was first translated to the position where the nonreflecting areas were observed and subsequently, the incident divergent beam was transformed into a parallel beam by increasing the distance between specimen and X-ray source and by placing a slit aperture in front of the specimen. Thus Fig. 7 was obtained.

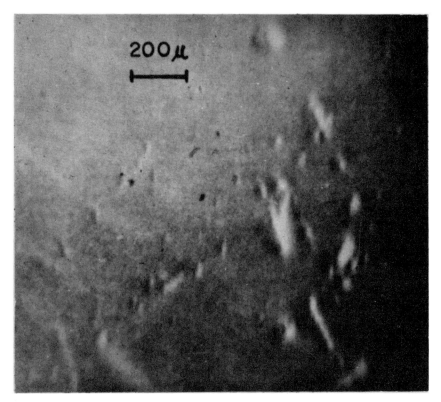

FIG. 7—*AT pattern of germanium by parallel beam method disclosing microcracks. Crystal bent, $\epsilon = 0.5$ percent.*

The beam conversion technique employed is quite analogous to that previously discussed, when the topographic information had to be extracted from the diffraction conics of the pseudo-Kossel pattern. In the latter case, however, the imaging of the defect structure was accomplished by employing the parallel beam transmission technique with normal absorption (Lang topography [19]), while in the former case the imaging was obtained by parallel beam AT. It is interesting to note that with copper $K_\alpha$ radiation and a specimen thickness of 1 mm the exposure time took 20 h for the parallel beam technique, while the preceding AT scan obtained by the divergent beam technique (Fig. 6) required only 2 h. Thus, the divergent beam scan functioned as an efficient surveyor of the defect structure which, once its location was established, could be subsequently imaged by converting the incident divergent beam to a parallel beam.

The imaged defect structure shown in Fig. 7 could be identified as microcracks which upon bending of the crystal expanded, and which, together with their concomitant elastic strain field, destroyed the AT locally. After removal of the bending moment the microcracks contracted again, relaxing the elastic strains and restoring the AT pattern. Following Cottrell [20], one may visualize the elastic microcrack as an elliptically shaped discontinuity in a homogeneous elastic solid, equivalent to a continuous array of dislocations [20], which under the influence of a suitable external force can be made to expand, and on removal of this force to contract.

## Instrumentation of X-Ray Divergent Beam Combination Method

Since the various aspects of the X-ray divergent beam method have been discussed for the transmission and back-reflection applications, and since it was shown that they work synergistically when used in combination, it may be useful to discuss the instrumentation which enables one to apply this combination method in practice. Figure 8a offers a front-side view of the instrumentation employed, and with the back-reflection film holder removed, represents essentially all the experimental features necessary for the various transmission techniques. Figure 8b offers a back view of the instrumentation and, with the back-reflection holder 1 in place, depicts the experimental

(1) Back-reflection film holder, (2) transmission film holder, (3) specimen holder with bending device, (4) divergent beam source, (5) vertical scan mechanism, (6) horizontal scan mechanism, (7) scan control, (8) electron gun housing, (9) electromagnetic lens, (10) X-ray tube, (11) optical bench with precision scale.

FIG. 8–*Experimental arrangement of combination method based on divergent beam techniques. (a) Transmission, and (b) transmission and back reflection.*

FIG. 8—(*Continued.*)

arrangement for the combined transmission and back-reflection divergent beam method. The sleeve design of the film holder *1* permits removal of the film holder from the horizontal X-ray tube *10* without any disturbance to the location of the specimen under investigation. Thus, back-reflection and transmission patterns can be obtained simultaneously. Various specimen holders and deformation devices were designed for different types of deformation, for example, tensile, compression, and bending devices, and a device of the latter type is shown as item *3* in Figs. 8*a* and 8*b*.

The electrons generated by the electron gun *8* held at high potential are being accelerated and focused by an electromagnetic lens *9* to the tip of the tube *4*. The tip, held at ground potential, contains the target foil which represents the source of the emergent, divergent X-ray beam. Tip and target may be replaced easily if a different characteristic radiation is required.[3]

The horizontal scan mechanism *5* and the vertical scan mechanism *6* provide for the coupled X-Y translation of specimen and film. Such translation motion is particularly useful if the sites of lattice defects are to be located by selected area topography, using either the normal or the AT technique. The optical bench with precision scale *11* is provided with precision spacers which facilitate the ray-tracing technique in back reflection. It will be recalled that upon this tracing technique rest the precision measurements of the lattice parameters and of the interatomic spacings, and hence, it represents an important experimental link to the stress-strain analysis of the crystal.

### Study of Fracture Mechanism in Crystals by a Combination Method Based on X-Ray Pendellösung Fringes, Double-Crystal Diffractometry, TEM, and SEM [13,22]

A useful combination method was recently developed which, applied to the study of fracture of crystals, is capable of detecting and assessing the microplastic regions and elastic stress fields generated by the crack tip [13]. The novel approach takes advantage of the disturbance of pendellösung fringes (PF) obtained by X-ray transmission topography of wedge-shaped crystals. This method is highly sensitive, since PF similar to AT are based on the dynamical interaction of the X-ray wave fields inside the crystal. Dynamical interaction occurs between the primary and secondary beams analogous to that which takes place between a pair of coupled pendulums whose frequencies are nearly equal. The two wave fields interact to give a beat effect, whereby the primary beam has all the energy at the surface, but at a certain depth this state of affairs is reversed, and the secondary beam has all the energy, and so the alternation goes on. The PF, therefore, can be obtained only from crystals of varying thickness, and it is for this reason that wedge-shaped crystals are being investigated.

The depth of the layer, called extinction distance, at which complete alternation takes place, is the greater the more nearly the velocities of the two waves approach. The extinction distance $\xi_g$ is measured along the normal to the X-ray entrance surface of the crystal.

The aspect of PF patterns most relevant to the fracture study is the fact that very small lattice disturbances have a profound effect on the dynamical interaction of the wave fields and, therefore, change drastically the PF pattern.

From the viewpoint of the materials scientist, the fracture study of silicon

---

[3] An X-ray tube of this type and a diffraction unit (Microflex) are commercially produced by the Rigaku-Denki Co., Tokyo, Japan.

crystals offers several attractive features. First of all, these crystals can be obtained nearly dislocation-free. Secondly, at elevated temperatures (650°C to 1000°C) silicon deforms plastically like a metal. It undergoes a ductile-brittle transition at lower temperature and is totally brittle at room temperature. Moreover, any lattice distortions introduced at elevated temperatures become frozen in at room temperature, so that the details of the defect structure which has been outlined by the preceding X-ray investigation can then be disclosed by TEM without fear that the defect structure was altered by the thinning process during specimen preparation. Lastly, it should be pointed up that $\xi_g$ is inversely proportional to the structure factor $F$ of the reflecting $(hkl)$ plane, and, via $F$, it is also inversely related to the atomic number $Z$ of the crystal. It is expected, therefore, that perfect wedge-shaped crystals of low $Z$ values, namely, silicon, will yield a well-resolved PF pattern.

Such crystal specimens into which a V-notch was introduced were prepared for tensile deformation. The crystal surface had a (211) orientation with the $[01\bar{1}]$ direction parallel to the tensile axis. Figure 9 shows a Lang projection topograph of a notched specimen deformed in tension at 800°C. The nominal stress, $\sigma_n$, was 1.6 kg mm$^{-2}$ and the strain rate $\dot{\epsilon}$ was 5.9 x 10$^{-5}$ s$^{-1}$ · $\sigma_n$ is defined by $F/A$, where $F$ is the applied load and $A$ the measured minimum cross-sectional area. This topograph was obtained by directing a finely collimated X-ray beam onto the crystal, which was placed approximately at right angles to the incoming beam so that the set of transverse (111) planes satisfied the conditions of Bragg reflections. The transmitted reflected beam was recorded on the film, while the transmitted primary beam was prevented by a stationary screen from striking the film. The crystal holder and film holder, being mechanically coupled, were moved to and fro during the exposure.

Figure 9 may serve to illustrate the type of information which can be

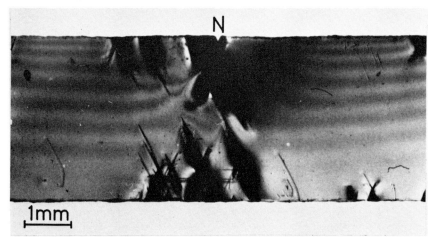

FIG. 9—*X-ray topograph of notched silicon crystal deformed in tension at 800°C, $\sigma_n$ = 1.6 kg mm$^{-2}$, $\dot{\epsilon}$ = 5.9 x 10$^{-5}$ s$^{-1}$.*

obtained from PF patterns in fracture studies. The regions of plastic zones, such as those associated with the notch $N$ or those generated from the specimen surface opposite to the notch, are characterized by the total destruction of the PF pattern. They appear as black or white (out of contrast) areas on the topograph. The regions of elastic strains are characterized by the bending of PF and by the systematic narrowing of the fringe spacing when the plastic zone is approached. Although the distortions of the PF patterns are quite reminiscent of the optical fringe contours encountered in photoelastic stress analysis of materials transparent to light, it must be remembered that the distortions of the PF pattern result from displacements on an atomic scale and depend only on the transparency of perfect crystals to X-rays.

To assess the dislocation density of the plastic zone quantitatively, the PF technique is supplemented by the method of double-crystal diffractometry. Thus, the primary beam is first reflected from a perfect silicon crystal and the monochromatized radiation is directed towards that area on the test crystal which is outlined by the destruction of the PF pattern. The reflecting power of the test crystal is measured by rotating ("rocking") the crystal through its angular range of reflection. The width $\beta$ at half maximum of the obtained rocking curve is a measure of the crystal perfection and can be related to the excess dislocation density of one sign $D$ by [21] $D = \beta/3bt$, where $b$ is the magnitude of the Burgers vector and $t$ the linear size parameter of the crystal area investigated. Thus, the PF technique functions as a "guiding eye" to locate the microplastic zone which is to be quantitatively evaluated by the double-crystal diffractometer method.

The sensitivity of detecting microplastic zones can be gaged from the fact that a lattice misalignment $\beta$ of 45 s of arc was sufficient to destroy the PF pattern which corresponds to a dislocation density of $\sim 10^5$ cm$^{-2}$. The dislocation structure of the microplastic zone itself can be disclosed by TEM, and Fig. 10 shows such a zone in proximity to the crack tip. Thus, one arrives again at a combination method in which each component part, namely, PF technique, double-crystal diffractometry, and TEM, fulfills a synergistic function.

Using this combination method, the zones of plastic deformation and elastic strains in notched silicon crystals were mapped out as a function of applied stress and deformation temperature [22]. It could be shown that at the low deformation temperature of 600°C silicon fractured in a brittle manner. Fracture was initiated by a small plastic zone at the crack tip, sensitively disclosed by the destruction of PF in the vicinity of the tip, and the crack propagated along one of the (111) planes without any lateral formation of a plastic zone. At more elevated deformation temperatures, namely, 700°C, other microplastic zones were generated besides those associated with the notch root. These microplastic zones, similar to those shown in Fig. 9, were strain-hardened zones which constrained regions of residual elastic strains. The formation of these strain-hardened microplastic zones and the associated regions of locked-in elastic strains explain the occurrence of the notch-brittle

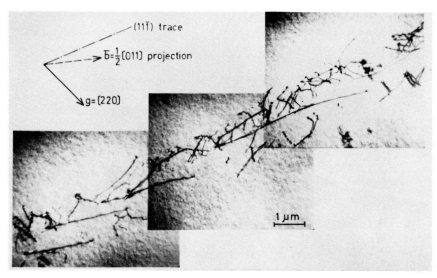

FIG. 10—*Electron micrograph of dislocation structure in silicon near crack tip.*

transition observed around 650°C. It was observed that for unnotched specimens, the fracture stress at 600°C was 15 kg mm$^{-2}$ and the yield stress at 700°C was 8 kg mm$^{-2}$. Such a decline in stress level with increasing deformation temperature is, of course, expected. For notched specimens, however, this trend was reversed. The fracture stress at 600°C was ∼ 3 kg mm$^{-2}$, while the yield stress at 700°C was virtually identical with that of the unnotched specimen. At the low deformation temperature of 600°C the microplastic zones other than the minute one associated with the notch root were absent, and all the elastic strain energy found catastrophic release at a critical stress level, resulting in cleavage fracture. At the elevated deformation temperature of 700°C the strain-hardened microplastic zones, which were generated principally at the specimen surface, formed effective boundaries of pockets into which residual elastic strains were locked (Fig. 9). Consequently, both the yield and fracture stresses increased considerably. At still higher deformation temperatures, both the yield and fracture stresses declined because the dislocations in the plastic zones could rearrange themselves into a configuration of lower energy by cross-slip and climb, and thereby decrease the efficiency of the barrier effect in confining residual elastic strains [22]. The efficiency of the plastic zones in constraining regions of locked-in, residual elastic strains, and the mechanism by which the elastic strains relaxed, were studied by controlled annealing experiments following the tensile deformation. It could be shown by X-ray topography that the relaxation of the locked-in elastic strains occurred through the formation of dislocation loops at the boundaries of the plastic regions. These loops interacted so as to form a relaxed three-dimensional dislocation configuration, with the sum of the Burgers vector tending toward zero (hexagonal network). Thus, relaxation of the residual elastic strains occurred by spreading of microplastic zones.

The formation of microplastic regions and the concomitant onset of ductility in notched silicon crystals at 650°C, revealed by the destruction of PF, could be also correlated to interesting results obtained by scanning electron microscopy (SEM). Examination of the fracture surface by SEM disclosed at this deformation temperature the appearance of the first cleavage steps, an indication that dislocations had been intersected and, consequently, that microplastic regions were formed [22].

The results obtained by applying the combination method to the study of silicon crystals underlined generally the importance of microplasticity in deformation processes. In particular they emphasized the impact of microplasticity on the fracture mechanism, for it could be shown [22] that the extent of the plastic region associated with the crack tip was invariably 10 to 15 times larger than that predicted on the basis of approximations used in continuum mechanics.

### Discussion—Interplay of Component Techniques in Combination Methods

In correlating the visualization of lattice defects, as disclosed by X-ray topography, to quantitative X-ray diffraction analyses of materials such as the stress-strain, line profile, and rocking curve analyses, one may well have achieved a research goal that can give one added confidence in interpreting the behavior of structure-sensitive properties. Nevertheless, it is important to realize that in transversing the material X-rays average out details of the defect structure, and hence, X-ray topography is capable of disclosing only relatively gross features of the defect structure. These may include subgrain formation, slip and deformation bands—in short, long-range cooperative phenomena of dislocation interaction. Individual dislocations can be disclosed only when the dislocation density is very low and even in the most favorable cases this would restrict the observation to only the initial stages of deformation of a material. TEM, on the other hand, is capable of revealing details of the defect structure such as the individual dislocations and dislocation networks shown in Fig. 10. Such resolution exceeds the resolving power of X-ray topography by many orders of magnitude. The principal disadvantage of TEM, however, lies in the fact that only small specimen areas of about $10\mu^2$ or in some cases $100\mu^2$ can be studied. Because of this limited restriction of the field of view, it is frequently difficult for TEM to discern the essential features and parameters that determine and govern the structure-sensitive properties of the material. The TEM method "sees frequently too much," and to be most effective it requires another research tool for guidance. In the combination methods of structural analysis described in this paper such guidance is provided by X-ray topography. X-ray topography, however, should be employed not only for quick and effective location of a defect structure, but principally for locating and discerning structural features of importance to the process under study. For example, in the deformation study of beryllium [8-10], X-ray topography was employed on the intersection of the deficiency conics pertaining to the basal, prismatic, and pyramidal planes of beryllium. Consequently, the anisotropic deformation behavior of a small, selected, irradiated crystal volume could be analyzed by studying the deformation (compression and tension) response of the different (*hkl*) planes. Subsequently, the complementary TEM study was able to focus attention on the mechanism of dislocation interaction which was responsible for the formation of the cell structure observed by X-ray topography and was able to disclose the development of the cell structure leading up to fracture [*10*].

Another example may serve to illustrate the synergistic interplay of the component techniques to make the application of the combination method most effective. In the fracture study of silicon [*13,22*], the PF topography was capable of distinguishing zones of elastic residual strains from those containing plastic deformation. The latter were analyzed by double-crystal diffractometry and the details of the dislocation configuration, particularly in the vicinity of the notch root, were revealed subsequently by TEM.

Corroborative evidence that microplastic zones were formed in notched silicon at the ductile-brittle transition temperature of about 650°C was obtained from the observations of fine cleavage steps on the fracture surface disclosed by SEM. It appears quite safe to predict that SEM, with its recent extension of X-ray analysis by energy dispersion, will play an increasingly important role in the future developments of the combination methods.

The greatest sensitivity in locating lattice defects by X-ray topography is achieved when the topographic method is based on phase contrast rather than on reflectivity contrast. Topography based on phase contrast, such as AT contrast (Figs. 6 and 7), or PF contrast (Fig. 9), requires crystals of very low dislocation density. There is ample evidence, however, that besides the transistor type of crystals there exists a host of other crystals of technological importance, namely, crystals used in laser operation, which might be suitable candidates for such study.

## Conclusions

Combination methods of structural analysis were developed which make it possible to correlate the visualization of lattice defects, disclosed by X-ray topography and TEM, to quantitative X-ray diffraction analysis of structure-sensitive properties of materials. Depending on the information desired, the quantitative diffraction analysis may consist of:

(*a*) line profile analysis, such as was performed in the analysis of deficiency conics of divergent beam patterns of beryllium,

(*b*) rocking curve analysis, as was carried out in the analysis of microplastic regions in fracture studies of silicon, and

(*c*) stress-strain analyses based on strain measurements of back-reflection divergent beam patterns. These were applied to precipitation-hardened and ordered alloys and to neutron-irradiated materials.

It was shown that the topographic disclosure of lattice defects was most effective when the techniques of X-ray topography and TEM were so employed as to complement each other. Owing to its larger field of view, X-ray topography was capable of locating the important, gross topographical features, the details of which were studied subsequently by TEM. It was shown that certain isolated lattice defects, such as microcracks, microplastic regions, or zones containing residual elastic strains, were most effectively revealed when X-ray topographic methods were employed which are based on phase contrast. Thus, the lattice defects were disclosed by the disturbance of AT or PF. SEM of fracture surfaces played an important part in assessing the early formation of microplastic regions.

## Acknowledgment

The partial support of this work by the Rutgers Research Council is gratefully acknowledged.

## References

[1]   Imura, T., Weissmann, S., and Slade, J.J., *Acta Crystallographica*, Vol. 15, No. 8, Aug. 1962, pp. 786-793.

[2]   Ellis, T., Nanni, L.F., Shrier, A., Weissmann, S., Padawer, G.E., and Hosakawa, N., *Journal of Applied Physics*, Vol. 35, No. 11, Nov. 1964, pp. 3364-3373.

[3]   Slade, J.J., Weissmann, S., Nakajima, K., and Hirabayashi, M., *Journal of Applied Physics*, Vol. 35, No. 11, Nov. 1964, pp. 3373-3385.

[4]   Nakajima, K., Slade, J.J., and Weissmann, S., *Transactions Quarterly*, American Society for Metals, Vol. 58, No. 1, March 1965, pp. 14-29.

[5]   Weissmann, S., Imura, T., Nakajima, K., and Wisnewski, S.E., *Journal of the Physical Society of Japan*, Vol. 18, Supplement III, March 1963, pp. 179-188.

[6]   Weissmann, S. and Shrier, A. in *The Science, Technology and Application of Titanium*, R. Jaffee and N. Promisel, Eds., Pergamon Press, New York, 1970, pp. 441-451.

[7]   Newman, B.A. and Weissmann, S., *Journal of Applied Crystallography*, Vol. 1, Part 3, Sept. 1968, pp. 139-145.

[8]   Glass, H.L. and Weissmann, S., *Journal of Applied Crystallography*, Vol. 2, 1969, pp. 200-209.

[9]   Glass, H.L. and Weissmann, S., *Metallurgical Transactions*, Vol. 2, 1971, pp. 2865-2873.

[10]  Kannan, V.C. and Weissmann, S., *Journal of Applied Physics*, Vol. 42, 1971, pp. 2632-2638.

[11]  Weissmann, S. and Kannan, V.C., *Journal of Materials*, Vol. 7, No. 3, Sept. 1972, pp. 279-285.

[12]  Stroh, A.N., *Philosophical Magazine*, Vol. 3, 1958, p. 597.

[13]  Weissmann, S., Tsunekawa, Y., and Kannan, V.C., *Metallurgical Transactions*, Vol. 4, Jan. 1973, pp. 376-377.

[14]  Weissmann, S. and Kalman, Z., *Philosophical Magazine*, Vol. 15, No. 135, March 1967, pp. 539-547.

[15]  Borrmann, G., *Physikalische Zeitschrift*, Vol. 42, No. 9/10, July 1941, pp. 157-162.

[16]  von Laue, M., *Acta Crystallographica*, Vol. 2, 1949, pp. 106-113.

[17]  von Laue, M., *Röntgenstrahlen Interferenzen*, Akademische Verlagsgesellschaft, Frankfurt/Main, 1960.

[18]  Penning, P. and Polder, D., *Philips Research Reports*, Vol. 16, No. 10, Oct. 1961, pp. 419-440.

[19]  Lang, A.R., *Journal of Applied Physics*, Vol. 29, No. 3, March 1958, pp. 597-598.

[20]  Cottrell, A.H., *Fracture*, Wiley, New York, 1959, p. 2.

[21]  Hirsch, P.B. in *Progress in Metal Physics*, Pergamon Press, New York, Vol. 6, 1956, p. 282.

[22]  Tsunekawa, Y. and Weissmann, S., "Importance of Microplasticity in Fracture of Silicon Crystals," paper accepted by *Metallurgical Transactions*.

*Leo Zwell*[1]

# X - Ray Diffraction – A Versatile, Quantitative, and Rapid Technique of Metallography

**REFERENCE:** Zwell, Leo, "X-Ray Diffraction–A Versatile, Quantitative and Rapid Technique of Metallography," *Metallography–A Practical Tool for Correlating the Structure and Properties of Materials, ASTM STP 557,* American Society for Testing and Materials, 1974, pp. 23–42.

**ABSTRACT:** X-ray diffraction is used to delineate the structure of materials, their chemical and phase analyses, grain and domain sizes, internal strain (stress), texture, imperfections, homogeneity, etc. In this paper, the practicality of the methods is emphasized; diffractometer techniques can be simple, quantitative, and rapid, and together with film techniques, permit examination of a wide range of materials. Examples are given of the characterization of structure by X-ray diffraction techniques and of the applications of the results in such different investigations as mechanical and physical properties of solid solutions, recrystallization of steel, pore structure of carbons, creep properties, surface stresses, and transformation of austenite to bainite.

**KEY WORDS:** X-ray diffraction, metallography, crystallography, preparation, lattice parameters, carbon, mechanical properties, recovery, crystallite size, texture

In the 1948 edition of "Metals Handbook" published by the American Society for Metals (ASM), metallography is defined as "the science concerning the constitution and structure of metals and alloys as revealed by the microscope." In the 1961 edition, metallography is "the science dealing with the constitution and structure of metals and alloys as revealed by the unaided eye or by such tools as low-powered magnification, optical microscope, electron microscope and diffraction or X-ray techniques." Now, in 1973, the field of metallography has been broadened to cover much more than metals and alloys—metallography is a tool for correlating the structure and properties of materials. In 1965, ASTM Committee E-4 defined metallography as "that branch of science which relates to the constitution and structure, and their relation to the properties of metals and alloys." As the old saying goes, metallography is what metallographers do.

One might say that the structure of a material is known when the following characteristics have been determined: the quantitative chemical elemental analysis; the existing phases and their relative amounts; the sizes, shapes, and distribution of these phases; and finally, additional factors such as texture, internal strain, ordering parameter, and homogeneity. The list grows with time—truly a large number of features required to describe structure. X-ray analysis comprising the three aspects of radiography, fluorescence, and

---

[1] Consultant, Swarthmore, Pa. 19081.

diffraction is certainly the most versatile method available because almost all aspects of structure can be investigated. These subjects have been described in the literature often and well, both in breadth and in depth.

The purpose of this paper is to demonstrate the practicality of X-ray diffraction in revealing the structure of materials and the correlation of the results to other properties of interest. Examples have been chosen to emphasize the diverse nature of problems which can be investigated with commercial or easily assembled equipment. Most of the work to be described has been performed at the United States Steel Corporation Research Center. In the natural course of events, the studies have been cooperative in nature. The joint efforts of many co-workers, too numerous to name individually, are acknowledged with much appreciation.

## Specimen Preparation

The ease, simplicity, rapidity, and versatility of specimen preparation merit emphasis. In the Debye-Scherrer camera technique, the aim is to center the specimen in the X-ray beam and rotate it so that many orientations and grains are seen. The three common ways of placing a specimen in this camera are: (1) to coat the outside of a thin nonreflecting fiber with the specimen using a binder such as Canada balsam, (2) to place powder inside a thin-walled capillary, and (3) to shape the specimen into a suitable rod. This can be done for solids by cutting the specimen and subjecting it to chemical attack. In other instances, a mixture of powdered material and a binder (balsam or collodion, for example) is either rolled into a rod or placed in a tube and extruded. The advantages of the camera method are that all diffraction peaks are recorded at the same time, that very small amounts of sample can be used, and a tremendous range of time of exposure is possible. Other cameras are available, like the Guinier-deWolff type which gives higher resolution and permits the simultaneous exposure of four powder patterns.

For examination on a diffractometer, the main requirement is that the specimen be flat—so flat sheets or ground and polished specimens can be examined without further preparation. Powders can be examined quickly by dusting them onto double-coated transparent tape mounted on a glass slide. Slurries of powder and a binder (lacquer, collodion, or cement) can be placed on a glass slide and warmed until the volatile part of the binder has evaporated. Pieces of material can be placed on a slide either with the tape or with a binder. Powders can also be placed in a recess in a nondiffracting plate flush with the surface of the plate. Finally, samples can be mounted in bakelite, epoxy resin, or other mounting material commercially available, and then made flat for examination on the diffractometer.

One advantage of X-ray diffraction analysis, especially in camera techniques, is that small specimens can be examined. Particles have been separated on the basis of appearance, density, or magnetic or chemical property, and identification obtained therefrom.

**Elemental Analysis**

The chemical analysis of materials is determined by X-ray techniques in several ways: (1) most accurately, by measuring characteristic X-rays produced by electron bombardment as in the electron microprobe or by X-ray bombardment as in X-ray spectrometers, (2) by determining lattice parameters where the change of lattice parameter with composition is known, and (3) by using the absorptivities of the elements (because of density or absorption edge) as in microradiography.

Microradiography has the great advantages of simplicity of procedure, low cost, and examination of the specimen in bulk. The drawbacks are serious or more investigators would be using the technique (low resolution and a long time required for specimen preparation and exposure). Microradiography is still being used to show segregation within specimens, but microprobe analysis has practically taken over the field, for example, the recent study on solidification of high speed tool steel by Barkalow et al [1].[2]

An example of the value of microradiography is its application to the investigation of surface defects produced during severe forming. Ridging is a defect caused by differences in the directional properties of sheets which arise from the nonrandomness of the orientations of the grains in the sheet. This condition of nonrandom orientation is called texture or preferred orientation. (Perhaps this paper should have been devoted mainly to a discussion of texture, because preferred orientation is a natural and ever present result of the working of materials and X-ray diffraction is the best way to determine texture. Since the aim of the paper is to emphasize the versatility and practicality of X-ray diffraction, subjects which are handled relatively quickly and easily have been chosen.)

At the United States Steel Corporation Research Laboratory, J.D. Defilippi and H.C. Chao [2] employed iron and chromium X-radiation to delineate a band-like segregation of chromium and molybdenum in hot-rolled AISI Type 434 stainless steel (17Cr-1Mo). Their thesis is that segregation of the elements in the ferrite and austenite phases may lead to retention of a harmful texture in the finished sheet. Because of selective absorptivity, chromium (and vanadium and titanium) will selectively absorb iron radiation; because of higher density, molybdenum will absorb both iron and chromium radiation more than the other elements in this steel. With the aid of a reference mark scribed on the surface, it was possible to take a light micrograph and then radiographs of the same area of a hot-rolled sheet ground and polished down to a thickness of 25.4 $\mu$m (1 mil). The results are shown in Fig. 1. The white areas in 1$b$ and 1$c$ represent regions of high absorptivity, chromium for iron radiation, and molybdenum for both iron and chromium radiations. The areas which are white in both radiographs indicate concentration of molybdenum; those areas white in the iron target radiograph and dark in the chromium

---

[2] The italic numbers in brackets refer to the list of references appended to this paper.

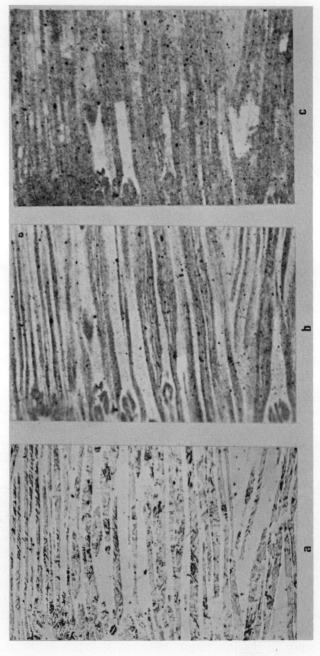

FIG. 1–Longitudinal section of steel plate (a) light micrograph, (b) radiograph by iron-Kα (c) radiograph by chromium-Kα. X101. Courtesy of Metallurgical Transactions, Ref. 2.

target radiograph indicate higher concentrations of chromium. By comparing these radiographs with the light micrograph, one sees that these alloying elements were concentrated in the ferrite. The martensite, a transformation product of the austenite existing at rolling temperatures, shows less of these solutes.

Examination of a rolled sheet which had failed in use provided an interesting lesson. The texture of the sheet was determined and then out of curiosity, a mil was ground off and texture redetermined. A marked change had occurred! The edge and surface of the sheet were then examined in the light microscope and the answer to the problem found—the surface of the sheet was fine-grained, but the bulk was coarse-grained. Once again, the value of using any and all available instruments was demonstrated; this experience is the background for the preference of the definition of metallography which includes "structure as revealed by the unaided eye or by such tools as ...".

Qualitative chemical analysis can be made of the first series of transition metals by choice of radiation. Because of absorption edge wavelengths, elements will absorb characteristic radiation of elements two atomic numbers higher or above and emit their own characteristic X-rays. High background or darkening of a film when cobalt radiation is employed reveals that manganese or chromium is present; likewise, iron radiation discloses the presence of chromium, and copper radiation that of cobalt, iron, or manganese, or a combination thereof.

Quantitative chemical analysis on an elemental basis can be made quite accurately if the change of unit cell parameters with composition is known. Relatively simple mathematical expressions for extrapolation to $2\theta = 180$ deg have been derived to take care of the nonrandom errors which arise from the film techniques and some persons have applied them to the diffractometer. However, it has been found that the extrapolation procedure is not required for the determination of changes in lattice parameter with solute content to an accuracy commensurate with that of the chemical analysis when a diffractometer is used with flat specimens that produce a Bragg peak in the far back-reflection region. The base material, usually solute-"free", serves as the fiducial, and the changes in lattice parameter with variation in solute content are determined from shifts in position of the back-reflection peaks. The shifts can be measured very accurately and corrections are unnecessary because the geometry is the same for all specimens. The peak shapes are visual indicators of the strain and chemical homogeneity of the phase, assuming that there is no broadening due to fine crystallite size or to rarely met uniform strain.

Many attempts have been made to relate properties of solid solutions to the electronic structure or relative sizes of the atoms in the solution. Because nature is quite complicated, these efforts have been only partially successful. The variation of lattice parameter with composition of iron-nickel alloys [3], (Fig. 2), illustrates several aspects of this type of study. First, there can be considerable differences among results published by different workers in the field. Second, the variation may not be linear; in this instance, in very unusual

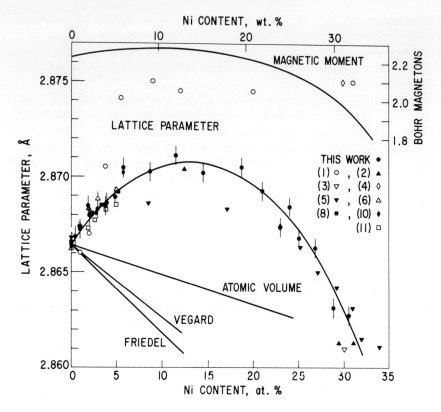

FIG. 2—*Lattice parameters of ferritic and martensitic iron-nickel alloys. Courtesy of Metallurgical Transactions, Ref.* 3.

fashion the dilation goes through a maximum as with increasing concentration, nickel expands and then contracts the body centered cubic (bcc) iron lattice. The identical effect occurs as iron goes into the face centered cubic (fcc) nickel-rich solution. Third, the explanation appears to be in the electronic and magnetic interactions in these alloys because the magnetic moment (Bohr Magneton number) exhibits the same behavior with composition as does the lattice parameter. A similar but smaller effect is found in iron-rich cobalt-iron alloys.

The relationship between relative dilation of the bcc iron lattice and solid solution strengthening has been discussed by Leslie [4]. Results of the effects of alloying elements in iron-base alloys on lattice parameters and on such varied mechanical properties as elastic constants, solid solution strengthening and softening, work hardening, strain aging, the effect of temperature on strength, hot working, and toughness are presented. The effects of solutes on the lattice parameter of bcc iron at 298 K is given in Fig. 3. As noted in the paper, a linear relationship has been used for the cobalt-iron, nickel-iron, and silicon-iron alloys for the purpose of treating all the data alike, though the

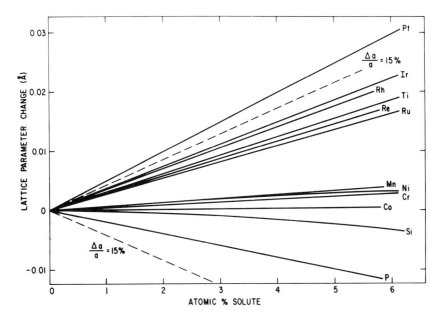

FIG. 3–*Effect of elements in solid solution on the lattice parameter of alpha iron at 25°C. Courtesy of Metallurgical Transactions, Ref. 4.*

dilation per atomic percent solute in these systems is not linear over this range of composition.

Leslie, despite all the work done on iron-base alloys or perhaps because of it, comes to the sad conclusion that there are more complexities than were expected. However, he concludes that the size misfit parameter, defined as the change in lattice parameter per atomic fraction divided by the lattice parameter $(1/a \times da/dc)$ is a rough guide to solid solution strengthening, defined as the change in shear stress with solute concentration—with some exceptions (Fig. 4). Interestingly, the most notable exceptions occur with those elements that decrease the lattice parameter.

Iron oxide (FeO), a defect structure at 1 atm pressure because of vacant iron sites, provides an example of the change of lattice parameter with composition. The lattice parameter varies from about 4.28 Å at $Fe_{0.83}O$ to 4.31 Å at $Fe_{0.95}O$. Many carbides, oxides, sulfides, and intermetallic compounds have defect structures—another use of lattice parameter measurement for chemical analysis after the phase has been identified. Pearson's two-volume handbook on lattice spacings is invaluable for this purpose [5].

## Phase Identification

The basis for the identification of the phases in a specimen is the fact that each crystalline substance gives its own characteristic diffraction pattern independently of other phases. Identification of phases in a specimen is accomplished by obtaining its diffraction pattern and comparing the pattern to those

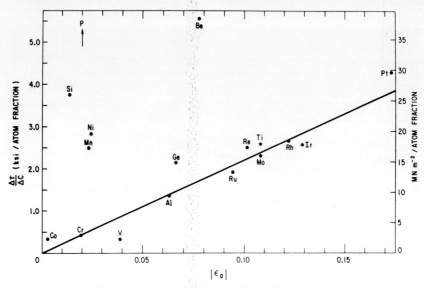

FIG. 4—*Correlation of solid solution strengthening of iron-base alloys at 25°C with size misfit parameter. Courtesy of Metallurgical Transactions, Ref. 4.*

of known substances. Some laboratories have their own collection of diffraction patterns; the set available to the public is that of the Joint Committee on Powder Diffraction Standards (JCPDS) which publishes an ever-growing Powder Diffraction File (PDF), now numbering well over 20 000 patterns.

A pattern from the PDF is that of FeO [6] shown in Fig. 5. Pertinent information such as crystal structure, method of preparation, and reference is on the card. The relative intensitives of the Bragg reflections, due to many

| d | 2.15 | 2.49 | 1.52 | 2.49 | (FeO) 8F | | | | | |
|---|------|------|------|------|----------|---|---|---|---|---|
| I/I₁ | 100 | 80 | 60 | 80 | Iron (II) Oxide | | | (Wustite) | | |

| Rad. CoKα  λ  1.7902    Filter  Fe    Dia.<br>Cut off          I/I₁ Diffractometer    I/I cor.<br>Ref. W.C. Allen, U.S. Steel Fundamental Res. Lab. | d A | I/I₁ | hkl | d A | I/I₁ | hkl |
|---|-----|------|-----|-----|------|-----|
| | 2.49 | 80 | 111 | | | |
| | 2.153 | 100 | 200 | | | |
| | 1.523 | 60 | 220 | | | |
| Sys. Cubic                        S.G.  Fm3m (225)<br>a₀  4.307    b₀            c₀          A          C<br>α            β            γ            Z    4    Dx 5.972<br>Ref. Ibid. | 1.299 | 25 | 311 | | | |
| | 1.243 | 15 | 222 | | | |
| | 1.077 | 15 | 400 | | | |
| | 0.988 | 10 | 331 | | | |
| εα            nωβ  2.32    εγ            Sign<br>2V          D  5.745    mp 1372°C  Color Opaque, Black<br>Ref. Ibid. Dana's System of Mineralogy 7th Ed. | .9631 | 15 | 420 | | | |
| Average of 13 patterns of sample prepared by fusion<br>of FeC₂O₄ or Fe₂O₃ in iron crucibles.  Fe₂O₃ varies<br>8-11% by analysis.  Crystals are rounded under mi-<br>croscope. | | | | | | |

FIG. 5—*Standard JCPDS diffraction data card (3 in. by 5 in.) for iron (II) oxide. Courtesy of JCPDS, Ref. 6.*

randomly oriented cyrstallites, are shown in the column $I/I_1$. It can happen, as in heavily deformed material or in electroplated deposits, that the treatment will bring grains into a nonrandom distribution of orientations, clustered to some particular plane or direction or both, called the preferred orientation or texture. In work on the oxidation of iron (in the form of sheets) to FeO in water-hydrogen atmospheres, only ($h00$) peaks were observed when the oxidized specimen was examined on the diffractometer, indicating a fiber [100] texture in the plane of the sheet. When the hydrogen was mixed with helium, the diffraction pattern was like the one on the card except that the ($h00$) peaks were absent indicating the presence of a [100] fiber texture perpendicular to the plane of the sheet. In this study, the orientation of the newly formed oxide apparently did not affect the rate of oxidation of the iron sheet; it may, however, lead to interesting information of the mobility of iron atoms or ions in different atmospheres.

Another point to be made is that frequently an educated guess of the texture of a material can be made by one run on a diffractometer. One must ascertain that missing peaks are not due to large grains. This is easily done by examining different areas of a specimen; a coarse-grained specimen with random texture will produce different Bragg reflections from different areas, while one with texture will produce the same reflections from all areas. For a complete pole figure or for quantitative determination of preferred orientation, the standard methods must be used.

In studying materials, identification of the phases present is very important. These phases can be extracted from the matrix in several ways; the one we've employed most often is the double-etching extraction technique. The method is as follows: after the specimen has been polished, it is etched for long periods of time (10 to 100 times the time used for microscopic observation) in a solution which will attack the matrix. The specimen is then washed, air-dried, and coated with collodion. After the collodion is dry (about 15 min), the specimen is etched in the same solution for about half the time, washed with isopropyl alcohol ($CH_3CHOHCH_3$) (to avoid dissolving the collodion), and air-dried. A thick coat of polyvinyl alcohol (about 50 percent solution Elvanol -Dupont 51-05 in water) is poured over the specimen and allowed to dry overnight in a dessicator. The composite film which now contains the precipitates is stripped from the specimen and floated in water (at about 50°C) until the polyvinyl alcohol dissolves (about 15 min). The extraction replica is picked up on a glass fiber and mounted in the camera for X-ray diffraction analysis. By changing etching times, it is possible to pick up precipitates of different sizes.

Electron micrographs of extractions taken from a stainless steel subjected to creep rupture are shown in Fig. 6. The particles were identified as cementite, chromium-rich $M_{23}C_6$ carbides, sigma phase, and chi phase [7]. In this investigation, by these methods it was shown that with increasing time at testing temperature, the sequence $Fe_3C$ to $M_{23}C_6$ to sigma phase took place. With new theoretical treatments and accurate measurements of thermal expan-

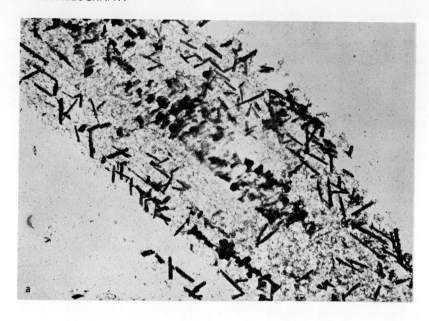

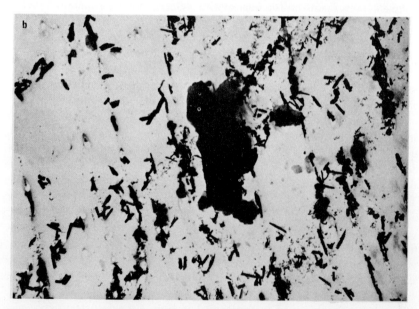

FIG. 6—*Electron micrographs of extraction replicas of Type 316 stainless steel subjected to creep rupture. (a) × 3200 and (b) × 4800. Courtesy of TMS-AIME, Ref. 7.*

sion and elastic moduli of these substances, it is now possible to determine more accurately the relationship of the phases to the. behavior of materials [8], whereas previously only their concomitance could be reported.

Another application of this technique was the identification of carbides of two different sizes in a steel after an aging treatment (Fig. 7). An extraction replica placed in a Debye-Scherrer camera was not rotated—so that the small particles would be expected to give a continuous pattern and the larger ones a spotty pattern. As can be seen, both patterns are coincidental; they have the same lattice parameter and, therefore, presumably the same composition.

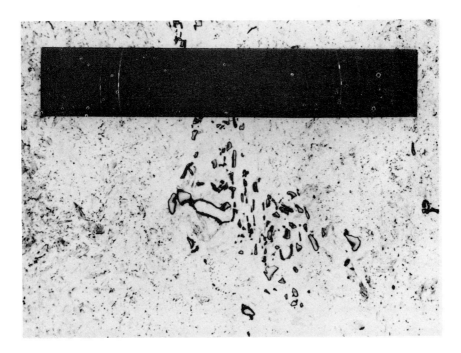

FIG. 7—*Light micrograph (≃ x 470) and X-ray diffraction pattern of carbides in steel.*

Quantitative analysis of phases existing in materials is possible because the intensity of the diffraction pattern of each phase is proportional to its concentration in the specimen under examination. The measured intensities of patterns from different phases can be related either to experimentally determined intensities from prepared standard mixtures or to intensities calculated from crystal structure data [9].

In the field of metallurgy, a very important application has been that of determining the amount of retained austenite in a martensitic matrix, both phases present in steels. This is of great commercial significance because of the significant effect of austenite on strength and other properties. Examples abound in the literature; the one chosen here is from recent work by Caton and Maniar [10] in developing a new high-strength maraging stainless steel. They determined the austenite content in their alloys as a function of composition and found that an austenite content of about 10 percent gave the optimum combination of strength and toughness.

The practical problems associated with the determination of austenite in steel are coarse-grain size, presence of other phases which are neglected in the simplification of the calculation, and, most importantly, the existence of texture. The effect of preferred orientation is shown by Miller [11] in the comparison of the determination of austenite by X-ray diffraction with that by light microscopy (Fig. 8). The departure from agreement of the values obtained by these two methods varies with the degree of preferred orientation in the austenite. The ratio of the intensities of the (220) and (311) peaks should be 0.9 for a randomly oriented austenite; as the ratio departs from this value, the agreement becomes poorer. To overcome this source of error, methods have been devised to measure intensities as the specimen is rotated and tilted through part of [12] or a full pole figure [13]. These procedures cost something, either larger uncertainty and increased minimum detectable amount or longer time for the determination.

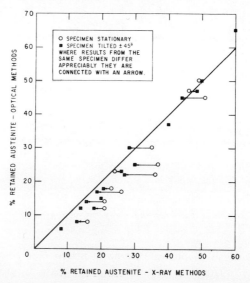

FIG. 8–*Comparison of austenite determinations by light microscopy and by X-ray diffraction. Courtesy of ASM, Ref.* 11.

## Other Structural Characteristics

The widths of diffraction peaks result from the spectral distribution of the X-ray beam, the experimental arrangements and the structure of the specimen. The first two features, usually fixed in an investigation, produce a finite peak width which is called the "intrinsic" or "instrumental" breadth. The peaks are broadened by many structural characteristics of the specimen such as fine particle size (coherently reflecting domains below about 3000 Å in size), inhomogeneity of strain, stacking faults, and inhomogeneity of composition. Although several analytical methods have been developed to separate the effects of each factor, they have not been applied to practical problems very often. The reasons may be the cost in time and effort, or hesitation on the part of the investigator to try something not easily understood or handled.

However, peak height and width are visible, line broadening may be obvious, and they frequently can be used as rapid and sometimes quantitative measures of one microstructural characteristic—provided the others can be neglected. The peak heights, the half-widths (width at half maximum) of back-reflection peaks resulting from $K_{\alpha_1}$ and $K_{\alpha_2}$ radiations, and the minimum between them can be measured quite accurately, and the measurements can be used as indications of changes in structural characteristics of materials under study. Large variations can be determined quantitatively by observations on forward-reflection (low-angle) diffraction peaks.

These parameters were used in an investigation by Michalak and Schoone [14] of the differences between nitrogen in solution and nitrogen precipitated as aluminum nitride (AlN) on the recovery, recrystallization, and texture development of a cold-rolled, aluminum-killed steel subjected to simulated box annealing. X-ray examination included determination of pole figures, measurements of integrated intensities and of line widths, and X-ray reflection macroscopy. Recovery was followed by means of an easily measured parameter first suggested by van Arkel and Burgers [15], the ratio of the intensity minimum (saddle point) between $K_{\alpha_1}$ and $K_{\alpha_2}$ peaks to the intensity of the $K_{\alpha_1}$ peak (less background intensity in each measurement). Michalak and Schoone normalized this parameter by using this ratio for the specimen after complete recrystallization as a base. The fractional residual line broadening was evaluated as the difference between this ratio for the specimen at annealing temperature $T$ and the ratio for the recrystallized specimen divided by the difference in the ratios of the specimen between the cold-rolled and recrystallized conditions. This was done for three reflections, the results for one being shown in Fig. 9. The data show that the high-AlN material, in which the nitrogen has been removed from solution by precipitation, recovers to a greater extent than the low-AlN specimen. The same result is shown in Fig. 10 where the measured relative intensities of the (100) and (112) reflections at different annealing temperatures are plotted. X-ray reflection macroscopy confirmed these findings but took more time.

A unique application of X-ray diffraction is the measurement of strain (and stress) in each phase existing in a specimen. Two different kinds of strain can be determined. Uniform (or mean) macrostrain causes a shift in position of the diffraction peaks to different Bragg angles as the lattice planes are moved under stress, and nonuniform microstrain causes a broadening of the diffraction peaks as the planes become distorted. The measurement of macrostrain (and stress) by X-ray diffraction is excellently described in Ref 16. Although

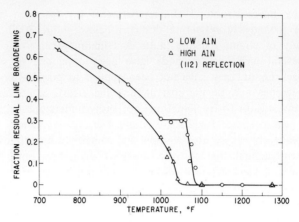

FIG. 9–*Effect of temperature on recovery of aluminum-killed steels cold-rolled 65 percent and heat at 40°F/h to different temperatures. Courtesy of TMS-AIME, Ref. 14.*

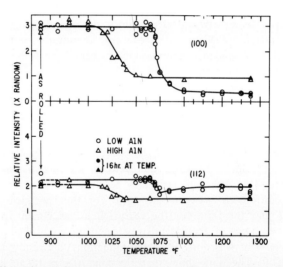

FIG. 10–*Effect of annealing temperature on the relative intensities of (100) and 112) reflections after 65 percent cold reduction and heating at 40°F/h to different temperatures. Courtesy of TMS-AIME, Ref. 14.*

in steels, only the stress of the bcc structure, martensite or ferrite, is usually determined, the stress on austenite or other phases that give diffraction peaks in the back-reflection region can also be obtained. As mentioned earlier, the various structural factors which go into line-broadening have been treated in several ways. The combination of automation and computer techniques (even to time-sharing procedures) allows routine analysis of particle size, micro-strains, and macrostrain [17].

Stresses arise for different reasons and X-ray diffraction can be used to differentiate between these various causes of stress. In an investigation by

Wriedt et al [18] of the stress resulting from a concentration gradient of nitrogen in the surface of a mild steel, the quenching stresses were found to be almost as large as the computed stress due to the gradient (Fig. 11). However, by aging specimens, one with and one without nitrogen, at temperatures between 100 and 300°C, the effects due to the concentration gradient, to quenching, and to precipitation of the dissolved nitrogen could be separated, semiquantitatively at least.

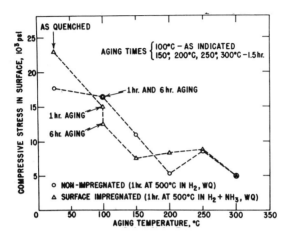

FIG. 11—*Cumulative effect of aging on residual surface stresses in mild steel with and without nitrogen impregnation. Courtesy of ASM, Ref. 18.*

In another investigation, that of the pore characteristics and rates of oxidation of graphite, coke, and charcoal by Turkdogan et al [19], line-broadening and lattice parameter measurements were made to determine the mean crystallite size of the carbons. A visual comparison of the Debye-Scherrer patterns (Fig. 12) shows the great differences in peak widths of the specimens and the concomitant variations in interplanar spacings. From measurements of the 200 peak widths taken from diffractometer charts, using the geometrical mean suggested by Taylor [20], the mean "apparent" particle sizes were determined to range from 6 Å to over 1000 Å. These values were in agreement with values of crystallite size determined from the relation of the change in lattice parameter with particle size published by Bacon [21]. Bacon shows that the distance between the basal planes increases and the perpendicular distance decreases as the crystallite size decreases. To complete this story, the result of the investigation was that the state of crystallinity apparently had no marked effect on the rate of oxidation, the difference in effective surface areas being the essential parameter for the difference in oxidation rates of the carbons.

The effect of variation of composition on line widths has been analyzed by Rudman [22], but it is difficult to determine when other causes are present, as they usually are. Stresses present because of concentration gradients existing on a microstructural scale would also contribute to line broadening.

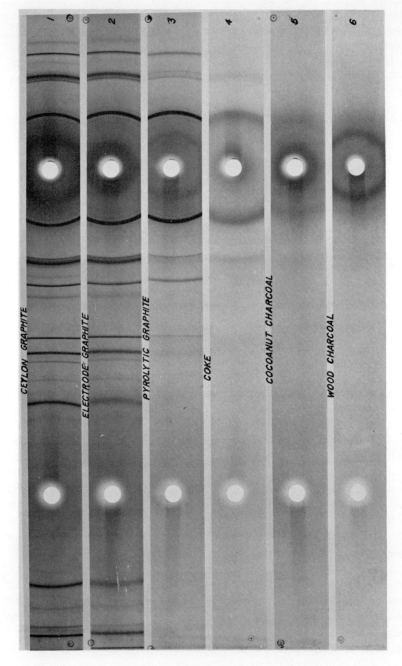

FIG. 12—X-ray powder diffraction patterns of different carbons.

Many of the methods described previously can be used to delineate the changes occurring in the transformation of austenite to upper bainite. Much work has been done on this interesting and important temperature range in the heat treatment of steels, yet it seems that no one investigator has yet determined all the information possible. By combining the quantitative determination of austenite in steel, the change in lattice parameter of iron-carbon austenite with carbon [5,23], the change in lattice parameter of ferrite with dissolved silicon [5], and the determination of stress in each phase, it should be possible to determine the relative amount, chemical composition, and state of strain and stress of each phase in a steel undergoing this transformation. Our work was on a 2Si-0.6C (SAE 9260) steel. Specimens, 1/8 in. thick and 1/2 in. in diameter were austenitized at 900°C (1650°F) for 15 min, quenched to 482°C (900°F) and held for times ranging from a few seconds to 24 h, and quenched in iced brine. The results, only partially revealed in Fig. 13, are: (1) the specimen held only momentarily at the upper bainite temperature of 482°C transformed to martensite and about 5 percent retained austenite, (2) after a 20 s incubation period, the amount of austenite increased until a maximum of 24 percent was reached at a holding time of about 300 s, and (3) the amount of austenite decreased with holding time thereafter, down to 5 percent after 24 h. Accompanying the increase in amount of austenite was an

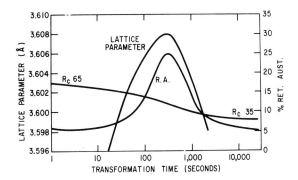

FIG. 13 –*Lattice parameter of austenite, percent austenite, and hardness in 2Si-0.6C steel (SAE 9260) during transformation to bainite at 482°C.*

increase in "$d$" spacing or lattice parameter of this phase, interpreted as enrichment by carbon (amount not established, but over 0.25C); the martensite peaks increased in width, an indication of a wide composition range, increased strain, or a decreasing crystallite size. The later decrease in amount of austenite was concomitant with a decrease in lattice parameter, an indication of a loss of dissolved carbon probably as a result of carbide precipitation. Occurring at the same time were a sharpening of the "martensite" diffraction peaks and a decrease of the bcc lattice parameter, indicating a loss of carbon and an increase of the silicon content in the ferrite to about 2.5 percent. The results of hardness measurements were as expected, the hardness decreasing with time. Unfortunately, the strains in the phases were not measured in these preliminary results.

A 2Si-0.2C steel showed the same results, but in diminished proportion; these changes were below the limits of detectability in a 2Mn-0.2C steel.

Many important subjects such as the determination of phase diagrams, small angle scattering, diffraction at high and at low temperatures, crystal structures, and other complex scientific studies have not been discussed in this paper, even though some of these should be considered practical in modern industrial practice.

Before the summary, some words might be appropriate on recent developments in the field. As mentioned previously in the determination of structural features from line-broadening measurements, automation and computer techniques are being applied to densitometers (for film readings) and to diffractometer outputs for determination of stress, percent austenite, pole figures, preferred orientation, and other characteristics. This is, of course, not new and has been done in individual laboratories for many years. The new aspect is that commercial manufacturers are thinking of or working on plans for automated diffraction analysis, tying the diffractometer output into the PDF on magnetic tape for phase identification.

Another relatively recent development has been the use of a semiconductor (lithium-drifted silicon) radiation detector coupled with a multichannel pulse height analyzer and a readout or display. This detection system, called energy dispersive analysis, has the advantages of obtaining the spectrum of data simultaneously and quickly and lends itself to computer techniques. The drawbacks are (1) the fluorescence and diffraction patterns are obtained at the same time (this may be an advantage), (2) liquid nitrogen and associated equipment are necessary in order to get the best resolution, and (3) the resolution is not sufficient for many studies. Papers on this subject have been given (see Refs 24-26); the first article on the subject was by Giessen and Gordon [27].

## Conclusion

The aim of this paper has been to give a broad view of the practicality of X-ray diffraction methods in correlating the structure and properties of materials. Necessarily, the presentation of each investigation has been brief and incomplete. The original articles are the proper sources for information on the subjects discussed here. Apologies are offered to the many authors of relevant papers that have not been mentioned. This paper closes with noteworthy remarks made in 1940 by C.C. Patterson, then director of General Electric Company Research Laboratory in Wembley, England at the conclusion of a talk by H.P. Rooksby [28] of that laboratory.

As time went on it was extraordinary what a large number of everyday problems in the laboratory found refuge and their solution, or partial solution, by submission to this technique in which Mr. Rooksby has made himself expert. At a guess I should think that 30 to 50 percent of the problems that come up in the course of our everyday activities touch his section of work at some stage or another in their career, and nearly always useful information is obtained. I do not think that until a laboratory has really used this technique and found of what it is capable, they realize how valuable it is.

*Acknowledgment*

I wish to thank the Joint Committee on Powder Diffraction Standards for its support and members of its staff for assistance in preparation of the manuscript.

# References

[1] Barkalow, R.H., Kraft, R.W., and Goldstein, J.I., *Metallurgical Transactions,* Vol. 3, April 1972, pp. 919-926.

[2] Defilippi, J.D. and Chao, H.C., *Metallurgical Transactions,* Vol. 2, Nov. 1971, pp. 3209-3216.

[3] Zwell, L., Carnahan, D.E., and Speich, G.R., *Metallurgical Transactions,* Vol. 1, April 1970, pp. 1007-1009.

[4] Leslie, W.C., *Metallurgical Transactions,* Vol. 3, Jan. 1972, pp. 5-26.

[5] Pearson, W.B., *Handbook of Lattice Spacings and Structures of Metals,* Pergamon Press, New York, Vol. 1, 1958; Vol. 2, 1967.

[6] Powder Diffraction File, Pattern #6-615, Joint Committee on Powder Diffraction Standards, Swarthmore, Pa. 19081.

[7] Zwell, L., Fasiska, E.J., and von Gemmingen, F., *Transactions,* The Metallurgical Society, American Institute of Mining, Metallurgical, and Petroleum Engineers, Vol. 224, No. 1, Feb. 1962, pp. 198-200.

[8] Brooksbank, D. and Andrews, K.W., *Journal of the Iron and Steel Institue,* Vol. 207, April 1969, pp. 474-483; Vol. 208, June 1970, pp. 582-586; Vol. 206, 1968, pp. 595-599.

[9] Clark, C., Smith, D.K., and Johnson, G.G. Jr. in *Progress in Analytical Chemistry Series,* Vol. 6, I.L. Simmons and G.W. Ewing, Eds., Plenum Press, New York, 1973, pp. 45-60.

[10] Caton, R.L. and Maniar, G.N., *Cobalt,* No. 55, June 1972, Centre D'Information Du Cobalt, Brussels, Belgium, pp. 92-98.

[11] Miller, R.L., *Transactions Quarterly,* American Society for Metals, Vol. 57, No. 4, Dec. 1964, pp. 892-899.

[12] Miller, R.L., *Transactions Quarterly,* American Society for Metals, Vol. 61, No. 3, Sept. 1968, pp. 592-597.

[13] Lopata, S.L. and Kula, E.B., *Transactions,* The Metallurgical Society, American Institute of Mining, Metallurgical, and Petroleum Engineers, Vol. 233, No. 2, Feb. 1965, pp. 288-293.

[14] Michalak, J.T. and Schoone, R.D., *Transactions,* The Metallurgical Society, American Institute of Mining, Metallurgical, and Petroleum Engineers, Vol. 242, No. 6, June 1968, pp. 1149-1160.

[15] van Arkel, A.E. and Burgers, W.G., *Zeitschrift für Physik,* Vol. 48, 1928, pp. 690-702.

[16] "Residual Stress Measurement by X-ray Diffraction," M. Hilley, J.A. Larson, C.F. Jatczak, and R.E. Ricklefs, Eds., SAE J784a, Society of Automotive Engineers, Two Pennsylvania Plaza, New York, New York, 10001, 1971.

[17] Nunes, T.L., Kim, J.G., and Mendiratta, S.K., *Journal of Applied Crystallography,* Vol. 5, No. 6, Dec. 1972, pp. 389-394.

[18] Wriedt, H.A., Zwell, L., Leslie, W.C., Scott, J.H., and Stoll, P.A., *Transactions Quarterly,* American Society for Metals, Vol. 59, No. 4, Dec. 1966, pp. 998-1002.

[*19*] Turkdogan, E.T., Olsson, R.G., and Vinters, J.V., *Carbon,* Vol. 8, 1970, pp. 545-564.

[*20*] Taylor, A., *Philosophical Magazine,* Series 7, Vol. 31, 1941, pp. 339-347.

[*21*] Bacon, G.E., *Acta Crystallographica,* Vol. 3, 1950, pp. 137-139; Vol. 4, 1951, pp. 558-561.

[*22*] Rudman, P.S., *Acta Crystallographica,* Vol. 13, No. 11, Nov. 1960, pp. 905-909.

[*23*] Ridley, N., Stuart H., and Zwell, L., *Transactions,* The Metallurgical Society, American Institute of Mining, Metallurgical, and Petroleum Engineers, Vol. 245, No. 8, Aug. 1969, pp. 1834-1836.

[*24*] Sparks, C.J. Jr. and Gedcke, D.A. in *Advances in X-ray Analysis,* Vol. 15, K.H. Heinrich, C.S. Barrett, J.B. Newkirk, and C.O. Ruud, Eds., Plenum Press, New York, 1972, pp. 240-253.

[*25*] Lin W. in *Advances in X-ray Analysis,* Vol. 16, L.S. Birks, C.S. Barrett, J.B. Newkirk, and C.O. Ruud, Eds., Plenum Press, New York, 1973, pp. 298-309.

[*26*] Carpenter, D. and Thatcher, J. in *Advances in X-ray Analysis,* Vol. 16, L.S. Birks, C.S. Barrett, J.B. Newkirk, and C.O. Ruud, Eds., Plenum Press, New York, 1973, pp. 322-335.

[*27*] Giessen, B.C. and Gordon, G.E., *Science,* Vol. 159, No. 3818, 1 March 1968, pp. 973-975.

[*28*] Rooksby, H.P., *Journal of the Royal Society of Arts,* Vol. 88, 1940, pp. 308-338.

*B.L. Bramfitt,*[1] *A.O. Benscoter,*[1] *J.R. Kilpatrick,*[1] *and A.R. Marder*[1]

# The Use of Hot-Stage Microscopy in the Study of Phase Transformations

REFERENCE: Bramfitt, B.L., Benscoter, A.O., Kilpatrick, J.R., and Marder, A.R., "The Use of Hot-Stage Microscopy in the Study of Phase Transformations," *Metallography—A Practical Tool for Correlating the Structure and Properties of Materials, ASTM STP 557,* American Society for Testing and Materials, 1974, pp. 43–70.

ABSTRACT: This paper summarizes the experimental techniques used in hot-stage light microscopy and the application of these techniques to ferrous transformations. In the hot-stage microscopy examples, particular emphasis is given on results of the martensite, pearlite, and ferrite transformations studied in this laboratory. Reference is also made to the results of many other investigators who have used the hot-stage microscope as a tool to study kinetics and morphology of ferrous transformations during both heating and cooling conditions.

KEY WORDS: metallography, phase transformations, ferrite, pearlite, bainite, martensite

The use of hot-stage microscopy has made it possible to study the dynamic and kinetic conditions of materials at elevated temperatures [1].[2] Generally, hot-stage microscopy does not require highly sophisticated and expensive equipment, thus allowing a wide use of the technique even in small laboratories with limited budgets. Although the technique has been used to study a wide variety of materials, this paper deals with only the study of transformations in steel.

The first section will discuss the technique of hot-stage microscopy and some of the problems encountered. The second section will discuss applications of the technique, with specific reference to various transformations that have been studied in our laboratory and by others.

## Experimental Technique

There are three high-temperature hot stages on the market in this country, namely, the Leitz Model 1750, the Reichert Vacutherm, and the Unitron Model HHS-3. Although Table 1 lists some comparative information for all

---

[1] Engineer, metallographer, metallographer, and supervisor, respectively, Homer Research Laboratories, Alloy Development Section, Bethlehem Steel Corp., Bethlehem, Pa. 18016.

The authors have been awarded the Joseph R. Vilella Award for the above paper. This award is under the jurisdiction of Committee E-4 on Metallography and is "given in recognition of a paper published by the Society of outstanding significance to the science of Metallography".

[2] The italic numbers in brackets refer to the list of references appended to this paper.

43

TABLE 1–*Commercial heating stages.*

| Manufacturer* | Model | Temperature Range, °C | Type of Atmosphere |
| --- | --- | --- | --- |
| Leitz | 1750 | room temperature to 2700[a] | vacuum, gas |
| Reichert | Vacutherm | room temperature to 1800 | vacuum, gas |
| Unitron | HHS-3 | room temperature to 1500 | vacuum, gas, pressure |

* The above data was taken from sales brochures of the three manufacturers.
[a] Temperature above 1750°C must be measured with an optical pyrometer.

three hot stages, we will deal mainly with the Leitz 1750 heating stage, which our laboratory has been using for several years.

Many of the details of our hot-stage technique have been published elsewhere and include modifications of the Leitz 1750 heating stage to accommodate a specially designed control system [2]. Figure 1 shows the basic system and the modifications.

FIG. 1–*Overall view of the hot-stage setup used for this study showing the basic system: (A) Leitz 1750 heating stage, (B) Leitz Ortholux microscope with xenon lamp, (C) Leitz power supply for 150-W xenon lamp, (D) power furnace transformer (5 V, 750 W), (E) regulating transformers, and the modifications: (F) control switching unit, (G) strip chart recorder (AZAR), (H) gas drying system, (I) gas flow meters, (J) liquid nitrogen bath (Dewar flask), (K) solenoid valve, and (L) Bolex 16-mm camera.*

The heating stage, optical system, and specimen preparation, as well as the control of atmosphere and cooling/heating rate, are described in the following discussion.

## Heating Stage

A cross-sectional exploded view of the Leitz heating stage is shown in Fig. 2. The water-cooled furnace chamber can operate under a vacuum (*A*) or in

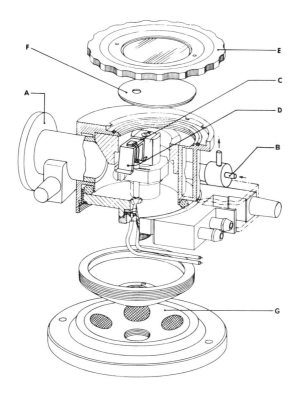

FIG. 2–*Exploded view of the Leitz heating stage showing (A) vacuum port, (B) gas inlet, (C) specimen, (D) heating element, (E) rotatable quartz window, (F) heat shield, and (G) magnetic, spherical bearing.*

an inert atmosphere (*B*). When an inert atmosphere is employed, the chamber is purged with research-grade argon or helium several times before operation. The 2.5 by 2.5 by 0.25-mm specimen (*C*), which rests upon a flat furnace (*D*), is observed through the quartz window (*E*) located above the radiation shield (*F*). The entire chamber is mounted on a spherical bearing (*G*) fitted with magnets. This arrangement makes it possible to keep the specimen surface perpendicular to the light beam of the microscope. A view of the furnace section is shown in Fig. 3 for two conditions of heating, namely, radiation heating (Fig. 3*A*) and contact heating (Fig. 3*B*).

*Furnace Design*–Various furnace configurations can be used, depending upon the type of study involved. Figure 4 shows four different furnaces that employ contact heating, where the specimen or crucible is in direct contact with the heating element. The crucible furnace (Fig. 4*A*) is used for melting and solidification studies where direct contact with a metal heating element must be avoided so as to prevent alloying and contamination. The furnace in Fig. 4*B* is used to heat powder specimens for sintering studies, and the other two furnaces are used for heating sheet and wire specimens. Furnace *D* (Fig. 4), used exclusively in this study, was preferred over furnace *C*. Furnace *C* is

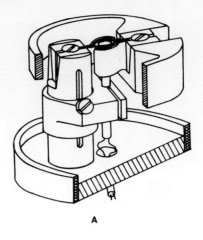

A

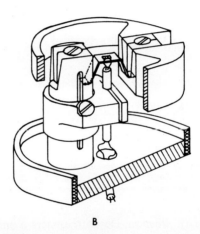

B

FIG. 3–*Internal portion of the hot stage showing two methods of heating: (A) radiation heating and (B) direct-contact heating.*

under more restraint than furnace *D* causing it to bend during heating and cooling, thus creating difficulty in focusing during observation.

In setups where the contact between the specimen and heating element is to be direct, it is advisable to tack-weld the specimen to the element to eliminate specimen movement during heating and cooling. Immobility is particularly important when the specimen is being cooled with a blast of inert gas.

Figure 5 shows another type furnace—one which operates mainly by indirect heating. The specimen may be of the cylindrical form shown in Fig. 5*A* or may be in powder form in a ceramic crucible, Fig. 5*B*. In the furnace arrangement for such specimens the heating element and radiation protection screens surround the specimen (Fig. 5*C*). The variant form of a cylindrical specimen shown in Fig. 5*A* is commonly used in a variety of heating stages [3-12]. In contrast to the furnace arrangement for the thin specimen (Fig.

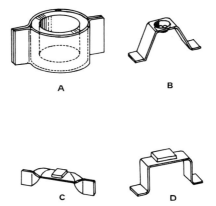

FIG. 4–*Furnace configurations for various heating applications.*

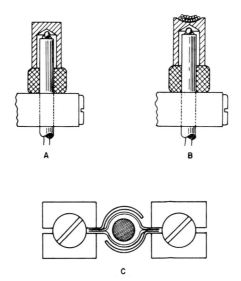

FIG. 5–*Configurations used for radiation heating of: (A) hollow cylindrical specimen and (B) powder specimen on a ceramic crucible. The top view of the furnace (C) shows the heating element, radiation shields, and specimen.*

4*D*), the main disadvantage of the cylindrical specimen is that the higher thermal inertia of this specimen precludes fast cooling rates.

For example, using a cylindrical specimen with a diameter of about 0.5 cm, Gabler [3] obtained a maximum rate of 80°C/s when cooling from 1000 to 200°C, with a blast of cold inert gas introduced into a Reichert Vacutherm heating stage. In contrast, Benscoter et al [2], working with thin specimens (Fig. 4*D*) and using a cold helium blast in a Leitz hot stage, obtained a cooling rate in excess of 2000°C/s. The control of cooling rate will be discussed in a subsequent section.

*Furnace Materials*—Furnace materials usually consist of high-melting-temperature metals such as tantalum, tungsten, molybdenum, and platinum as well as platinum-rhodium and platinum-iridium alloys [13]. High-resistance alloys such as Nichrome V can also be used [2]. In some cases, the resistance of the specimen itself makes it possible to use it as the heating element. Speich and Miller [14] found this latter method advantageous when, as in the case of a steel strip specimen, the low thermal inertia necessitates rapid quenching, for example, greater than 500°C/s.

Before selecting a furnace material for a particular application, one must consider the following factors:

1. *Type of atmosphere used*—Since the refractory metals tantalum, molybdenum, and tungsten are highly susceptible to high-temperature oxidation, they must be used in a reducing or inert atmosphere or in high vacuum. Oxidation-resistant elements and alloys, such as platinum and platinum alloys, can be used in most atmospheres.

2. *Thermal expansion characteristics*—Thermal expansion and contraction affect the movement of the specimen during heating and cooling and, therefore, can create a focusing problem when one is observing and photographing a transformation under nonisothermal conditions. Thus, thermal expansion is particularly important in furnace designs where the furnace and specimen are in direct contact (Fig. 4), and materials with a low coefficient of expansion within the temperature range of the study should be used.

3. *Electrical resistivity*—The resistivity of the furnace material determines how fast a specimen can be heated and, therefore, becomes important when a rapid heating rate is employed.

4. *Alloying behavior*—Alloying of the specimen and the heating element can obviously create drastic changes in the transformation characteristics. Therefore, in heating stages where the specimen and furnace material are in direct contact, one should avoid materials that readily alloy. For example, we found that a 0.8C steel specimen severely alloyed with a platinum heating element at temperatures above 1080°C. On the other hand, when we used a pure iron specimen, we were able to run the same furnace continuously at 1100°C for 2.5 min without appreciable alloying occurring.

5. *Transformation characteristics*—Since a transformation creates a nonlinear expansion/contraction condition, one should avoid a furnace material that exhibits a phase transformation during heating and cooling. Fortunately, most of the common heating elements do not go through an allotropic phase transformation.

6. *Ductility*—The material used for the heating element should exhibit ductility so that it can be drawn into wire for wound furnaces or into sheet for the furnace design shown in Fig. 4. Although many furnace designs are available from suppliers, reasons of economy or test design may require a special configuration. For example, at our laboratory we shape our own heating elements (Fig. 4D) with a special fixture shown in Fig. 6.

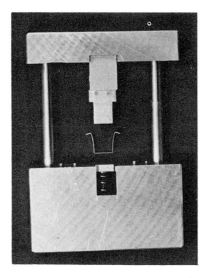

FIG. 6—*Fixture used to form heating elements from strip.*

## Optical System

*Microscope*—Since a variety of microscopes can be used to observe phenomena in a hot stage, only the optical system used in the present study will be discussed in detail. As seen in Fig. 1, a Leitz Ortholux microscope with a 150-W xenon light source (with diffuser and green filter) was employed. We used both phase-contrast and regular objectives, which were corrected for the quartz window of the heating stage. The free working distance ranges from 5.7 mm for the 32X objective (0.60 numerical aperture (NA)) to 8.3 mm for the 20X objective (0.40 NA). In the case of our 5 and 10X objectives, the working distance is 13 mm, and such lenses need not be corrected for quartz since correction is not necessary at these lower magnifications. The minimum working distance of our heating stage is 5 mm, which includes the 2-mm-thick quartz window and the specimen 3 mm below the window. The distance between the window and the specimen can be controlled by changing the height of the heating element, which is particularly easy when elements are fabricated in one's own laboratory. For transformations such as austenite to martensite that create a large amount of surface relief, phase-contrast objectives are unnecessary. Of course, more subtle transformations, for example, pearlite, require special optics to reveal the slight change in surface relief. Possibilities include phase contrast, oblique or polarized light, as well as dark field and interference microscopy.

*Photography*—A 16-mm Bolex H16 reflex motion picture camera was employed for timed sequence studies and cinephotomicrography. The motion picture camera is capable of filming at speeds ranging from 12 to 64 frames/s. This range of film speed is sufficient for most ferrous phase transformations, including the martensitic transformation, although Mitsche et al [15] used film speeds up to 4000 frames/s to study the discontinuous growth of a martensite needle. Most of our filming is done at 24 frames/s by means of a constant speed motorized drive attached to the camera. A constant speed is necessary when the film is used to obtain kinetic data such as growth rate measurement.

## Specimen Preparation

Specimens used in the ferrous transformation studies described in the *Applications* section of this study were prepared as follows:

1. Normal metallographic polishing technique was employed to produce a specimen 0.25 mm thick with a scratch-free surface of about 1 cm$^2$.

2. The polished specimens are then ultrasonically cleaned in high-purity ethyl alcohol and sheared into 2.5-mm squares.

3. Each 2.5-mm square is placed in the center of the heating element as seen in Fig. 4D.

A platinum/platinum-10Rh thermocouple is spot welded to the exposed top surface of the specimen near the area to be observed. The diameter of the thermocouple wire should be smaller than the specimen thickness so that the cooling of the thermocouple wires does not cause a large temperature gradient during cooling. The wire diameter used for these studies was 0.2 mm. A thermocouple bead was not used with this small specimen; instead, each thermocouple wire was welded directly to the specimen. The current used in welding was sufficient to simultaneously tack weld the specimen to the heating element.

Early in our studies, the thermal gradient across the specimen was measured using a 0°C-reference junction with the platinum/platinum-10Rh thermocouple. With an argon flow of 800 cm$^3$/min, the temperature difference across the top surface of a specimen (2.5 mm) was 1.5°C at a holding temperature of 680°C and 2.5°C at 820°C. This temperature difference is quite small and well within the range of experimental error of temperature measurement.

## Control of Atmosphere

Most heating stages can employ either a vacuum or a gaseous atmosphere. Although the Leitz heating stage was designed for both types of atmosphere, we generally employ a slightly positive pressure of inert gas flowing at the rate of 150 to 800 cm$^3$/min. Too much flow chills the specimen during heating and soaking, thus creating a steep thermal gradient. Chilling the specimen and furnace material also requires more current during heating.

An inert gas, usually argon, was preferred to a vacuum because of the following disadvantages of heating a metal or alloy under vacuum:

1. *Decarburization*—It has long been established that decarburization takes place during vacuum heating [7]. Due to this loss of surface carbon the transformations that take place may not be representative of the bulk material.

2. *Alloy loss*—Alloy loss due to the high vapor pressure of an alloying element can cause a composition change on the surface. For example, working at $10^{-5}$ torr, Speich, in studying an Fe-0.3C-3Cr alloy, limited his austenitizing temperature to below 1000°C to prevent excessive loss of chromium from the free surface [16]. Working at $5 \times 10^{-4}$ torr and 1200°C, Stransky and Kralova found a rapid decrease in chromium at the surface of a 20Cr steel and eliminated the problem with an overpressure of argon [8].

3. *Evaporation*—Due to evaporation of metal under vacuum, the quartz window of the heating stage becomes coated with a film that can obstruct the view during observation. Many heating stages employ a movable window to minimize this problem.

Due to these compositional changes that take place under vacuum, abnormal effects take place on the surface. For example, Okamoto et al [10] found that the austenite grain size on the surface of a low-alloy steel heated to 950°C in vacuum ($3 \times 10^{-5}$ torr) was much coarser (ASTM No. 2) than the interior region of the specimen (ASTM No. 8). When they repeated the experiments under argon at 0.6 atm, the grain size at the surface was identical to that in the interior at all temperatures up to about 1200°C.

The main problem in the use of an inert gas is oxidation of the specimen. However, the use of a thoroughly dried high-purity gas can eliminate this problem. In our laboratory we dry a research-grade argon (99.999A) using first a Lectro-dryer, then a desiccating column of $CaSO_4$ chips. Details of the gas flow system are shown in Fig. 7. The use of the system as a quenching device will be discussed in the next section.

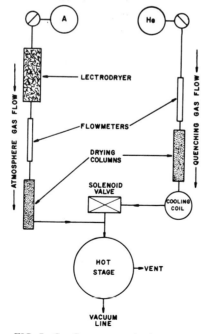

FIG. 7—*Gas-flow system for hot stage.*

Atmospheres other than an inert gas or vacuum can be used in the heating stage for special applications. For example, Naumann [17] used an ammonia atmosphere at 500°C in his study of nitride formation on the surface of pure iron. He found that nitride crystals formed at several nucleation sites, for example, grain boundaries, inclusions, and etch pits, and that the needle-shaped crystals grew rapidly along certain crystallographic planes of the iron. Our experience has shown that using a nitrogen atmosphere creates nitride needles which pin the movement of austenite grain boundaries at the specimen surface.

### Control of Heating/Cooling Rate

Phase transformations are studied under either isothermal or continuous heating and cooling conditions. Under isothermal conditions it is necessary to maintain a constant temperature during transformation. However, under continuous cooling the rate must be controlled, since it drastically influences the transformation temperature of many ferrous transformations such as austenite to pearlite, austenite to ferrite, and austenite to bainite.

The heating rate is controlled by varying the current to the furnace. The furnace current is controlled by means of a rheostat which can be manually or automatically adjusted. Figure 8 shows the electrical system for the hot stage used in our laboratory. The heating rates for this setup were on the order of 145°C/s. If extremely fast heating rates were required, a pulse-heating device could be adapted to the electrical system.

Most of the studies in this laboratory were concerned with the effect of continuous cooling on transformations. We were able to vary cooling rates from less than 1°C/s to a maximum of 2000°C/s. For purposes of discussion, we will describe our control of cooling rate in terms of a "slow" and "fast" cooling rate. The cooling rate provided by our normal furnace cooling (which occurred when the power to the furnace was turned off and the specimen was allowed to cool at a rate between 50 to 100°C/s) will serve as the division between the "slow" and "fast" cooling rates. The normal cooling rate of a furnace depends on many factors, including furnace material, furnace thickness, and specimen thickness.

The "slow" cooling rates below 50°C/s were obtained by gradually decreasing the furnace current by means of the motorized rheostat shown in Fig. 8. The minimum rate on our system was determined to be 0.4°C/s. Changing the gearing in the motorized drive could provide still slower cooling rates if required.

For "fast" cooling rates, for example, those greater than 100°C/s, a gas quench was employed. The quenching system shown in Fig. 7 uses helium gas (99.995He) dried in a desiccating column of $CaSO_4$ chips. The specimen was cooled by a blast of helium gas, the pressure of which was controlled by the regulator valve on the helium tank. Flow rates up to 140 000 cm$^3$/min were used for gas quenching. To increase the flow of gas through the hot stage, a vacuum pump can be used. The fastest cooling rates were obtained with a

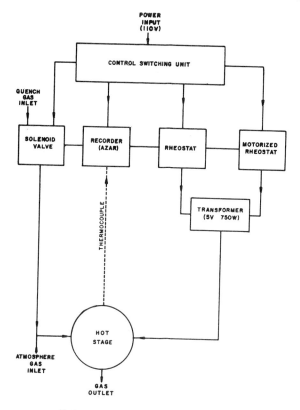

FIG. 8–*Electrical system for hot stage.*

high flow of chilled helium gas. The gas was chilled by a cooling coil submerged in liquid nitrogen. Liquid nitrogen maintained a quantity of gas, larger in volume than the furnace chamber, at a temperature of $-196°C$.

Caution must be taken in the selection of the coolant and the quenching gas. For example, using liquid nitrogen at $-196°C$ as a coolant eliminates the use of argon as a quench gas since argon liquifies at $-186°C$. In a study of the martensite transformation, Benscoter et al obtained cooling rates in excess of $2000°C/s$ with the previously described technique [2]. In measuring cooling rates of this magnitude, one can no longer rely on normal temperature recording instruments such as a strip-chart recorder, due to their response times, usually on the order of 1 s full scale. More sophisticated techniques are needed such as oscillograph traces or relating the motion picture time sequence (elapsed frames) to some known transformation interval [2].

The electrical system shown in Fig. 8 is capable of controlling the cooling rate (*A*) from a given soaking temperature directly down to room temperature, or (*B*) from the soaking temperature to some intermediate temperature and then, after isothermal holding at that temperature, down to room temperature. These two main patterns consist of the following variations:

A. *Cooling Directly to Room Temperature*
  1. Fast cooling to room temperature.
  2. Furnace cool to room temperature.
  3. Slow cool to room temperature.

B. *Interrupted Cooling*
  1(*a*) Fast cool to an intermediate temperature and furnace cool, or
    (*b*) fast cool to an intermediate temperature and slow cool.

  2(*a*) Furnace cool to an intermediate temperature and fast cool, or
    (*b*) furnace cool to an intermediate temperature and furnace cool, or
    (*c*) furnace cool to an intermediate temperature and slow cool.

  3(*a*) Slow cool to an intermediate temperature and fast cool, or
    (*b*) slow cool to an intermediate temperature and furnace cool, or
    (*c*) slow cool to an intermediate temperature and slow cool.

Interrupted cooling of types 1(*a*) and (*b*) can be followed by a rapid quench only if enough time is allowed during holding at the intermediate temperature for a new supply of helium gas to be chilled to below $-196°C$.

## Applications

Using the equipment and procedures just described, we have, over a period of several years, studied primarily the range of ferrous phase transformations of practical interest to ferrous metallurgists concerned with the effect of heat treatment on steel properties. One of the main purposes of this paper is to provide workers in our field with a useful state-of-the-art guide for these transformations. Therefore, our hot-stage studies summarized in the following sections cover both our unpublished applications and accompanying cine-photomicrographs, as well as new cinephotomicrographs relating to our previously published studies on pearlite and martensite. Key findings from pertinent English and other languages are also referenced where appropriate. Table 2 is an outline of ferrous transformations studied, using the hot-stage microscope together with references and brief comments.

### Melting and Solidification

Melting and solidification have been studied by several investigators. Kulmburg et al [18-20] studied the effect of segregation on the incipient melting in steel as well as the melting of low-temperature constituents such as eutectic phases and precipitates. Mitsche and Jeglitsch [21] were also able to take photomicrographs illustrating the melting of complex eutectics in high-speed steels. Jeglitsch [22] studied dendrite formation and solidification front movement in stainless steels and also observed supercooling and the subsequent remelting of small areas. Thorsen [5] studied dendritic growth and cellular formation on a number of unalloyed steels.

Figure 9 illustrates some solidification experiments accomplished on our hot-stage microscope. Cinephotomicrographs were taken of the liquid surface

TABLE 2—*Hot-stage microscopy of ferrous transformations.*

| Parent Phase | Product Phase | References | Comments |
|---|---|---|---|
| \multicolumn{4}{c}{Transformations on Cooling} | | | |
| Liquid | δ-Ferrite | 5 | dendritic growth and cell formation in low-carbon steel |
| Liquid | Austenite | 5,22 | dendrite formation in plain-carbon and stainless steels |
| δ-Ferrite | Austenite | | |
| Austenite | α-Ferrite | 7,24-26,31,32 | equiaxed and Widmanstätten ferrite studied |
| Austenite | Cementite | | |
| Austenite | Pearlite | 25-27,33-35 | lack of surface relief requires special optics, for example, dark field or phase contrast |
| Austenite | Upper Bainite | 37-39 | isothermal studies of growth rate and morphology |
| Austenite | Lower Bainite | 16,36,37,39-41 | very slow growth independent of time (isothermal) |
| Austenite | Lath Martensite | 2,11,42,44-47 | large surface shears, morphology characterized |
| Austenite | Plate Martensite | 15,43 | large surface shears, morphology characterized |

Transformations on Heating

| Parent Phase | Product Phase | References | Comments |
|---|---|---|---|
| Plate Martensite | Austenite | | |
| Lath Martensite | Austenite | | |
| Lower Bainite | Austenite | | |
| Upper Bainite | Austenite | | |
| Pearlite | Austenite | 26,27 | etched samples used to show pearlite decomposition |
| Cementite | Austenite | | |
| α-Ferrite | Austenite | 8,9,24,25 | wrinkling of surface due to volume change |
| Austenite | δ-Ferrite | 20,23 | pronounced surface relief and needles growing from grain boundaries (stainless steels and tool steels) |
| Austenite | Liquid | | |
| δ-Ferrite | Liquid | | |

Special Studies

| Type of Transformation | References | Comments |
|---|---|---|
| Austenite grain growth | 1,10,24,28,29,30 | surface grain growth depends upon alloy, atmosphere, and specimen size |
| Cementite spheroidization | 6 | spheroidization of a 1.17%C steel |
| Nitride formation | 3,16 | AlN and $Fe_2N$ at austenite grain boundaries |
| Segregation phenomena | 18-21 | incipient melting of low-temperature constituents (eutectics and precipitates) in high-alloy steels |

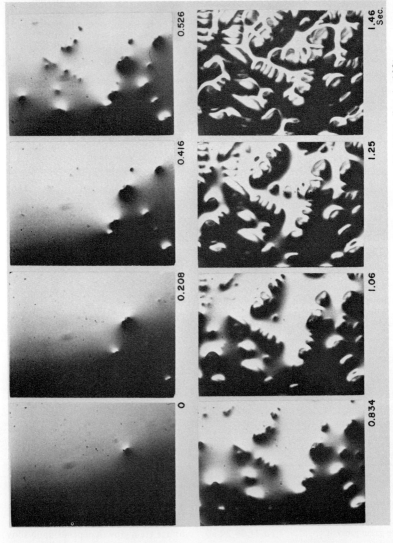

FIG. 9—Cinephotomicrographic sequence showing solidification in a Fe-0.8C alloy (× 109).

of an Fe-0.8C alloy. At time zero, one large and two small crystals of austenite have nucleated and begun to grow on the surface. After 0.21 s, seven crystals appear on the surface, and the beginning of a dendrite can be seen. Therefore, these crystals are interconnected beneath the liquid surface and are branches of a single dendrite. As time progresses, several dendrites form, grow, and impinge until all the liquid is expended, thus creating interdendritic shrinkage as seen in the last photograph of the sequence.

## Austenite to δ-Ferrite Transformation

Investigations of δ-ferrite have been limited because of the high temperature requirements. However, Kulmberg et al [23] were able to show the formation in stainless steels and tool steels. They found on heating that the δ-ferrite was precipitated on austenite grain-boundaries as fine polygonal grains distinguished by pronounced surface relief. They also found that the δ-ferrite can form as well-defined needles which grow inward into the grain from the grain boundaries in much the same way that Widmanstätten ferrite does. The effect of segregation of δ-ferrite formation was also demonstrated with chromium and molybdenum which favor the formation of δ-ferrite.

## α-Ferrite to Austenite Transformation

Quite naturally, the ferrite to austenite transformation was one of the first phase changes studied in the hot-stage microscope. Rogers [24] first observed the formation of austenite as an "occurrence of a number of new lines and the wrinkling of the surface," the "wrinkling" being attributed by Esser and Cornelius [25] to the lattice volume change. Esser and Cornelius did not see the wave across the crystal that was reported by Rogers for some of his specimens. Other investigators also studied the $\alpha \rightarrow \gamma$ transformation [7,9] and the transformation of $\alpha$ + pearlite to austenite [26,27].

Studies in our laboratory have shown that the $\alpha \rightarrow \gamma$ transformation occurs very quickly, is often completed within 0.04 s, and looks, at least superficially, something like a martensitic transformation. In Fig. 10 it is seen that allotromorphs (arrows) of $\gamma$ are forming on the ferrite grain boundaries of pure iron, in precisely the same way ferrite allotromorphs form during the $\gamma \rightarrow \alpha$ transformation.

## Austenite Grain Growth

Since Rogers' [24] first experiments on grain growth in 1933, many investigators have studied austenite grain growth. Pfeiffer [28] and later Lozinskii [1] documented the movement of austenite grain boundaries at high temperature. At this point the relationship between surface grain size and bulk grain size was questioned, and Kulmberg [29] attempted to explain the difference by temperature differences within the specimen. Taking exception to Kulmberg's conclusion, Jeglitsch cited other factors such as atmosphere, diffusion, and oxides, that affect grain size [30]. Carefully investigating the

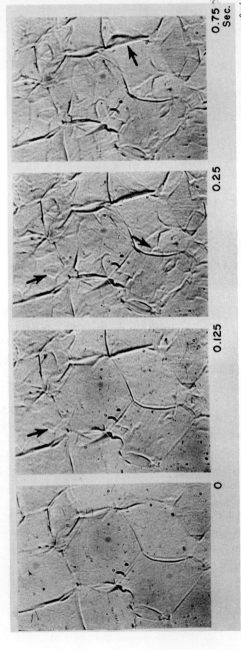

FIG. 10—*Cinephotomicrographic sequence showing the ferrite to austenite transformation in pure iron at a heating rate of 145°C/s. Arrows show growth of allotromorphs on ferrite grain boundaries (× 218).*

effects of atmosphere, argon, and vacuum, Okamoto et al found that success in getting the surface grain size to match the interior grain size depends on selecting the right atmosphere for a particular alloy [10].

The cinephotomicrographs in Fig. 11 show grain growth at 1000°C in an alloy steel (0.26C, 0.77Mn, 0.95Cr, 1.00Mo, and 0.25V) which we studied in our laboratory. In this sequence one can see older boundaries (A) being replaced by new boundaries (B).

*Austenite to Ferrite Transformation*

Several investigators [7,24,25,27] have recorded the austenite to ferrite transformation in the hot-stage microscope. Generally, they reported the transformation as the formation of new grains on the previously formed austenite grain boundaries. Mitsche et al [26] were the first to report the needle-like growth of Widmanstätten ferrite.

Because of the surface relief generated in the Widmanstätten ferrite region, the kinetics of the transformation become easier to study. Leont'yen and Kachanov [31] studied the isothermal growth rate of Widmanstätten ferrite (acicular ferrite) in iron containing 0.03C. They found that even in the same colony of needles the growth rate varied because of the barriers encountered in the austenite by these ferrite needles. By decreasing the reaction temperature, they found that the growth rate ranged from 3 to 18 $\mu$m/s at 800°C to 150 to 350 $\mu$m/s at the lower temperatures of 650 to 700°C. When Kogan et al [32] studied Widmanstätten ferrite formation in the hot stage, they found that the reaction was analogous to the bainite transformation where the growth rate is controlled by the rate of carbon diffusion. They also found that as the austenite grain size was increased and the reaction temperature was lowered, the proportion of Widmanstätten ferrite being formed increased in relation to the common polygonal ferrite. They noted that increased carbon content lowered the transformation start temperature for the Widmanstätten ferrite.

We have been able to follow the formation of three different types of ferrite. (1) Widmanstätten ferrite growth in an Fe-0.8C alloy at a cooling rate of 10°C/s is seen in Fig. 12. (2) Allotromorphs, as seen (arrows) in Fig. 13, that develop on the austenite grain boundaries in a 0.1C, 0.3Mn steel at a cooling rate of 12°C/s. (3) As for the third type of ferrite morphology, which represents the movement of a phase front generated from the allotromorphs and grain boundaries, this phenomenon can be shown in the motion pictures but not in still photographs.

The correlation of surface shears to the bulk microstructure in Fig. 14 demonstrates that both the Widmanstätten and allotromorphic types of ferrite are not merely surface phenomena.

*Austenite to Pearlite Transformation*

The lack of surface relief [33] makes it difficult to follow the austenite to

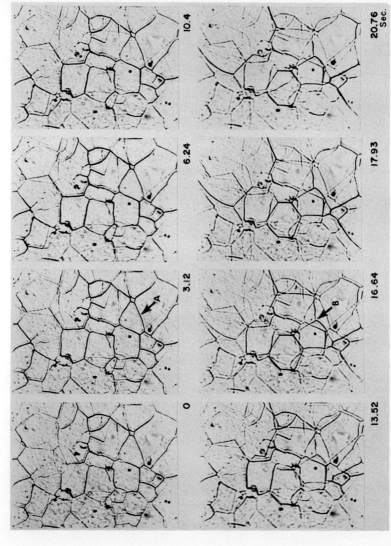

FIG. 11—Cinephotomicrographic sequence of austenite grain growth at 1000°C in a low-alloy steel. Arrow at (A) indicates old set of boundaries being replaced by new set (B) (× 244).

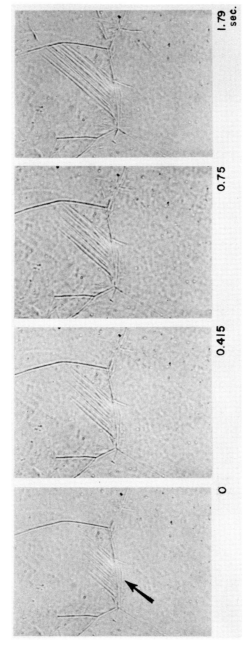

FIG. 12—Cinephotomicrographic sequence showing the growth of Widmanstätten ferrite (arrow) from Fe-0.8C austenite at 617°C (cooling rate of 10°C/s) (× 250).

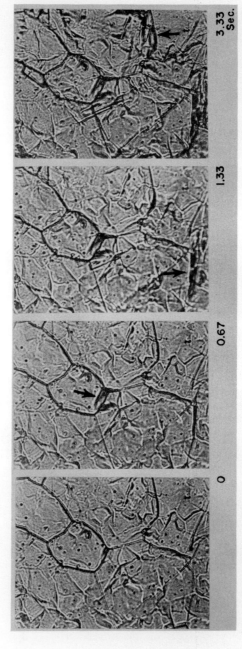

FIG. 13—Cinephotomicrographic sequence showing the formation of ferrite allotromorphs (arrows) on austenite grain boundaries in pure iron at 825°C (cooling rate 12°C/s) (× 125).

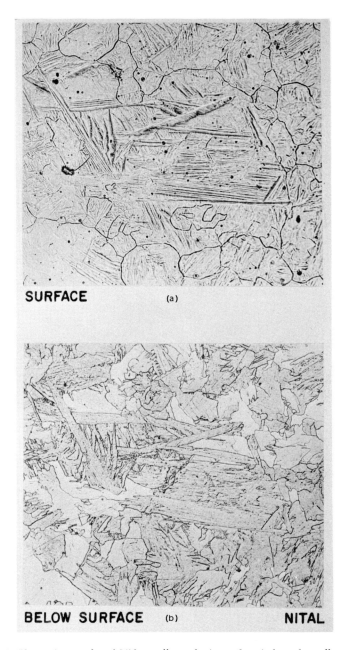

FIG. 14—*Photomicrographs of Widmanstätten ferrite and grain-boundary allotromorphs in a low-carbon steel:* (a) *at the surface and* (b) *just below the surface* (× 200).

pearlite transformation using the hot-stage microscope. However, special optical techniques help discern pearlite formation. For example, Mitsche et al [26] used dark-field optics to see the transformation. However, because of the dark-field optics, the pearlite did not clearly appear in photographs. Esser and Cornelius [25] reported that the formation of pearlite was seen as a darkening of the polished surface due to the development of surface relief during the transformation.

In recent work in our laboratory we made use of phase-contrast objectives to study the pearlite transformation in a binary Fe-0.8C alloy and in ternary iron-carbon alloys containing molybdenum, nickel, cobalt, manganese, and silicon. An example of this hot-stage technique applied to the pearlite transformation in an Fe-0.8C alloy is shown in Fig. 15 where the arrows indicate four different pearlite nodules growing in a matrix of austenite. This technique facilitated studying the effects of alloying on the C-curve behavior of pearlite [34], as well as the effect of cooling rate on the growth rate of pearlite [35]. It has been our experience that as contrasted with the tedious isothermal salt-bath techniques, the hot-stage technique has the advantage that measurements can be made on a single specimen in which growth rates of various nodules can be measured simultaneously.

*Austenite to Bainite Transformation*

The study of the bainite transformation by hot-stage microscopy found immediate application because of the surface shears and slow growth associated with this phase change. A major contribution to the study of bainite was made by Speich [16] and Speich and Cohen [36] who used hot-stage microscopy to determine the isothermal growth rates of lower bainite. These results showed that growth rate was independent of time at constant temperature and that edgewise and sidewise growth rates increased with temperature, the edgewise growth being in the range of $10^{-1}$ $\mu$m/s and the sidewise growth being about an order of magnitude less. For upper bainite Goodenow et al [37] found that the isothermal growth rate continued to increase with temperature, in the range of 5 by $10^{-2}$ to 1 $\mu$m/s, depending on the alloy. In such studies the hot stage was also used to characterize the morphological differences between upper and lower bainite. Kurdman and Freiwillig's studies [38] of bainite with both hot-stage microscopy and quantitative microscopy gave identical results for both methods but pointed up the advantage of less time required for the hot-stage method. Other investigators used hot-stage microscopy to study the effect of carbon and nickel on the bainite transformation [39], the effect of stress on the transformation [40], and the effects of segregation on the bainite transformation in alloy steels [41].

Our hot-stage microscope, incorporating controlled cooling, was well suited for the study of the morphological changes taking place during the formation of continuously cooled bainite. Thus, for a low-alloy steel (0.26C, 0.77Mn, 0.95Cr, 1.00Mo, and 0.25V) that we continuously cooled at the rate of 6°C/s,

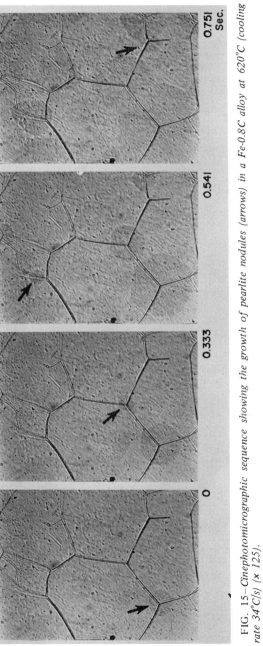

FIG. 15—Cinephotomicrographic sequence showing the growth of pearlite nodules (arrows) in a Fe-0.8C alloy at 620°C (cooling rate 34°C/s) (× 125).

Fig. 16 shows sequentially the development of a bainite which is like "upper bainite" produced by isothermal treatment. Measurements showed the edgewise growth rate to be about 3 to 5 $\mu m/s$.

## Austenite to Martensite Transformation

Hot-stage microscopy is easily adaptable to the study of martensite because of the surface shears associated with this type of transformation. $M_s$ temperatures [42] and the effects of grain size on the martensite transformation [43] have been determined by direct visual observation in the microscope. High-speed cinephotomicrography has been used by Mitsche et al [15] in determining the growth rates and morphology of plate martensite in high-alloy steels. They found that the longitudinal growth rate of plates ranged from 16 to 2000 $\mu m/s$ and that the plates developed by the multiple repetition of individual steps similar to twinning.

The lath martensite transformation in iron-nickel alloys was studied in the hot stage by both Dubrov [11] and Bryans et al [44]. This transformation in iron-nickel and other iron alloys has also been carefully studied in a series of hot-stage microscopic studies in our laboratory, and some of the key results on growth rate and morphology are as follows. Studies on iron-nickel [45], iron-carbon [46], and iron-molybdenum [47] alloys show recorded growth rates ranging from 70 to 800 $\mu m/s$. More significantly, these hot-stage studies made it possible to document the morphological development of a packet of lath martensite. The sequence of cinephotomicrographs prepared for the present paper (Fig. 17) show the formation of lath martensite in a low-alloy steel (0.26C, 0.77Mn, 0.95Cr, 1.00Mo, and 0.25V). A striking similarity can be seen between the formation of lath martensite in Fig. 17 and the formation of bainite in Fig. 16. However, the cooling rates and growth rates are very different. For example, the cooling rate for the formation of lath martensite is about three times faster than that for the bainite transformation and the time lapse shown in Fig. 17 is about eight times faster than for the bainite transformation shown in Fig. 16. That the lath martensite transformation is not merely a surface phenomenon was also clearly demonstrated by these studies, which provided ample metallographic evidence of direct correspondence between the bulk microstructure and surface shears produced by the hot stage [45-47].

In summary, this paper has shown how the effectiveness of hot-stage microscopy as a tool for the study of ferrous phase transformations has been increased by improvements in associated equipment and procedures. These improvements include furnace arrangements, specimen preparation, choice of atmosphere, control of temperature and cooling rate, and the use of special optics.

The use of hot-stage microscopy was discussed in terms of examples from a range of phase transformations of practical interest to ferrous metallurgists. It is hoped that these examples, together with key findings drawn from both American and foreign literature, will provide a useful reference on the state of the art of hot-stage microscopy studies of ferrous transformations.

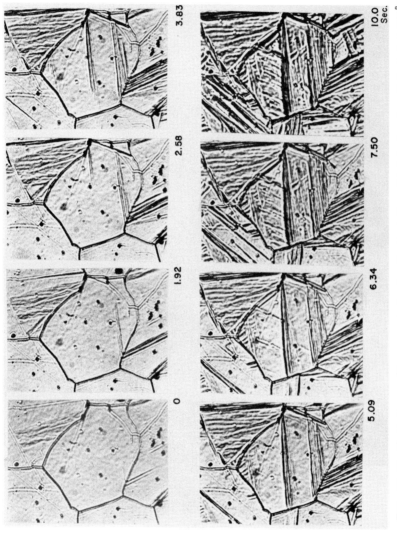

FIG. 16—*Cinephotomicrographic sequence showing the formation of bainite in a low-alloy steel at 550°C (cooling rate of 6.2°C/s) (× 227).*

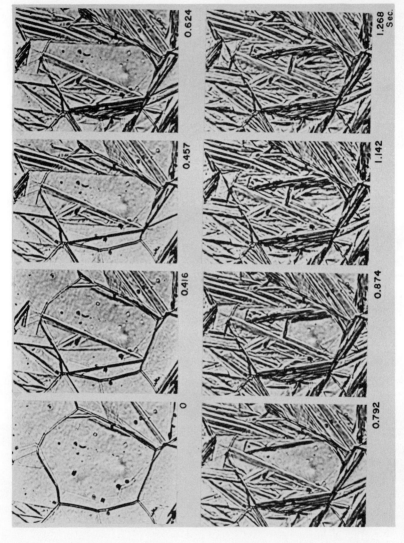

FIG. 17—Cinephotomicrographic sequence showing the formation of lath martensite in a low-alloy steel at 330°C (cooling rate of 17°C/s) (× 227).

*Acknowledgments*

We wish to express appreciation to B.S. Mikofsky for his assistance in the editing of this paper.

## References

[1]  Lozinskii, M.G., *High Temperature Metallography,* Pergamon Press, New York, 1961.

[2]  Benscoter, A.O., Kilpatrick, J.R., Wolf, R.P., and Marder, A.R., *Microstructures,* Vol. 1 No. 1, 1970, p. 21.

[3]  Gabler, F., *Freiberger Forschungshefte,* No. B111, Dec. 1965, p. 27.

[4]  Olson, D.M., Brixner, B.B., and Smith, M.C., *Metal Progress,* Vol. 81, No. 6, 1962, p. 75.

[5]  Thorsen, K.A., *Praktische Metallographie,* Vol. 4, No. 9, 1967, p. 443.

[6]  Olney, M.J. and Smith G.C., *Journal of the Iron and Steel Institute,* Vol. 193, 1959, p. 107.

[7]  Saller, H.A., Dickerson, R.F., and Carlson, R.J., *Metal Progress,* Vol. 67, No. 5, 1955, p. 105.

[8]  Stransky, K. and Kralova, M., *Metal Treatment and Drop Forging,* July 1964, p. 255.

[9]  Jenkins, J.E., Buchele, D.R., and Long, R.A., *Metal Progress,* Vol. 67, No. 5, 1955, p. 101.

[10]  Okamoto, M., Miyagana, O., and Saga, T., *Transactions,* Japan Institute of Metals, Vol. 7, 1966, p. 217.

[11]  Dubrov, V.A., *Fizika Metallov I Metallovedeniee,* Vol. 21, No. 4, 1966, p. 551.

[12]  Ko, T. and Cottrell, S.A., *Journal of the Iron and Steel Institute,* Vol. 152, 1952, p. 307.

[13]  Mitsche, R., Gabler, F., and Jeglitsch, F., *Powder Metallurgy in Nuclear Engineer,* 4th Plansee Seminar, June 1961, Reutte/Tirol, Austria, p. 799.

[14]  Speich, G.R. and Miller, R.L., *Review of Scientific Instruments,* Vol. 31, No. 6, 1960, p. 658.

[15]  Mitsche, R., Gabler, F., Jeglitsch, F., and Burkert, D.G., *Radex-Rundschau,* Vols. 3 and 4, 1967, p. 705.

[16]  Speich, G.R., *Decomposition of Austenite by Diffusional Processes,* Interscience, New York, 1962, p. 353.

[17]  Naumann, F.K., *Praktische Metallographie,* Vol. 5, No. 9, 1968, p. 473.

[18]  Kulmberg, A., Rudolfs, M., and Swoboda, K., *Praktische Metallographie,* Vol. 1, No. 1, 1964, pp. 19-24.

[19]  Kulmberg, A., Block, R., Swoboda, K., and Plockinger, E., *Berg und Hüttenmannische Monatshefte,* 109, 1964, pp. 114-119.

[20]  Kulmberg, A. and Bloch, R., *Radex-Rundschau,* Vols. 3 and 4, 1967, pp. 699-704.

[21]  Mitsche, R. and Jeglitsch, F., *Haerterei: Technische Mitteilungen,* Vol. 15, 1961, pp. 201-218.

[22]  Jeglitsch, F., *Praktische Metallographie,* Vol. 4, No. 2, 1967, pp. 53-64.

[23]  Kulmberg, A. and Swoboda, K., *Praktische Metallographie,* Vol. 7, No. 1, 1970, pp. 25-38.

[24]  Rogers, B.A., *Metals and Alloys,* Vol. 2, 1931, pp. 9-12.

[25]  Esser, H. and Cornelius, H., *Stahl and Eisen,* Vol. 53, 1933, pp. 532-535.

[26]  Mitsche, R., Gabler, F., and Wurz, W., *Aluminum,* Vol. 10, 1961, pp. 652-662.

[27]  Borchers, H. and Boxhorn, G., *Archiv fuer das Eisenhüttenwessen,* Vol. 29, 1958, pp. 47-56.

[28]  Pfeiffer, I., *Zeitschrift fur Metallkunde,* Vol. 48, 1957, pp. 171-175.

[29]  Kulmberg, A., *Radex-Rundschau,* Vols. 3 and 4, 1967, pp. 685-691.

[30]  Jeglitsch, F., *Radex-Rundschau,* Vols. 3 and 4, 1967, pp. 691-694.

[31]  Leont'yen, B.A. and Kachanov, G. Ye., *Fizika Metallov I Metallovedeniee,* Vol. 27, 1969, pp. 856-860.

[32]  Kogan, L.I., Fayvilevich, G.A., and Entin, R.I., *Fizika Metallov I Metallovedeniee,* pp. 696-702.

[*33*] Dichtl, H.J. and Jeglitsch, F., *Radex-Rundschau,* Vols. 3 and 4, 1967, pp. 716-722.

[*34*] Bramfitt, B.L. and Marder, A.R., *Metallurgical Transactions,* to be published.

[*35*] Bramfitt, B.L. and Marder, A.R., unpublished research.

[*36*] Speich, G.R. and Cohen, Morris, *Transactions,* American Institute of Mining and Metallurgical Engineers, AIME, Vol. 218, 1960, pp. 1050-1059.

[*37*] Goodenow, R.H., Matas, S.J., and Heheman, R.F., *Transactions,* American Institute of Mining, Metallurgical and Petroleum Engineers, AIME, Vol. 227, 1963, pp. 651-658.

[*38*] Kurdman, J. and Freiwillig, R., *Praktische Metallographie,* Vol. 5, No. 12, 1968, pp. 386-393.

[*39*] Yada, H. and Ooka, T., *Journal Japan Institute of Metals,* Vol. 31, 1967, pp. 766-771.

[*40*] Dubrov, V.A., *Fizika Metallov I Metallovendeniie,* Vol. 28, No. 2, 1969, pp. 309-314.

[*41*] Kulmberg, A. and Swoboda, K., *Praktische Metallographie,* Vol. 6, No. 7, 1969, pp. 383-400.

[*42*] Banerjee, B.R. and Hauser, J.J., *Metallography,* Vol. 1, No. 1, 1968, pp. 157-159.

[*43*] Swoboda, K., Kulmberg, A., and Schwarz, L., *Radex-Rundschau,* Vols. 3 and 4, 1967, pp. 819-824.

[*44*] Bryans, R.G., Bell, T., and Thomas, V.M., "The Mechanism of Phase Transformations in Solids," Institute of Metals, London, Monograph No. 33, 1969, p. 181.

[*45*] Marder, J.M. and Marder, A.R., *Transactions,* American Society for Metals, Vol. 62, 1969, pp. 1-10.

[*46*] Marder, A.R. and Krauss, G., *Transactions,* American Society for Metals, Vol. 62, 1969, pp. 957-964.

[*47*] Krauss, G. and Marder, A.R., *Metallurgical Transactions,* Vol. 2, 1971, pp. 2343-2357.

*R.J. Schaefer,*[1] *J.A. Blodgett,*[1] *and M.E. Glicksman*[1]

# Examination of Materials by Coherent Light Techniques

REFERENCE: Schaefer, R.J., Blodgett, J.A., and Glicksman, M.E., "**Examination of Materials by Coherent Light Techniques**," *Metallography—A Practical Tool for Correlating the Structure and Properties of Materials, ASTM STP 557,* American Society for Testing and Materials, 1974, pp. 71–85.

ABSTRACT: The diffraction and interference of coherent light from lasers can be used to record and analyze metallographic structures. Optical transforms, holography, optical correlation, and other coherent light methods are presently being applied to materials problems ranging from basic research to testing and inspection. This paper describes the basic concepts used in some of these methods and describes examples of their application. Holography is a particularly attractive method for measuring changes in the shapes of objects, especially because it allows interferometric measurements without special surface preparation. The use of holography for studies of crystal growth and electropolishing is described in some detail, and reconstructed holograms are shown. Holography and other coherent light techniques can often reveal the presence of defects or inhomogeneities even when quantitative evaluation of the optical output is difficult.

KEY WORDS: metallography, diffraction, holography, coherence, optical properties

The recent availability of lasers as sources of coherent light has stimulated extensive experimentation in new optical techniques for the evaluation of images. A wide variety of diffraction and interference effects can be used to measure shapes and shape changes and to analyze periodic structures. Applications range from basic research to assembly line inspection of manufactured products.

A coherent light image evaluation system may be thought of as a high speed analog computer. A major virtue of many such systems is their ability to simultaneously process optical information from an entire two-dimensional field of view. The optically processed information may thus be generated virtually as fast as specimens can be moved into position. Measurement and interpretation of the optical output, however, may be much more difficult. The output can be examined visually, photographically, or by photoelectric devices which can be part of a computer or servo system.

Materials scientists have used coherent light for many years in interference microscopy, and these techniques have become so well developed, and are so widely known, that they will not be reported here. Our attention will be

[1] Physicist, Metallurgy Division, physicist, Optical Sciences Division, and metallurgist, Metallurgy Division, respectively, Naval Research Laboratory, Washington, D.C. 20375.

directed to some less familiar or newer techniques, especially those which require better coherence of the illuminating light than that needed for conventional interference microscopy.

## Coherence

Coherence is a measure of the phase relationships in different parts of a beam of light. In an ideal perfectly coherent beam of light, the relative phase of the light at all points would remain fixed, a condition possible only with perfectly monochromatic light. No source of such light has yet been invented, but many lasers produce light which approaches this ideal condition.

Coherent light techniques generally utilize the interference between different portions of a light beam which have traversed different paths. If we consider a system in which a light beam is divided into two beams (by a beam splitter, for example) which later overlap after traversing different paths, we can distinguish several factors which could cause changes in the relative phase of the two beams and thus change the interference. Changes in the optical path difference, due either to the motion of optical components or to changes in the refractive index of the traversed media, produce corresponding changes in the relative phase of the overlapping waves. Furthermore, a change in wavelength of the light means that an optical path difference which remains constant when measured in centimeters will change when measured in wavelengths, thus again changing the interference pattern. Finally, if the light source produces more than one wavelength, the relative phase of the different wavelengths in the two beams cannot remain constant, except when the path difference is zero.

Analyses of partially coherent light and its influence on interference effects may be found in several texts on coherent optics and holography [1-3].[2] For many applications, a conveniently defined coherence length serves as a useful description of the coherence properties of the light source. For a source with spectral bandwidth $\Delta\nu$, we can define the coherence length $L = c/\Delta\nu$, where $c$ is the speed of light. Alternatively, the definition can be based on the visibility of the fringes produced by splitting the beam and recombining after traversing different path lengths. The visibility $(V)$ is defined as $V = (I_{max} - I_{min})/(I_{max} + I_{min})$, where $I_{max}$ and $I_{min}$ are the intensities at the brightest and dimmist parts of the fringes. The coherence length is defined as the maximum path difference which gives $V = 1/2$. The coherence length required for metallographic techniques will vary according to the technique used.

## Optical Transforms

A lens can be used to form the Fourier transform of the amplitude distribution in an image formed by coherent light. It is thus possible to view directly the spatial frequency spectrum of the amplitude in the image, and the

---

[2] The italic numbers in brackets refer to the list of references appended to this paper.

presence of periodic structures will be immediately apparent. Optical transforms can thus be used for inspection of machined surfaces, or of dendritic, eutectic, or fibrous materials.

The scattering of electromagnetic waves by periodic structures is a familiar subject to crystallographers. The very close analogy between the diffraction of X-rays by crystal lattices and the diffraction of light by macroscopic scatterers has been used to construct optical analogs to X-ray systems. Books by Taylor and Lipson [4] and by Lipson [5] describe the analogies between X-ray and optical diffraction and the significance of optical transforms as applied to the study of X-ray phenomena. Masks consisting of plates which are opaque in some regions and transparent in other regions are prepared, such that the light passing through them is analogous to the X-rays scattered from a crystal lattice. Many such masks and their optical transforms are shown in these works.

The formation of Fourier transforms by lenses is described in standard references on coherent optics [1,2]. The basic phenomenon is illustrated simply by considering a regular periodic object, such as a Ronchi ruling, placed in front of a lens and illuminated by coherent collimated light (Fig. 1).

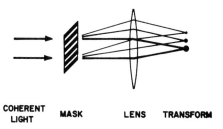

COHERENT LIGHT    MASK    LENS    TRANSFORM

FIG. 1—*Formation of an optical transform by a lens. Each Fourier component of the light amplitude in the object (in this case, a Ronchi ruling mask) produces a diffracted beam which comes to a focus in the back focal plane of the lens. The optical transform of the Ronchi ruling is a linear array of bright spots, only three of which are illustrated here.*

The amplitude distribution of this object is simply a square wave, which can be represented as the sum of Fourier components. Each component acts as a grating, diffracting a collimated beam at a specific angle. The diffracted collimated beam from each Fourier component will be focused at a point in the back focal plane of the lens, and the array of points will map out the Fourier spectrum of the Ronchi ruling.

An exact Fourier transform is produced in the back focal plane only when the object is placed in the front focal plane. However, objects placed any distance in front of the lens will produce a pattern which differs from the exact transform in phase distribution only. This difference is generally unimportant. The object can even be placed between the lens and the back focal plane; in this case the size of the transformed image will vary with the position of the object.

Application of optical transform techniques to the study of metal surfaces can be accomplished in several ways. Light can be reflected directly from the metal surface and through the lens, or photographs of the surface can be recorded and subsequently used as masks. The former has obvious advantages for routine testing, while the latter offers the possibility of processing for enhanced contrast or other desired characteristics.

In an application of coherent light to production line inspection, a beam of light from a small laser can be directed onto metal objects moving past an inspection station. At the back focal plane of a lens which gathers the light scattered from the objects, an optical transform will be formed. In many cases, the objects will normally have a surface structure which will be conspicuous in the transform. Arrays of parallel scratches or striations from machining or grinding operations will cause bright radial streaks in the transform plane. When such surface structures are present and acceptable, a mask can be prepared and placed in the transform plane to block the light in these radial streaks. No light will then be transmitted unless scratches running in directions other than that normally expected are present. These anomolous scratches will diffract light into unmasked portions of the transform plane, and a photodetector can then indicate a faulty unit. Sjolin [6] has described the application of such a system to the continuous inspection of sheet metal.

The radial and angular distribution of the light in the transform plane can be measured by an array of photodetectors, and compact units designed for this specific function are now commercially available. If an illuminating beam of rather small diameter is made to periodically scan across the object under study, more information is obtained about the size and form of the defects which scatter into the transform plane. The output from the photodetectors can then be analyzed by a computer to identify different types of defects [6].

Optical transform techniques have obvious potential for the inspection of periodic metallurgical microstructures such as eutectics or dendrites. The scarcity of such applications may be due in part to the prior availability of versatile and automated quantitative metallography systems. However, an optical transform system can be set up very easily by anyone possessing a small laser, yielding results which are informative, even if not always easily converted into quantitative data. Small irregularities in orientation or spacing of the microstructures can produce readily visible changes in the optical transform, thus indicating areas which require direct visual examination. Similarly, the transform of light scattered from the etched surface of a single crystal can indicate the magnitude of the misorientation at subboundaries, and thus serve as a convenient guide to X-ray investigation. The use of the transform allows very rapid scanning of a specimen surface, because the transform remains stationary when a periodic structure is scanned through the object plane, changing only when the periodicity or orientation of the structure changes.

To illustrate the application of optical transforms to the study of a solidification phenomenon, Ostwald ripening in a transparent analog to a metal alloy [7] was observed. A two-component organic mixture was sandwiched between glass microscope slides, heated to produce complete melting, and then allowed to cool to room temperature, where the equilibrium state was a mixture of solid and liquid. A circular area ~ 5 mm in diameter was illuminated by a helium-neon laser and the transform of the transmitted light was formed by a 50-mm lens. During cooling, dendritic crystals grew through the field of view and diffracted the coherent laser light. Figures 2a and b show the transforms of one area immediately after appearance of the dendrites and 5 min later. The bright streaks due to the primary dendrites are relatively stable, but satellite clouds due to small branches disappear as the branches coarsen by an Ostwald ripening process.

Quantitative evaluation of these observations is complicated by the finite thickness of the specimen and by an image consisting primarily of phase rather than amplitude variations. This is a common situation, however, in fiber technology, and light scattering by translucent fibers has been analyzed in detail [8]. Phase variations also occur in light reflected from metal surfaces, because the path length is affected by scratches. Phase variations in the object plane affect the amplitudes in the transform plane, but they do not change the position of spots caused by features of a given periodicity.

## Holography

A hologram is a recording, on some photo-sensitive medium, of the amplitude and phase of coherent light scattered from an object. When the hologram is illuminated by monochromatic light, it can reproduce the amplitude and phase of this scattered light, and thus reconstruct an image of the original object. This reconstructed image has unique properties which make it especially useful for quantitative observations of the shapes of objects. Objects everywhere within the field of view of the hologram are reconstructed in sharp focus, irrespective of their distance from the plane of the hologram. Because the hologram reconstructs the phase, as well as the amplitude, of the light scattered from the object, several interferometric techniques can be used to make precision measurements of the object. Holography is more difficult and costly than conventional photography, and its application is usually advantageous only when one makes use of these special depth-of-focus and phase information properties. Holography can be useful for applications ranging from basic research to nondestructive testing.

To form a hologram, an object is illuminated by coherent monochromatic light from a laser. The light scattered from the object is allowed to fall upon a high resolution photo-sensitive emulsion (film or plate). Simultaneously, a portion of the laser beam is split off before striking the object, and is directed onto the emulsion by a path which bypasses the object (Fig. 3). The second, or reference, beam forms an interference pattern when combined with the

*a.*
Immediately after growth of dendrites.

FIG. 2—*Optical transforms of transparent organic materials with dendritic morphology, showing the effect of the elimination of small branches by Ostwald ripening.*

*b.*
Five minutes after growth of dendrites.

FIG. 2–*Continued.*

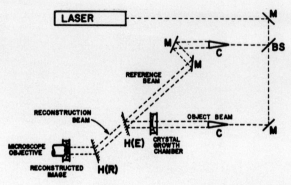

FIG. 3—*An optical system for recording and reconstructing holograms of a crystal growth chamber.* M = mirror, BS = beam splitter, C = collimator, H(E) = hologram during exposure, ' H(R) = hologram during reconstruction. A real image of the crystal growth chamber is reconstructed, to allow high resolution microscopic viewing.

first, or object, beam, and this interference pattern is recorded on the emulsion to form the hologram. Because the reference beam must be coherent with the object beam, the path lengths of the object and reference beams must be approximately equal, with their path difference less than the coherence length of the laser.

When the processed hologram is illuminated by laser light, the recorded interference pattern diffracts light to reconstruct an image of the original object. If the reconstruction beam duplicates the original reference beam, then a virtual image is seen by looking through the hologram. A reconstructed real image is formed when the reconstruction beam is the conjugate of the original reference beam. This real image is most easily produced if both reference and reconstruction beams are collimated, and the hologram is rotated 180 deg about a vertical axis between exposure and reconstruction (Fig. 3).

For studies of microscopic phenomena, it is preferable to reconstruct a real image which can be studied conveniently at higher magnification with a microscope. The best resolution is generally obtained by using optical elements (for example, lenses) between the object and the hologram [9,10], although this restricts the field of view of the resulting hologram.

For the materials scientist, the most exciting applications of holography involve interferometry. To date, several techniques have proven useful. When a real image is used, the dimensions of a reconstructed object can be measured by interference between the reconstructed image and a plane wave, introduced by a beamsplitter positioned between the hologram and the reconstructed image (Fig. 4). In double-exposure holography, two exposures of a scene are recorded on the same hologram. Interference fringes in the reconstructed image then reveal the minute changes in the scene which occurred in the interval between the exposures. In real-time holography, a hologram of an object is developed in place, or carefully repositioned, so that the reconstructed virtual image coincides with the object itself. Any changes in the dimensions of the object are then revealed in real time by interference fringes.

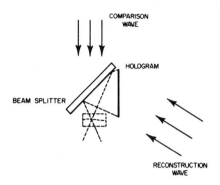

FIG. 4–*Interferometric analysis of a real image reconstructed from a hologram. The reconstructed image is reflected from the front surface of the beam splitter, and it interferes with a comparison wave transmitted through the beam splitter.*

In time-averaged holography, a hologram of a vibrating object is recorded with an exposure several times as long as the vibration period. Interference fringes in the reconstructed hologram delineate contours of constant vibrational amplitude. Many variations on these basic interferometric techniques are being constantly developed and applied.

There are several situations in which holographic interferometry is advantageous over conventional interferometry, especially where materials are being observed while undergoing shape changes. When transient events of interest take place at unpredictable locations, holography can record an entire specimen for later detailed interferometric observation at all points. Double-exposure and real-time holography record changes in specimen shape, even when the surface of the specimen is much too rough for conventional interferometry. Holographic interferometry has no particular advantages for the study of static polished metallographic specimens.

In applications of holography to research on phase transformations, we have recorded holograms of the solidification of transparent analogs to metals [*11,12*] and of the electropolishing of metals. For the observation of solidification, holography uniquely makes possible the recording of transient events occurring at unpredictable locations. Crystallization events throughout the volume of a relatively large study chamber can be observed microscopically in the reconstructed image. Moreover, the transient shapes of the crystals can be measured in detail, and interferometric techniques can be used to map out the growth rates at all points on the crystal surface.

Transmitted light is used to record the holograms of transparent materials as shown in Fig. 3. The laser indicated here is a continuous wave argon ion laser producing approximately 2.5 W in each of the two major lines, 488.0 and 514.5 nm. For our experiments, the 514.5-nm line is used because it is more visible to the eye in reconstruction. The holograms are recorded in plane "H(E)". In normal usage, 35-mm film is exposed in a motorized camera body. This is a standard rangefinder type camera with a focal plane shutter. Agfa-

Gevaert Scientia 10E56 emulsion is used in most of our studies. This film has a holographic resolution of better than 2800 cycles/mm and requires approximately 10 ergs/cm² to expose for a density of 0.6.

On reconstruction, the real image is examined with a microscope in an X-Y-Z mount. The resolution of the reconstructed image is ~ 400 cycles/mm, and to obtain optimum image quality it is necessary to sandwich the film between two pieces of flat glass with an index matching fluid. Emulsions on glass plates are used when still better image quality is required.

Double-exposure techniques and interferometry on reconstructed real images are used to measure the growing crystals. Each interference fringe corresponds to an optical path length difference of one wavelength ($\lambda$), corresponding to a crystal thickness of $\Delta h = \lambda / \Delta n$, where $\Delta n$ is the refractive index difference between solid and liquid. Figure 5 shows a reconstructed hologram of a region of solid-liquid interface, with interference fringes showing surface relief developing near grain boundaries and near an undissolved impurity particle. Figure 6 shows an array of dendrites with side branches beginning to form. We have used interferometric measurements from these and other holograms to study the stability of solid-liquid interfaces, the influence of defects on this stability, and the anisotropy of crystal growth.

The electropolishing of copper in a phosphoric acid solution is now under study by double-exposure techniques, which allow measurement of the streaming of electrolyte and of local rates of metal removal. In this case, the system of Fig. 3 is modified to record light reflected from the surface of the metal specimen. Figure 7 shows reconstructions from two double-exposure holograms of a copper specimen which was masked by a transparent coating except for a 5 mm square in which electropolishing occurred. In Fig. 7a, the exposures were made before the start of polishing and 2 min after the start of polishing. The fringes within the unmasked square area result from optical path length changes due to both metal removal and change in composition of the electrolyte. The fringes in the area below the square result only from the accumulation of streaming electrolyte. In Fig. 7b, the exposures were recorded 8 and 10 min after the start of polishing. The absence of fringes in the area below the square indicates that the streaming of electrolyte has reached a steady-state condition. The fringes within the unmasked area are, therefore, due only to metal removal. Each fringe represents a line of constant metal removal rate. From this hologram, it is not possible to determine the absolute rates of removal, because a sharp step, on which the fringes are unresolved, is forming at the edge of the unmasked area. The fringes show local differences in removal rate, with successive fringes differing in removal by $\Delta R = \lambda / 2n\Delta t$, where $\lambda$ is the wavelength, $n$ is the refractive index of the electrolyte, and $\Delta t$ is the time interval between exposures. In this case, $\lambda = 514.5$ nm, $n = 1.424$, and $\Delta t = 120$ s, so $\Delta R = 1.51$ nm/s. These experiments are being used to identify the factors which lead to nonuniform polishing.

Our own experiments illustrate the use of holography for research in phase transformations. Holography also has many applications to nondestructive

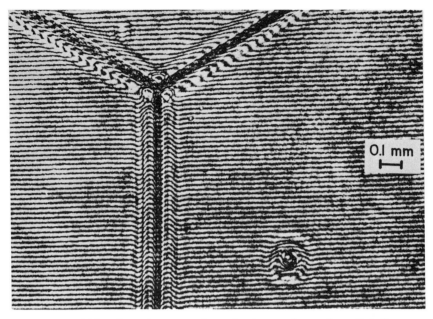

FIG. 5–*A solid-liquid interface in camphene, showing transient surface relief adjacent to a grain boundary trijunction and an impurity particle. The interference fringes were generated using the arrangement of Fig. 4, and each fringe represents a height* $\Delta h$ *of 18.5* $\mu$m.

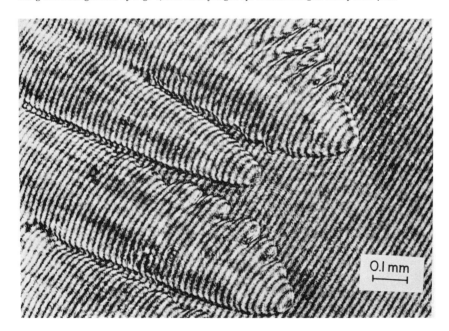

FIG. 6–*Dendrites of camphene, reconstructed from a hologram. The arrangement of Fig. 4 was used to generate the interference fringes, with the beam splitter being tilted to align the fringes perpendicular to the dendrite axis.*

*a.*
0 to 2 min, showing accumulation of viscous surface layer streaming from polishing area.

FIG. 7—*Double-exposure holograms of an electropolishing copper specimen. The surface is masked by a transparent, nonconductive coating except for the 5-mm-square window.*

*b.*
8 to 10 min, showing removal of metal after streaming electrolyte has reached steady state.

FIG. 7–*Continued.*

testing, with double-exposure techniques being especially useful. When two exposures of an object in different states of stress are recorded on a single hologram, the reconstructed image will show fringes delineating the change in shape of the object. Any weak point or flaw which produces an inhomogeneous displacement of a few microns will produce conspicuous interference effects. This technique is particularly useful in testing bonded composites [13]. Holography now promises to become one of the major tools of nondestructive testing and experimental mechanics [14,15].

## Optical Correlation

Optical correlation is a method for comparing one image to another, and it has obvious applications in fields such as pattern recognition or the reading of printed characters. Marom and Mueller [16] demonstrated that it can also be a sensitive detector of deformation in metals.

The first step in an optical correlation experiment is to record a hologram of the object which is to be the standard for comparison, for example an undeformed metal specimen. The processed hologram is then illuminated not by a duplicate of the original reference wave, but by light scattered from the test object. If the test object is identical to the comparison standard, (for example, if the metal specimen has remained undeformed) then the light scattered from the test object will be diffracted by the hologram to reconstruct the original reference beam. This reconstructed reference beam can be focused to a small diameter spot, which can pass through a pinhole and be measured by a photodetector. Distortions in the test object will cause corresponding distortions in the reconstructed reference beam. The light passing through the pinhole, which is a measure of the optical correlation, will then decrease. Marom and Mueller showed that this technique can readily detect the small deformations due to impending fatigue failure in metal specimens. They found that no special surface preparation was necessary, and in fact polished surfaces were less desirable than rough surfaces.

Although optical correlation cannot provide such detailed information on the localization of strains as can real-time holographic interferometry, it produces an output signal in a convenient form which is easy to monitor.

## Summary

Coherent light provides new opportunities for the evaluation of metallographic structures and for studying the response of materials to external stimuli. The most significant applications lie in the detection by holography or optical correlation of small displacements or deformations of surfaces. In many cases, no special surface preparation is required. For microscopic phenomena, the application of interference techniques is broadened greatly by the use of holography. Optical transforms provide a rapid method for studying periodic structures, and the output is relatively easy to process.

We have described here only the most basic forms of some coherent light techniques. A wide variety of modifications and combinations of these techniques can be used for specific applications. The information content in the output of a coherent light experiment is immense, and interpretation of this output is frequently the major challenge to the investigator.

# References

[1] Goodman, J.W., *Introduction to Fourier Optics,* McGraw-Hill, New York, 1968.
[2] Smith, H.M., *Principles of Holography,* Wiley-Interscience, New York, 1969.
[3] Françon, M., *Optical Interferometry,* Academic Press, New York, 1966.
[4] Taylor, C.A. and Lipson, H., *Optical Transforms,* Cornell University Press, Ithaca, New York, 1965.
[5] Lipson, H.S., *Optical Transforms,* Academic Press, New York, 1972.
[6] Sjolin, Ulf, *Laser Focus,* Vol. 8, No. 7, July 1972, pp. 41-42.
[7] Jackson, K.A. and Hunt, J.D., *Acta Metallurgica,* Vol. 13, 1965, pp. 1212-1215.
[8] Charrier, J.M. and Marchessault, R.H., *Fibre Science and Technology,* Vol. 5, 1972, pp. 263-284.
[9] van Ligten, R.F. and Osterberg, H., *Nature,* Vol. 211, 1966, pp. 282-283.
[10] Toth, L. and Collins, S.A., *Applied Physics Letters,* Vol. 13, 1968, pp. 7-9.
[11] Glicksman, M.E., Schaefer, R.J., and Blodgett, J.A., *Journal of Crystal Growth,* Vols. 13 and 14, 1972, pp. 68-72.
[12] Blodgett, J.A. and Schaefer, R.J., "Design and Applications of a Holographic System for Crystal-Growth Studies," NRL Report 7498, Naval Research Laboratory, Washington, D.C., Jan. 1973.
[13] Wells, D.R., *Materials Evaluation,* Vol. 27, 1969, pp. 225-231.
[14] Vest, C.M., *International Journal of Nondestructive Testing,* Vol. 3, 1972, pp. 351-374.
[15] Sampson, R.C., *Experimental Mechanics,* Vol. 10, 1970, pp. 313-320.
[16] Marom, E. and Mueller, R.K., *International Journal of Nondestructive Testing,* Vol. 3, 1971, pp. 171-187.

*J.I. Goldstein*[1]

# The Electron Microprobe as a Metallographic Tool

**REFERENCE:** Goldstein, J.I., "The Electron Microprobe as a Metallographic Tool," *Metallography—A Practical Tool for Correlating the Structure and Properties of Materials, ASTM STP 557,* American Society for Testing and Materials, 1974, pp. 86–136.

**ABSTRACT:** The electron microprobe (EMP) is an electron optical instrument in which compositional and topographic information are obtained from regions $\leqslant 1 \mu m$ in diameter on a specimen. Photographs of compositional and topographic changes in $1\text{-mm}^2$ to $20\text{-}\mu m^2$ areas on various types of specimens can also be obtained which are strikingly similar to optical photomicrographs. This paper discusses the various signals that are measured in the EMP (X-rays, secondary electrons, backscattered electrons, etc.), their resolution, and the types of information that can be obtained. In addition to elemental analysis, the solid state detector and scanning techniques will be discussed. The last sections will cover characterization of phases-homogeneity-trace element analysis-quantitative metallography and various techniques which extend the instrument capabilities such as deconvolution and soft X-ray analysis. Various applications will be discussed and illustrated.

**KEY WORDS:** metallography X-ray spectra, quantitative analysis, electron probe, spectroscopy, resolution, background, microanalysis, X-ray spectrometers, solid state counters, trace element analysis, homogeneity

The electron microprobe (EMP) is one of the most powerful techniques for the examination of the microstructure of materials. The instrument employs a high voltage electron beam (1 to 30 kV) focused to $\leqslant 1$ $\mu m$ in diameter, and information such as composition and topography are obtained from the bombarded region. The characteristic X-ray spectra emitted by the specimen allows its elemental composition to be determined. By combining electron beam scanning and X-ray detection, the EMP becomes a logical extension of the optical microscope. The spatial distribution of one or several elements in a fixed area of a specimen can be obtained by this technique. In addition, topographic information is obtained when other signals, specimen current, backscattered electrons (BSE), cathodoluminescence, and secondary electrons (SE) are collected in the scanning mode. General descriptions of the electron probe technique can be found in various references [1-3].[2]

---

[1] Associate professor, Department of Metallurgy and Materials Science, Lehigh University, Bethlehem, Pa. 18015.

[2] The italic numbers in brackets refer to the list of references appended to this paper.

## Electron Microprobe

### Electron Probe Diameter and Current

In the EMP a two- or three-lens system is used to demagnify the crossover image formed in the electron gun. The submicron electron beam which is produced bombards the specimen surface. A schematic drawing of the electron optical column of the Applied Research Laboratory (ARL) electron optical system is shown in Fig. 1. The amount of current in the finely focused electron

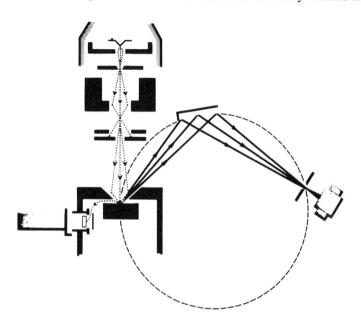

FIG. 1—*Schematic drawing of the electron optical column of the ARL electron microprobe. The X-ray focusing optics and secondary electron collection system are also illustrated.*

beam which impinges on the specimen determines the magnitude of the signals (X-ray, sample current, etc.) emitted, other things being equal. In addition, the size of the final probe spot determines the resolution of the instrument, although in many cases it does not determine the excitation volume from which the signal is produced. Therefore, the electron optical system in the EMP is designed such that the maximum possible current is obtained in the smallest possible electron probe.

It is possible to determine the maximum current ($i$) available in an electron probe of diameter ($d_p$) when the effects of aberrations in the electron optical system, chromatic, spherical, and diffraction are considered together. Pease and Nixon [4] calculated the theoretical limits to probe current and probe diameter by considering only spherical aberrations and diffraction. They obtained the following relation

$$i_{max} = 1.26 \frac{J_c}{T} \left(\frac{0.51 \, d_p{}^{8/3}}{C_s{}^{2/3} \, \lambda^2}\right) - 1 \quad 10^{-10} \tag{1}$$

where

$J_c$ = emission current density ($A/cm^2$) of the filament,
$T$ = temperature of the filament (K),
$C_s$ = spherical aberration coeefficient (cm), and
$\lambda$ = wavelength of the electrons (cm).

It can be seen from Eq 1 that the incident beam current will vary with the 8/3 power of the probe diameter. Figure 2 illustrates the relationships between probe current and the size of the electron beam as given by Eq 1 at two operating voltages of 15 and 30 kV. The values of $C_s$ (2 cm), $J_c$ (2.0 to 4.0A /cm²), and $T$ (2700 to 2820 K) that were chosen, are typical of operational instruments using a tungsten hairpin filament.

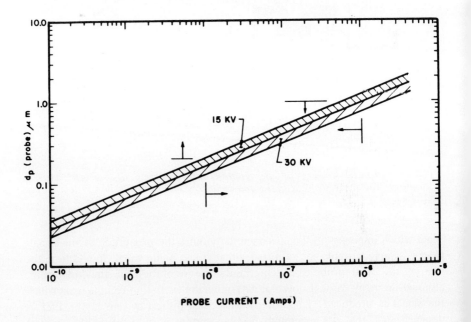

MICROANALYSIS RANGE

FIG. 2–*Relationship between probe current and electron beam diameter,* $d_p$. *The curves are given for two accelerating voltages, 15 and 30 kV.*

It can be observed from Fig. 2, that the maximum current available in a 1-$\mu$m electron beam using a conventional tungsten filament is 0.5 to 1.0 x $10^{-6}$ A at 15 kV and 1.0 to 2.0 x $10^{-6}$ A at 30 kV. This amount of current is well above the minimum (1.0 x $10^{-8}$ A) normally considered necessary to perform satisfactory quantitative X-ray analysis with X-ray, wavelength dispersive spectrometers. Successful X-ray analysis can, therefore, be obtained using a tungsten filament with minimum electron beam sizes ($d_p$) of the order of 0.25 $\mu$m. As will be discussed later, a spot size of 0.25 $\mu$m is usually well below the diameter of the region of X-ray emission from the specimen.

## Resolution of the Emitted Signals

A large number of interactions occur when a focused electron beam impinges on the specimen surface. Among the signals produced are SE, BSE, characteristic and continuum X-rays, and photons of various energies (Fig. 3). Each of these signals are obtained from specific emission volumes within the specimen and these are strong functions of electron beam voltage and the atomic number of the specimen. In fact the resolution of the EMP, for a particular signal, is primarily determined by its excitation volume and not by the electron probe size.

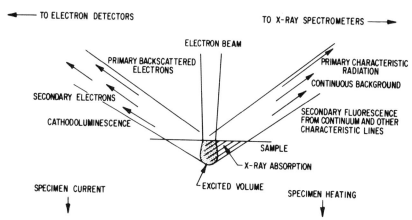

FIG. 3–*Signals produced when a focused high voltage electron beam bombards the specimen surface.*

Electrons having energies in the range 1 to 30 kV impinging on the solid specimen, undergo elastic scattering (change of direction with negligible energy loss) and inelastic scattering (energy loss with negligible change in direction). Elastic scattering is caused mainly by interactions with the nucleus and significant deviations from the incident direction occur. Inelastic scattering is caused by two mechanisms; inelastic interaction with the atomic nucleus and inelastic interaction with the bound electrons.

Inelastic scattering is primarily responsible for producing the signals that one attempts to utilize (Fig. 3). If inelastic scattering occurs through interaction with the nucleus of the atoms, the moving electrons lose energy in the coulomb field of the nucleus and emit white or continuum X-ray radiation. If inelastic collisions occur between the loosely bound outer electrons and the incoming beam, energy is lost and SE are produced. The SE which are no longer bound to the original atom have an energy typically less than or equal to ~ 50 eV. If the SE recombine with the holes formed during the scattering process, a photon of energy is produced which has a wavelength in the visible or near infrared range. This visible luminescence can be seen optically when one is analyzing transparent materials. In all of these inelastic collisions, the process is combined with the loss of some or all of the incoming energy of the electrons. Inelastic collisions can also occur between the incident electrons and the inner electrons of the atoms. In this case characteristic X-ray lines are obtained. The primary electron (PE) beam loses energy equivalent to the binding energies of the $K, L, M$, etc. shells, $V_K, V_L, V_M$, etc.

Elastic scattering results in a large change of direction of the impinging electron beam. At some depth within the target the original direction of the electron beam is lost and the electrons diffuse through the material at random. The position at which this occurs is called the depth of complete diffusion ($X_d$). The scattering cross section at constant energy varies with $Z^2$, and the probability of scattering through a given angle varies as $Z^2/V^2$. For low atomic number specimens, there is not much scattering near the surface of the specimen as the electrons enter. Only a few electrons are scattered through large angles and leave the specimen as BSE. In a high atomic number specimen, however, there is considerable scattering close to the surface and a large fraction of the incoming electrons are backscattered. In the case of a heavy element, such as gold, diffusion sets in much nearer the surface than for a light element. The shape of the electron distribution within the target as a function of voltage and atomic number can, therefore, be determined qualitatively as discussed by Duncumb and Shields [5], Fig. 4. This figure shows the electron distribution as a function of depth $z$ and the outside limits of the distribution represent zero voltage. At the same voltage, the electrons appear to penetrate more deeply into the low atomic number element and the electron distribution appears to be more pear-shaped. If the energy of the incident electrons is increased, the path length of each electron is lengthened, and the envelope is expanded but retains essentially the same shape.

*Electron Range and Spatial Resolution of the Primary Electron Beam*

The electron range ($R$) is defined as the distance (measured from the surface of the specimen) that the electron penetrates into the specimen. The spatial resolution is the spread of the electron beam laterally from the center of impact. For the incident electrons, the electron range and the spatial resolution are similar in value since they are both defined by the amount of elastic scattering.

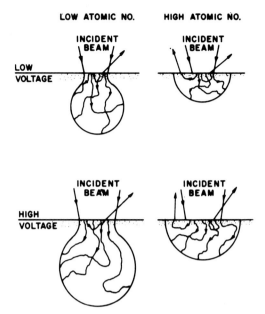

FIG. 4–*The shape of the electron scattering distribution within the target as a function of voltage and atomic number.*

Kanaya and Okayama [6] have derived an expression for the maximum range $(R)$ where the electron beam energy is reduced to zero using a total scattering cross section which takes into account both elastic and inelastic collisions. The range $(R)$ is expressed as

$$R = 0.0276 V_o^{1.67} \, (A/Z)^{8/9}/\rho \qquad (2)$$

where $V_o$ is the high voltage given in kV, $\rho$ is the density in g/cc, and $R$ is in microns. Table 1 gives a comparison of experimental values of $R_{max}$ [7] and the calculated ranges $(R)$.

TABLE 1–*Electron range, maximum range* $R_{max}$ *measured versus R calculated* $(\mu m)$.

|     | 2.5 kV | | 5 kV | | 10 kV | | 15 kV | |
| --- | --- | --- | --- | --- | --- | --- | --- | --- |
|     | $R_{max}$ | $R$ | $R_{max}$ | $R$ | $R_{max}$ | $R$ | $R_{max}$ | $R$ |
| Al | 0.21 | 0.12 | 0.48 | 0.32 | 1.1 | 1.25 | ... | 2.4 |
| Cu | 0.07 | 0.05 | 0.18 | 0.13 | 0.47 | 0.47 | ... | 0.9 |
| Au | 0.03 | 0.03 | 0.08 | 0.10 | 0.22 | 0.28 | ... | 0.54 |

The calculated maximum range [6] appears to agree quite closely with the measured values of $R_{max}$ and can be used in a practical sense to determine the electron range for analysis. Other expressions for electron range are also available [3]. It is obvious that the electron range varies greatly with atomic number at a given voltage and that the spatial resolution of the electron beam can be improved by selecting low voltages for analysis.

## Backscattered Electrons

Backscattered electrons (BSE) are produced by elastic scattering of the primary electron beam. Because the amount of elastic scattering increases with atomic number $Z$, the fraction $\eta$ of electrons which are backscattered also increases [8,9]. If the specimen surface is rough, the BSE yield can be selectively absorbed or increased depending on the beam position. Therefore, the intensity of the BSE in the direction of the detector is also a function of the topography of the specimen. However, it should be noted that if the specimen is polished flat, as in the preparation of specimens for quantitative analysis, one can obtain the average atomic number of the analyzed area of the specimen.

The BSE have an electron range which is smaller than that of the electron beam $(R)$ and, therefore, the range and also the spatial resolution of the backscattered signal is improved over that of the primary electron beam. According to Cosslet and Thomas [10] the backscattered fraction comes from a "mean" depth of about $0.3\ R$ in copper to $0.2\ R$ in gold at 25 kV. Shimizu and Murata [11] have calculated that the vast majority of electrons are backscattered laterally with a small diameter, about $R/2$.

## Low Energy Secondary Electrons

The secondary electrons (SE) have an energy typically less than 50 eV. If these SE are produced within a few hundred angstroms of the surface, they have a high probability of escaping from the specimen. These electrons are absorbed, however, if they are produced much below (>500Å) the surface of the specimen. For metals and coated specimens this value is smaller (>250Å). Within this maximum depth the spread of the primary beam is small. Therefore, the area from which the SE are produced, by the incident electron beam, is primarily limited by the electron probe spot size $(d_p)$. It is these low energy SE which are used in the scanning electron microscope (SEM) to obtain surface topography.

## X-ray Range and Spatial Resolution

When the electron beam strikes a specimen both continuum and characteristic X-rays are produced. The X-ray continuum varies in wavelength and can be excited as long as the electron beam voltage is greater than zero. The X-ray continuum forms the background X-ray radiation and determines the minimum detectability limit for the particular element that is measured, assuming that instrumental factors are negligible. The range for continuum X-ray production will be similar to that of the primary electron beam since X-radiation can be produced even at low electron energies.

The characteristic radiation is produced by the interaction of incident electrons with the inner shell electrons of the atoms in the specimen and the wavelengths of the characteristic radiation are specific for each element. Detection of a characteristic X-ray line indicates that the element is present in the specimen and these characteristic lines may also be used to obtain the composition of the specimen. The range for characteristic X-ray radiation $(R(x))$ will usually be smaller than that of electrons, since characteristic X-rays can only be produced at energies above the critical excitation potential $(V_c)$. Several equations for X-ray range $(R(x))$ have been developed [1,12-14]. The range equation obtained by Anderson and Hasler [13] where

$$R(x) = 0.064 \ (V_o^{1.68} - V_c^{1.68})/\rho \tag{3}$$

was based on experimental data and is probably more correct.

Figure 5 shows the X-ray range, calculated from Eq 3, for various X-ray lines $Al_{K\alpha}$, $Cu_{K\alpha}$, $Cu_{L\alpha}$, $Au_{L\alpha}$ generated within the element targets aluminum, copper, and gold as a function of operating voltage $V_o$. The three matrix elements shown in Fig. 5 were chosen to represent the

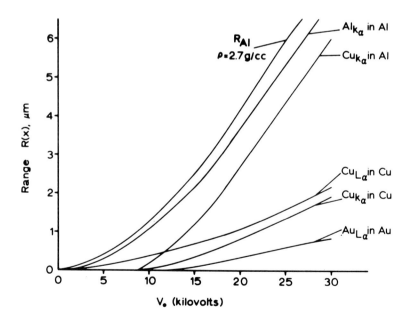

FIG. 5—*X-ray range* R(x) *for various X-ray lines (*$Al_{K\alpha}$, $Cu_{K\alpha}$, $Cu_{L\alpha}$, $Au_{L\alpha}$*) in selected targets* (aluminum, copper, gold).

range of specimen densities which are likely to be analyzed, and the X-ray lines were chosen to represent the common X-ray wavelength ranges measured. The electron range $(R)$ for aluminum [6] is shown for comparison purposes. The X-ray ranges depend not only on the density of the matrix (aluminum = 2.7 $g/cm^3$, copper = 8.93 $g/cm^3$, and gold = 19.3 $g/cm^3$) but, also, on the value of the energy of the X-ray line produced. One can see that, in general, to obtain an X-ray source size $\leqslant 1$ $\mu$m the voltage of the electron beam may have to be adjusted depending on the matrix material and line measured.

To define the X-ray source size or spatial resolution one can assume that the lateral X-ray production range is the same as $R(x)$, the X-ray range. This relation, however, assumes that the size of the electron beam impinging on the specimen is vanishingly small. The total X-ray spatial resolution $R_x$ is, therefore, equal to the sum of the X-ray range $(R(x))$ and the size of the electron beam $(d_p)$ hitting the specimen. As discussed previously, the electron beam size $(d_p)$ can be as small as 0.25 $\mu$m. Since the X-ray range $(R(x))$ is usually a micron or more, the total X-ray spatial resolution is essentially given by $R(x)$. Generally, there is little advantage for the X-ray spatial resolution, in reducing $d_p$ below 0.25 $\mu$m.

*Summary–Range and Spatial Resolution*

The result of electron beam specimen interactions is to produce various complex interactions. These interactions are responsible for the signals which can be used to reveal the topography and local chemistry of the specimen. Figure 6 summarizes the range and spatial resolutions of the various signals (BSE, SE, and X-rays) available from the EMP for a pure element of low to medium atomic number. The spatial resolution for X-rays and BSE are approximately the same as their respective ranges $(R(x)$ and $X_d)$. On the other hand, the spatial resolution of the SE is independent of the range of these signals. The spatial resolution of SE is approximately the same as the probe diameter $(d_p)$, whereas the spatial resolution of the BSE and X-ray signals are usually much larger than $d_p$. As illustrated in Fig. 5, the X-ray spatial resolutions of several X-ray lines measured in the same material are different.

**Elemental Analysis**

*Element Detection*

In the EMP, the crystal spectrometer is the principal method of measuring X-ray spectra. Figure 1 shows the typical X-ray focusing optics in an EMP. The system includes a source, the bombarded area, a crystal for diffracting the X-ray spectra, and a counter for X-ray detection. The source, crystal, and detector are all maintained on the same circle, called the focusing circle. In addition, the angle between the specimen surface and the measured X-ray beam is the X-ray emergence angle or take-off angle. In most EMP's this angle is held constant as the diffraction angle at the crystal $(2\theta)$ is varied.

Qualitative spectral scans of the type shown in Fig. 7 involve displaying the

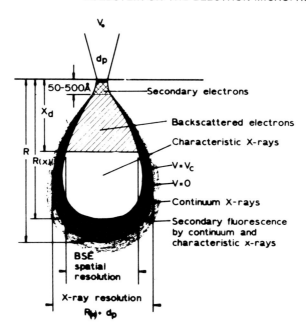

FIG. 6–*Schematic of the range and spatial resolution of the various signals produced in the EMP.*

X-ray ratemeter output as a function of diffraction angle ($2\theta$) or wavelength. Once the peaks are detected their identity can quickly be established. Figure 7 shows a spectral scan of the matrix and of inclusions in a stainless steel [*15*]. The carbide inclusion is rich in titanium, manganese, and chromium, while the matrix exhibits normal iron, chromium, and nickel, and small amounts of cobalt and manganese.

Usually one or more crystal spectrometers are available in the EMP. A broad selection of analyzing crystals is used to cover and optimize spectrometer performance in the range from 0.2 to 140 Å and elements from beryllium upward can be detected. Among the most useful crystals are lithium fluorine (LiF) for wavelength coverage 3.5 to 0.2 Å, ammonium dihydrogen phosphate (ADP) for 10 to 2 Å, potassium acid phthalate (KAP) for 25 to 5 Å, and lead sterate for 90 to 20 Å. For element detection, the spectrometers scan portions of the spectrum for periods of a few minutes to several hours depending on the desired level of sensitivity.

To obtain an optimum count rate of X-ray intensity with a wavelength dispersive detector, a probe current of $10^{-8}$ A is sufficient for most elements at concentration levels above 0.1 percent. However, a lower count rate of $10^3$/s can be used for scanning and point analysis. The typical efficiency of a dispersive detector allows count rates of $10^3$/s at 25 kV for most elements with atomic number 12 (Mg) at a beam current of $10^{-9}$ A [*16*]. Using Fig. 2, this beam current allows a probe diameter of $< 1000$ Å.

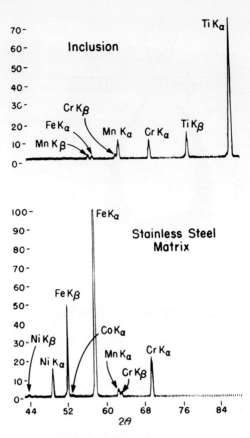

FIG. 7—*Spectral scan, intensity versus diffraction angle 2θ, of a stainless steel using a crystal spectrometer, carbide and inclusion* (top), *stainless steel matrix* (bottom).

Recently, improved lithium-drifted silicon solid state detectors allow detection and energy dispersion of X-rays of $\sim$ 1 to 30 kV energy in the EMP [17-19]. The energy resolution of such energy dispersive detectors is still significantly inferior to the standard focusing crystal spectrometer. As discussed by Lifshin [20], they have attracted widespread interest because (1) X-ray signals of all detectable energies from element 11 (sodium) and above are collected simultaneously, and a whole spectrum can be obtained in a few minutes, (2) higher counting rates at low beam currents greater than those obtained with a crystal spectrometer are possible, and (3) the detector responds to X-ray energy independent of specimen position, unlike the crystal spectrometer which requires the source of the X-ray spectra to be on the focusing circle.

The operating principles of the solid state detector system are shown schematically in Fig. 8. The X-ray signal passes through a thin window into

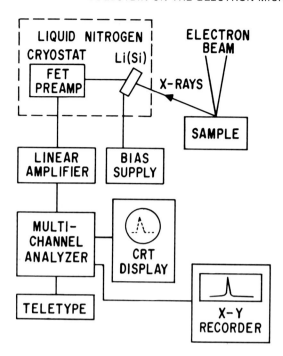

FIG. 8—*Block diagram of a solid-state detector system.*

the lithium-drifted silicon crystal. Energy is lost both to the crystal and in the formation of electron-hole pairs. These electron-hole pairs are swept away by an applied bias and are eventually converted to a voltage pulse and amplified by the preamplifier and linear amplifier. These pulses are stored by a multi-channel analyzer which sorts the incoming pulses by amplitude. The resulting spectrum can be displayed on a cathode ray tube, an X-Y recorder, a teletype, or transmitted to a computer.

Figure 9 shows the spectra obtained, with a solid state detector on an EMP, from a stainless steel specimen similar to that used for the data in Fig. 7. The difference in resolution can clearly be seen in a comparison between Figs. 7 and 9. In practice, the resolution of crystal spectrometers, which can be 5 eV for $\text{iron}_{K\alpha}$, is limited to the mosaic spread of the analyzing crystal. The resolution of the solid state X-ray detector is about 160 eV for $\text{iron}_{K\alpha}$ and is limited by both the statistical nature of electron-hole pair formation and electronic noise [20].

By far the most useful application of solid state detectors on EMP's is for qualitative analysis. The speed of obtaining useful spectra for identifying elements present in the specimen is a great advantage. Multichannel analyzers equipped with large enough memories also make it relatively easy to compare the spectra obtained from several different points on a specimen with each

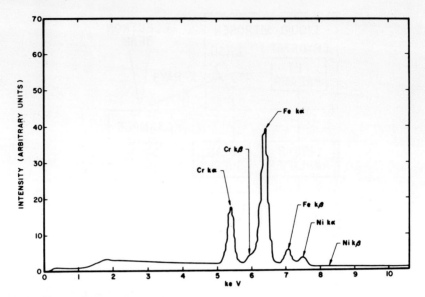

FIG. 9 – *Spectra, intensity versus voltage (kV) of a stainless steel suing a solid state detector.*

other or with standards. What the detector lacks in resolution is partially compensated for in total collected counts. However, the need for optimum resolution is particularly important when one analyzes complex multielement specimens in which peak overlap occurs. It is unfortunate that as the X-ray counting rate increases the resolution of the solid state detector is degraded [21].

Crystal spectrometers are not being replaced for qualitative analyses. They provide the highest sensitivity in most wavelength ranges, and their superior energy resolution virtually eliminates peak overlap problems and ambiguities in spectral identification. Crystal spectrometers are, so far, still the only means of measuring in the light element range (beryllium, boron, carbon, nitrogen, oxygen, and flourine) where large "*d-*" spacing crystals make analyses down to beryllium possible. Programmable spectrometers now make qualitative scans more efficient by only scanning through specific wavelength ranges corresponding to suspected peak positions.

*Composition Measurement*

Since much of our understanding of how materials behave depends on knowing the composition of the various phases in a microstructure, the method of quantitative electron probe microanalysis has been highly developed. In his doctoral thesis, Castaing [22] laid out the basis for the theory of quantitative electron probe microanalysis. He pointed up that the intensity of characteristic radiation generated directly in complex multielement specimens is approximately proportional to the mass fraction of the emitting element. He proposed that the corrections which need to be applied to each of the measured characteristic lines to obtain mass fractions are:

1. An atomic number correction $(Z)$ to correlate the effects of energy dissipation and electron backscattering with the atomic number of the specimen.

2. An absorption correction $(A)$ which takes into account the absorption of X-rays emerging from the specimen.

3. A fluorescent correction $(F)$ which takes into account the effect of any indirect X-ray generation by other elements.

The proportionality constant between the measured intensity $(I_A)$ and the concentration of a given element $(C_A)$ is given by the above corrections.

Because of the difficulties involved in making absolute intensity measurements, the X-ray intensity from the unknown specimen $(I_A)$ is always compared with that from a standard specimen $(I(A))$ under identical external conditions of excitation. In both cases the continuum background radiation is subtracted from the peak intensity. Where possible it is convenient to use the pure element $A$ as the standard, but less of a correction is necessary if the standard of composition $C(A)$ is close in composition to the unknown specimen.

The ratio $I_A/I(A)$ can be measured and related to the ratio of the concentrations $C_A/C(A)$ by the relation

$$\frac{I_A}{I(A)} = \left[\frac{ZAF_A}{ZAF(A)}\right]\frac{C_A}{C(A)} \tag{4}$$

This "classical" $ZAF$ scheme of data reduction has essentially remained the commonly used approach to quantitative analysis. It has been described along with potential sources of error in many publications [3,23,25] and numerous examples of its use have been published [3,26,27]. The objective of this section is to point up some of the problems and newer developments in quantitative analysis.

For quantitative X-ray analysis it is necessary to have a flat polished specimen for analysis free from the effects of selective etching. In addition, the specimen should not be affected by the impinging electron beam. The use of the EMP for the examination of alkali-containing glasses, and to a lesser extent, minerals, presents specific difficulties not encountered in conducting materials. Under the action of the beam, the glass apparently undergoes a composition change as shown by the change in intensity of the characteristic X-ray emission of the alkali metal present [28-30]. It is clear that before glasses can be analyzed, their stability under the beam should be proved for the conditions of kilovolt and beam current to be used. For biological specimens, unbound water must be removed from the specimen to make it suitable for vacuum insertion. In addition, the specimen must be electrically and thermally conductive, and the surface must be smooth and flat for analysis. The critical requirement is that in preparing the specimen, the structural-chemical relationships existing at the level of spatial resolution of the microprobe should not be disturbed [30].

Although the methods for quantitative microprobe analysis have been worked out in great detail, there are surprisingly few standards available for microprobe analysis. In many cases pure elements can be used for standards. For geological specimens pure oxides have been used as standards when the Bence-Albee correction [31] is employed. Recently, the National Bureau of Standards (NBS) certified and issued alloys of nominal composition 80W, 20Mo, and 3Si in iron and a series of binary alloys in the gold-silver and gold-copper systems. The major uses of these NBS alloys are to give the analyst experience with specimens which are well characterized to check out their own measurement procedures, data reduction, and calculation procedures.

In any composition measurement with the EMP the continuum background which underlies the characteristic X-ray peak must be measured and subtracted from the peak intensity. Generally, two methods are available. One can measure continuum background at a wavelength or energy adjacent to the X-ray peak, or one can use a specimen which is of similar composition but does not contain the element of interest. It is, however, difficult to obtain specimens for the latter method. With the solid state detector the background measurements are complicated by spectral overlap of peaks (Fig. 9). To overcome this problem, deconvolution techniques (spectrum stripping) using digital analysis are very helpful [32]. Another technique is to calculate the size of one of the interferring peaks from another peak from the same element that has no interference and subtract it from the total count of the composite peak [33]. Quantitative analysis with the solid state detector has been demonstrated for certain applications [3]. However, under normal microprobe operating condition, with the beam current $10^{-8}$ A or above, the total X-ray intensity available and the system count rate can be much higher than that acceptable by a solid state X-ray detector, and, as discussed earlier, resolution is degraded. Along with the fact that the peak to background ratios of a tuned crystal spectrometer are higher, the crystal spectrometer has a decided edge in quantitative EMP work over that of the solid state detector.

There are several ways in which the computer is used to provide the microprobe user with more and better information. For quantitative microprobe analysis, the ZAF correction procedure as given in Eq 4 is calculated using a computer. For a given X-ray line, operating voltage, and a particular X-ray optics, the emergent intensitites contained in Eq 4 can be calculated as a function of the composition of the specimen or standard. However, it is not possible to simply invert the equation in order to obtain the unknown mass-fraction of the emitting element corresponding to the intensity ratio $I_A/I(A)$ since the values for the correction factors depend on the specimen composition. The calculation of the mass fraction, therefore, requires an iterative procedure in which a computer is necessary.

Several dozen computer programs now exist to accomplish the task of converting X-ray intensity ratios to chemical compositions, for example,

[*34-36*]. In the more widely used programs the constants are stored in matrix form within the program making input quite simple and printout fairly extensive. These programs have generally required fairly large storage requirements and must be run on fairly large machines. If extended output is not required, and, if one is willing to input the constants required for the various corrections at the necessary time, then the program for data reduction may be small enough to fit into a standard minicomputer.

Automation of the EMP with the computer can vary greatly from one laboratory to another depending on the degree of sophistication desired. Several parts of the EMP can be automated, for example (1) the stage: specimens and standards are moved under the electron beam, and (2) the spectromers: they are moved through their wavelength ranges and intensities are read out. For quantitative analysis, accurate peaking of spectrometers is also necessary. In addition, other components which can be automated are the pulse height analyzer, X-ray amplifier, and high voltage, or even the high voltage and current of the electron gun.

Software as well as hardware must be obtained in order to operate efficiently. The software consists of a peak seeking program, sequencing of data collection, statistical analysis of data, and *ZAF* quantitative calculations. Several different automation systems have been developed [*37-40*]. The design of the system is often dictated by the major type of specimen to be studied (geological, thin film, etc.) and the types of analyses desired.

Quantitative EMP analysis of the light elements is particularly difficult, since the correction models developed for quantitative analysis may not be applicable in the light element range. In addition, the attenuation of the primary radiation is large when these long wavelength, low energy X-rays are measured. A large absorption (*A*) correction is usually necessary and unfortunately, necessary parameters such as the mass absorption coefficient are not well known. One can minimize the absorption effect by working at low electron energies and using high X-ray emergence angles from the specimen. Nevertheless, reliable quantitative results are best obtained by comparison with standards of known composition close to that of the specimen.

Calculations of oxygen content on well characterized oxides have been made using oxygen intensities measured with the EMP [*41*]. The results do not agree well in all cases, and the disagreement is due mainly in the uncertainty of the mass absorption coefficient and the influences of chemical bonding. When the same measurements were repeated in a later study [*42*] and after more accurate mass absorption coefficients became available, the relative errors between the electron probe microanalysis and the wet chemical analysis at various operating potential 5, 10, 15, 20, 25, and 30 kV were less than a few percent.

Complications in light element analysis also arise because of the presence of the *L*-spectra from heavier metals. Duncumb and Melford [*43*] have shown that even if overlapping occurs, a qualitative analysis can be obtained. In steels, for example, titanium carbonitride (TiNC) inclusions which are probably solid solutions of titanium nitride (TiN) and titanium carbide (TiC) are found. Figure 10 shows a comparison of the titanium $L$-spectra obtained from TiN, TiC, and pure titanium. The TiNC phase gave a more intense peak at the titanium$_{L_1}$-wavelength than that of pure titanium. This peak contains mainly titanium$_{L_1}$ at 31.4 Å (18.3° $\theta$) together with a small amount of nitrogen$_{k\alpha}$-emission indistinguishable from it at 31.6 Å (18.5°$\theta$), Fig. 10. The titanium $L_\alpha$-line at 27.4 Å (16.0°$\theta$) is heavily absorbed by nitrogen and is about one third as intense as that from pure titanium. The titanium$L_1$-emission, however, is only slightly absorbed by nitrogen.

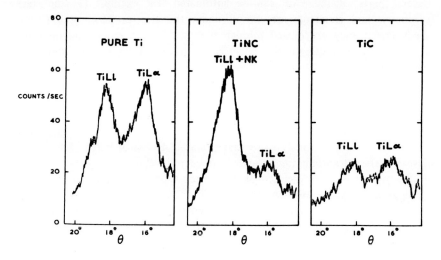

FIG. 10–*Comparison of the titanium L-spectra (intensity versus diffraction angle, $\theta$) obtained from pure titanium* (left), *TiN* (center), *and TiC* (right) *at 10 kV operating potential.*

The analysis of this type of inclusion may appear to be impossible, but Duncumb and Melford analyzed the titanium content by using the $K_\alpha$-radiation and analyzed the carbon content by use of the TiC standard, Fig. 10. The results indicate about 80Ti and 4C. The analysis for nitrogen was not possible for reasons already stated and was obtained by difference from 100 percent. In another study, Shiraiwa et al [44] also attempted to analyze TiNC inclusions in steel. They measured the nitrogen$_{K\alpha}$ directly, however, by setting the spectrometer slightly off the nitrogen$_{K\alpha}$-peak at 31.7 A where the intensity of the titanium $L_1$-peak was negligible.

It is well known that a specimen subjected to electron bombardment in a diffusion pumped vacuum gradually becomes covered with a "contamination" layer due to polymerization, under the action of the beam, of organic matter absorbed on the surface [1]. The organic molecules come from the oil vapors from the vacuum pumps and the outgassing of any organic material present in the instrument. The effect is not very troublesome unless the deposited layer absorbs the emitted X-rays to a great extent. For the light element radiation, particularly beryllium, boron and carbon, the absorption of the long wavelength X-radiation can be severe. The problem in the case of carbon analysis is increased because the "contamination" layer is composed to a large extent with carbon. It is crucial, however, that the specimen should be free of contamination from polishing and storage before insertion in the EMP.

Two methods have been used to avoid the contamination layer. Castaing and Descamps [45], as early as 1954, showed that directing a low pressure jet of gas on the specimen at the region bombarded by the beam in the microanalyzer permits the practical suppression of contamination. Air jets have been installed on various EMP's [46-48]. Not only is the contamination rate reduced to zero, but previously absorbed surface layers are removed. Although the vacuum system in the EMP is degraded by this process and the accompanying decrease in filament life is not severe.

The other generally used method is to provide a surface within the EMP which is cold relative to the surface of the specimen. Organic molecules will then tend to collect on the colder surface rather than on the specimen. The cold surface or cold finger must however be placed in very close proximity to the specimen. Cold fingers have been installed on various EMP's [49-52] and have effectively reduced the contamination rate to close to zero. In one case [53] both an air jet and a liquid $N_2$ cold finger have been used.

In one example, for the determination of carbon in steels, calibration curves of counting rate versus percent carbon were constructed from a series of high purity iron-carbon alloys which had been transformed to martensite to ensure homogeneity. Figure 11 shows the linear calibration curve between count rate and carbon content for the iron-carbon alloys and Fig. 12 shows a plot of carbon content versus distance across a proecutectoid ferrite grain boundary allotriomorph in an Fe-0.11C-1.95Mo alloy [49].

## Scanning Electron Probe

Cosslett and Duncumb [54] demonstrated that a beam deflecting or scanning system can be added to an EMP so that a magnified image of the scanned specimen area appears on the oscilloscope system. The image can be formed by the various signals that are obtained such as BSE, SE, target current, cathodoluminescent photons, and X-rays. The addition of scanning to the normal X-ray capability of the EMP allows one to obtain photographs of the composition distribution across a selected area on the surface of the specimen. Positive identification of phases can be made and compared directly to the optical micrographs. The resolution of the various images obtained depends on the range of the signal as discussed earlier in this paper. Since it is difficult to reduce the effective volume of X-ray emission below 1 $\mu$m, X-ray pictures are limited to about X3000. An excellent review of the various scanning techniques is presented by Heinrich [55].

Figure 13 shows a comparison of scanning X-ray pictures obtained from a solidified section of a *M2* tool steel [56]. The eutectic interdendritic areas are

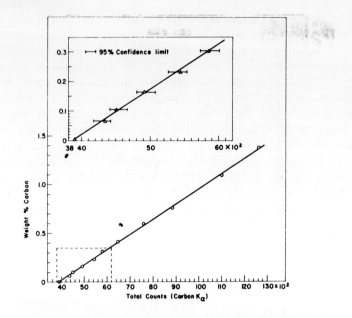

FIG. 11—*Linear calibration curve between carbon* $K_\alpha$ *count rate and carbon content for iron-carbon alloys. A more detailed view at carbon levels below 0.3 percent is given by the insert.*

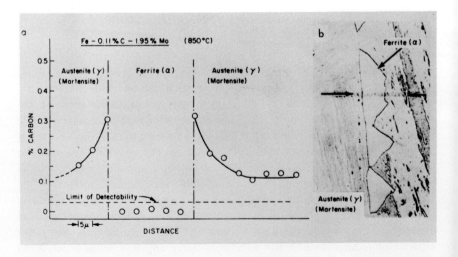

FIG. 12—*Variation of carbon content with distance across a proeutectoid ferrite grain boundary allotriomorph in an Fe-0.11%-C-1.95% Mo alloy. The metallographic view of the analyzed area is also shown. The specimen was heated 15 min at 1300°C, isothermally reacted 50 s at 850°C, and quenched.*

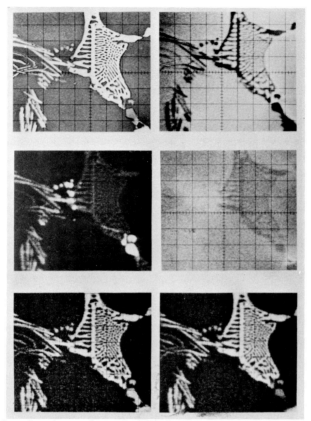

FIG. 13–*Scanning pictures from a solidified section of a* M2 *tool steel. The scanned area is 90 × 80 μm in size. The various signals are tungsten* $L_\alpha$ *(upper left),* molybdenum $L_\alpha$ *(upper right),* chromium $K_\alpha$ *(center left), Vanadium* $K_\alpha$ *(center right), iron* $K_\alpha$ *(bottom left), and BSE (bottom right).*

rich in chromium, molybdenum, and tungsten while the dendritic areas are iron-rich. In many cases the scanning X-ray analysis pictures may be much more important to the analyst than detailed quantitative analyses of specific areas. In most EMP laboratories scanning X-ray analysis represents a major portion of the analysis work. Various examples of scanning X-ray work can be found in review articles concerned with applications in geology [27], metallurgy [26,57], and biology [58,60].

X-ray images showing the distribution of a specific element are normally obtained by using the output of a crystal spectrometer to modulate the brightness of the scanning system cathode ray tube (Fig. 13). The same type of X-ray imaging is possible using a solid state detector. Figure 14 shows an example of a scanning X-ray distribution in a nickel matrix containing blocky tantalum carbide (TaC) particles [20]. If the discriminators on the multichannel analyzer of the solid state detector are set to include only the portion of the energy spectra corresponding to a nickel or tantalum line, it is possible

FIG. 14—*Scanning pictures from a nickel matrix containing blocky tantalum carbide particles. The X-ray scanning pictures are for tantalum* $L_\alpha$ (left bottom) *and nickel* $K_\alpha$ (right bottom).

to get an output much the same as with the crystal spectrometer. This output can be used to modulate the oscilloscope image as shown in Fig. 14.

Black and white photographs showing the topographic distribution of a single signal are widely used. It is difficult, however, to show the correlation of signals from two or more X-ray lines without the use of color. Composite color photographs using X-ray images from the EMP have been produced. One such method uses the black and white scanning images as color-separation-positives and with appropriate filters, color prints are made [61].

A more quantitative approach to X-ray scanning can be taken by using a device that produces abrupt changes of the oscilloscope beam brightness at predetermined signal levels. The contrast produced by a signal which is only slightly higher than the background can be enhanced so that only signal levels above background are obtained. Melford [62] demonstrated such an expanded contrast method in which brightness modulation by the ratemeter signal has been employed for image formation. This method can also be used to enhance differences at high concentration levels. Another technique developed by Heinrich [55] is called concentration mapping. In principle, this method shows the location of defined concentration ranges. To obtain this information, all concentration differences within each range are suppressed.

Since the backscattering fraction is a function of atomic number, a useful contrast between regions of differing atomic number can be obtained in the BSE images taken on flat specimens (Fig. 13). Since the intensity of the signal also varies with the specimen topography, a contrast can be developed between regions of different height. Figure 14 shows the mixed effects of topographic and atomic number contrast in the BSE pictures taken of the TaC particles in a nickel matrix. The backscattering image can be improved however. If one only collects BSE at a relatively low angle to the specimen surface and only electrons that have lost less than a few hundred eV in the specimen, the BSE range can be as small as 100 A below the specimen surface [63]. These BSE are assumed to travel in a straight line into the specimen until they are deflected by a single wide-angle scattering event.

The SE have spatial resolutions close to that of the primary electron beam. Most newer EMP's have secondary electron detectors. Although resolutions below 500 to 1000 Å are not usually available in EMP's, most instruments have secondary electron detectors in order to take advantage of the superior quality of the images they produce, Fig. 14, even at relatively low magnifications (X10 to 2500).

A simple way of obtaining a signal for image formation is to isolate the specimen from ground and observe the variations in the current flowing from the target to ground during the scanning process. This output is called the target or specimen current. The signal is complex because it is the current left over after the backscattered and low energy SE have been lost from the specimen. It is affected not only by the topography of the specimen but also by variations of the electron backscatter coefficient of the target. In conventional target current images the gray level is a function of both composition and topography. If a specimen contains areas of widely differing atomic numbers, topographic details are difficult to see. The images produced on the oscilloscope screen can also be mixed electronically with its first derivative [64]. The use of a mixed signal reduces the effects of composition variation so that topographic details appear more clearly.

Besides the signals already discussed, the emission of light in the visible and infrared ranges (cathodoluminescence) can also be used to obtain information concerning the region excited by the electron beam. The intensity and spectral distribution of the radiation is usually affected by trace amounts of some elements which activate the process.

Cathodoluminescence has found particular application in several fields. In geology studies, the EMP is a very suitable tool since the instrument has an optical microscope which allows viewing and photography of the specimen while under electron bombardment. In addition, the wide variation in beam size allows the examination of < 1 to > 300 $\mu m^2$. Long and Agrell [65] studied the visual luminescence of several minerals. They showed that identification of small grains can be accomplished because of a particular color. Variations in trace elements which behave as activators or as quench agents can also be observed. Since the concentrations involved are often small, their variation would not be easily observed except for detailed EMP measurements involving long counting times. The spatial resolution obtainable by using an optical microscope to observe cathodoluminescence is limited by diffraction to ~ 0.6 $\mu m$.

In insulators and semiconductors an appreciable fraction of the energy which is dissipated from the electron beam is used for the excitation of excess carriers and the excitation of optical energy levels. Radiation can result from the recombination of excess hole-electron pairs that are produced. In a study carried out by Kyser and Wittry [66], excess carriers were produced in gallium arsonide (GaAs) using an EMP with instrumentation for measuring infrared radiation. Local fluctuations in the intensity of recombination radiation over 10 to 50 $\mu$m regions were observed indicating a wide variation in the concentration of impurities or lattice defects. In a later study, Wittry [67] measured tellurium concentration by quantitative EMP analysis and found a correlation with the local variations in cathodoluminescence efficiency. Previous attempts to observe such a correlation failed because the practical limits of detectability using X-rays in the EMP are of the same order as the solubility limit of tellurium in GaAs.

Spectral analysis of cathodoluminescence was conducted by Kyser and Wittry [66] and others [68-71]. A typical emission spectrum may have a width of 500 Å, with a peak at 5000 Å, and different activators may not give distinguishable emission spectra. The effects of altering the accelerating potential and other parameters, and the effects of charging on the spectra were studied by Muir et al [68], also small single crystal cathodoluminescence characteristics of common phosphors were studied [72]. Analysis of rare earth materials have also been made using the cathodoluminescence spectra [69] in the ultraviolet and visible regions. Potentially, the cathodoluminescence method should be able to measure trace elements contents well below that of the X-ray EMP technique. However, it should be noted that the cathodoluminescence signal exhibits saturation effects and is not always proportional to beam current.

## Characterization of Phases

### Specimen Preparation

For quantitative X-ray analysis we need to have the flatest specimens possible. The effect of roughness of the specimen on the type or quality of data obtained increases as the take-off angle of the instrument (Fig. 1) decreases [73]. This relation exists because the relative errors in the calculation of the composition, due particularly to the absorption effect, increase with decreasing take-off angle. Although a high take-off angle probe may minimize the effect of surface roughness, a flat specimen is, nevertheless, desirable. Another reason for analyzing flat specimens is to obtain accurate composition measurements at phase boundaries and edges of the specimen. If flat specimens are not available, the total path length which the X-rays traverse on their way out of the specimen can be changed. The effects of corners and edges cannot be corrected for and must be minimized. Depending on the type of specimens to be analyzed, it may be necessary to try to maximize the flatness of the specimen at the expense of any other of the type of specimen preparation.

Limited qualitative microprobe analyses can be accomplished on rough fracture surfaces if several precautions are taken [74]. To make sure that scanning X-ray measurements of the elements present in the alloy are real and not just the effect of topography, the spectrometer can be set off-angle and a scanning image taken of the distribution of background intensity. In this way fluctuations in the X-ray signal caused by surface irregularity can be seen and spurious indications in the characteristic line image can be rejected to determine the distribution of elements of interest.

For organic materials, 1 to 4-μm-thick specimens are mounted on substrates. An ultramicrotome is used and tissues are usually dehydrated and embedded before they are cut. One can use dyes with tissues to highlight areas of interest as long as the materials which make up the dyes do not interfere with the concentrations to be measured within the specimen. It is also important to note that for biologic materials, all the standards should be of the same thickness as the specimens themselves. If the specimens and standards are prepared at different times this is very difficult to achieve.

Most geological and biological specimens are coated to ensure electrical and thermal conductivity. The most frequently employed coating is carbon. The coating should be as thin as possible, transparent to visible light for microscopy and also yield a stable sample current. Furthermore, the thinner the coating, the less is the X-ray absorption within it and the less is the energy loss of the primary electron beam entering the specimen. Usual coating thicknesses vary from 50 to 500 Å. It is desirable to have the same thickness of coating on both specimen and standards, but, for light element analyses it is a necessity.

*Statistics—Homogeneity, Composition Differences, and Trace Analysis*

It is important to note that X-ray production is statistical in nature. X-rays which are produced from a given specimen and interact with radiation detectors are completely random in time but have a fixed mean value. The distribution or histogram of the number of determinations of X-ray counts from one point on a specimen versus the number of X-ray counts for a fixed time interval may be closely approximated by the continuous normal (Gaussian) distribution. The individual X-ray "counts must lie upon the unique Gaussian curve for which the standard deviation is the square root of the mean ($\sigma_c = \sqrt{\bar{N}}$). Here, $\bar{N}$ is considered to be the most probable value of $N$, the total number of counts for a given time ($t$). In as much as $\sigma_c$ results from fluctuations that cannot be eliminated as long as quanta are counted, this standard deviation is the irreducible minimum for X-ray emission spectrography. For example, to obtain a number with a minimum of a 1 percent deviation in $N$, at least 10 000 counts must be accumulated.

However, as Liebhafsky [75] pointed up, the actual standard deviation ($S_c$), given by

$$S_c = \sum_{i=1}^{n} (N_i - \bar{N}_i)^2 / (n - 1)^{1/2} \tag{5}$$

where $n$ is the number of determinations of $i$ and $S_c$ equals $\sigma_c$ only when operating conditions are ideal. In most electron probes, instrument drift and specimen positioning create operating conditions which are not necessarily ideal. The high voltage-filament supply, the lens supplies, and other associated electron equipment may drift with time. After a specimen is repositioned under the electron beam, a change in measured X-ray intensity may occur if the effective "depth of focus" for the X-ray spectrometers is smaller than the "depth of focus" of the light optical system. In actual practice, for the usual counting time of 10 to 100 s/point, $S_c$ is about twice $\sigma_c$. If larger counting times are used, $S_c/\sigma_c$ increases due to instrument drift. Only when counting times are short and the instrument has stabilized does $S_c$ approach $\sigma_c$. Besides the specimen signal, sources of variation may also occur if data from reference standards and background are required [76]. These, as well as faulty specimen preparation, may also effect the precision of an analysis. Therefore, both instrumental factors and signal variations must be considered when the precision of an analysis is given. Very rarely will the percent coefficient of variation $(CV)$ of an analysis $(S_c/\overline{N}\ (100))$ approach the theoretical limit $(\sigma_c/\overline{N}\ (100))$.

Several studies have been made characterizing standard materials for use as electron probe standards [77,78]. The usual procedure for checking these standards is first to investigate inclusions and secondary phases if present. After this is done, a preliminary check on homogeneity of the matrix is made using a set of mechanical line scans. These line scans will point up any gross inhomogeneities ($>$10 percent of the amount present) on the 1 to 100-$\mu$m level. The possibility of gross inhomogeneities on the 1-mm to 1-cm level should also be investigated by conventional means such as X-ray fluorescence. To check for inhomogeneities of less than 10 percent of the amount present, a static probe is used and X-ray quanta are accumulated at each point. The procedure normally used it to take data at many points, usually between 10 and 200 spread across the specimen. The criterion used for homogeneity is [77-79] that all points fall within the $\overline{N} \pm 3\sqrt{N}$ limits. If 100 000 counts are accumulated at each point, a variation of more than 1 percent of the amount present can be detected. Therefore, a homogeneity level of within $\pm$ 1 percent of the amount present can be ensured.

A more exacting criterion for homogeneity would include ($a$) the use of the actual standard deviation $S_c$ which accounts for instrument drifts and for focusing errors, and ($b$) the use of a confidence level for the determination of $\overline{N}$. The confidence level, given as $1-a$, is usually chosen as 95 or 99 percent. This means that we would expect on the average, only 5 (or 1 percent) of repeated random points to be outside the limits $W_{95}$ or $W_{99}$.

The width of a 99 percent confidence interval $(W_{99})$ is

$$W_{99} = \pm C_i \frac{t_{n-1}{}^{99}}{\sqrt{n}}\ \frac{CV}{100} = \pm \frac{C_i t_{n-1}{}^{99}}{\sqrt{n}}\ \frac{S_c}{\overline{N}} \tag{6}$$

where

$C_i$ = true chemical weight fraction of element $i$,

$CV$ = percent coefficient of variation, and

$t_{n-1}^{99}$ = student's $t$ value for 99 percent confidence for $(n-1)$ degrees of freedom [80]. Other confidence intervals can be used by choosing other values of $t$. Student's $t$ values for $t_{n-1}^{95}$ and $t_{n-1}^{99}$ for various degrees of freedom $(n-1)$ are given in Table 2 [81].

TABLE 2–*Values of student* t *for 95 and 99 percent confidence level.*

| $n-1$ | $t_{n-1}^{95}$ | $t_{n-1}^{99}$ |
|---|---|---|
| 3 | 3.182 | 5.841 |
| 7 | 2.365 | 3.499 |
| 11 | 2.201 | 3.106 |
| 15 | 2.131 | 2.947 |
| 24 | 2.064 | 2.797 |
| ∞ | 1.960 | 2.576 |

In a study of NBS Standard Reference Material 479, an austenitic iron-chromium-nickel alloy, the Eq 6 was applied for a criterion of homogeneity [80]. Using a 40-s counting interval on the specimen 900 000 iron counts, 340 000 chromium counts and 270 000 nickel counts were obtained at each point. In no case was $CV > 1.5$ percent for any element present. Therefore, if $CV = 1.5$ percent is used as a conservative value, and, if $n$ is set equal to 16 in Eq 6

$$W_{99} = \pm C_i \frac{2.947}{\sqrt{16}} (0.015) = \pm 0.0111 \, C_i$$

or $C_i \pm 1.11$ percent relative. The time to collect data for the 16 points was not prohibitive, being about 30 min. It is also possible to predict the degree of homogeneity as a function of $N$, $n$, and the desired confidence level that would be measured under typical operating conditions [26].

Several different methods have been devised for obtaining homogeneity data. The objective in all these cases is to obtain data from enough points to be representative, obtain a minimum number of counts per point for each element of interest and, yet, do this within a reasonable time interval so as not to run into stability problems due to instrument drift. Systems for automatic displacement of the electron beam [2,82] or the specimen stage by some sort of automation equipment are available. A matrix of a single string of points along a line or a square or rectangular area can be developed. The data must be handled efficiently (computer, multichannel analyzer, or tape) and a computation is needed to transform the mass of data into a format that permits easy interpretation. In most cases it is advantageous to obtain both statistical output (standard deviations, frequency distributions, etc.) and top-ographical output (isoconcentration maps).

Normally the data are collected with crystal spectrometers. If the electron beam is displaced far enough from the electron optical axis of the EMP, the emitted X-rays will no longer be on the focusing circle of the X-ray spectro-meter, and a loss of X-ray intensity will occur. Typically, electron beam displacements over 50 $\mu$m will cause defocusing effects. An interesting feature of the solid state detector, as compared to the crystal spectrometer system, is that the counting rates are not altered by displacement of the beam on the specimen. Therefore, the use of a solid state detector for the analysis of points in a raster as big as 1 mm$^2$, simplifies the operation and interpretation of data by eliminating a major source of error [2].

Analytical sensitivity usually indicates the ability to distinguish, for a given element $A$, between two compositions $C_A$ and $C'_A$ that are close together. X-ray signals for both compositions $\bar{N}$ and $\bar{N}'$ have a similar statistical variation. If one determines two compositions $C_A$ and $C'_A$ by $n$ repetitions of each measurement, taken for the same fixed time interval $\tau$, then these two values are significantly different at a certain confidence level $(1-a)$ if

$$\bar{N} - \bar{N}' \geqslant \sqrt{2}\ t_{n-1}{}^{1-a} S_c / \sqrt{n} \tag{7a}$$

and

$$\Delta C = C_A - C'_A \geqslant \frac{\sqrt{2}\ C_A\ t_{n-1}{}^{1-a} S_c}{\sqrt{n}\ (\bar{N}_A - \bar{N}_B)} \tag{7b}$$

where

$C_A$ = element composition of one element in the specimen,

$\bar{N}_A$ and $\bar{N}_B$ = average number of X-ray counts of element $A$ for the speci-men and the element continuum background on the specimen,

$t_{n-1}{}^{1-a}$ = "student's" factor dependent on the confidence level 1-$a$ (Table 2) and,

$n$ = number of repetitions.

Ziebold [83] has shown that the analytical sensitivity for a 95 percent confidence level can be approximated by

$$\Delta C = C_A - C'_A \geqslant \frac{2.33}{\sqrt{n}}\ \frac{C_A}{(\bar{N}_A - \bar{N}_B)}\ \sigma_c \tag{8}$$

Equation 8 represents an estimate of the maximum sensitivity that can be achieved when signals from both compositions have their own errors but instrumental errors are disregarded. Since the actual standard deviation $(S_c)$ is about two times larger than $\sigma_c$, $\Delta C$ is approximately twice that given in Eq 8.

If $\bar{N}_A$ is much larger than $\bar{N}_B$, Eq 9 can be rewritten as

$$\Delta C = C_A - C'_A \geqslant \frac{2.33 \ C_A}{\sqrt{nN_A}} \tag{9}$$

and the analytical sensitivity that can be achieved is given as

$$\frac{\Delta C}{C_A} \ (\%) = \frac{2.33 \times 10^2}{\sqrt{n \ \bar{\bar{N}}_A}} \tag{10}$$

Shastry and Judd [84] investigated grain boundary solute segregation in an Al-6.86Zn-2.35Mg alloy which is susceptible to corrosion cracking. They found depletion or enrichment at the grain boundaries depending on the type of heat treatment and quench rates employed. They designed their experiments so values of $\Delta C/C_A$ (percent) for both zinc and magnesium were about 1 percent. In one case the relative change in concentration at the boundary was $\simeq$ 5 percent for both zinc and magnesium. To study olivine $(FeMg)_2 \ SiO_4$ compositional equilibration in large pallasite meteorites, olivine crystals from the opposite ends of several specimens $\sim$ 50 cm apart were obtained [85]. Using Eq 7b at the 95 percent confidence limit, a sensitivity of $\Delta C/C_A$ (percent) was about 1 percent. In all three meteorites, differences between the olivine crystals were less than this limit.

As the elemental composition $C_A$ approaches 0.1 percent in EMP analysis, $N_A$ is no longer much larger than $\bar{N}_B$. This composition range, below 0.1 percent is called the trace element analysis range. The analysis procedure now is to detect significant differences, between the specimen and the continuum background generated from the specimen. The detectability limit is governed by the minimum value of the difference $\bar{N}_A - \bar{N}_B$ which can be measured with statistical significance. Analogous to Eq 7a we have

$$\bar{N}_A - \bar{N}_B \geqslant \frac{\sqrt{2} \ t_{n-1}^{1-a} \ S_c}{\sqrt{n}} \tag{11}$$

where $S_c$ is essentially the same for both the specimen and background measurement.

For trace analysis, $<$ 1000 ppm, the X-ray calibration curves (Eq 4) may be taken as a simple linear function. Therefore, $C_A$, the unknown composition, can be related to $\bar{N}_A$ by the equation

$$C_A = \frac{(\bar{N}_A - \bar{N}_B)}{(\bar{N}_S - \bar{N}_{BS})} \ C(A) \tag{12}$$

where

$\bar{N}_S$ and $\bar{N}_{BS}$ = mean counts for the standard and standard background for element $A$, and

$C(A)$    = percent of element $A$ in the standard.

Using Eq 11 and 12, the detectability limit $C_{DL} = C_A$ is [86]

$$C_{DL} = \frac{C(A)}{(\bar{N}_S - \bar{N}_{SB})} \frac{\sqrt{2}\ (t_{n-1}{}^{1-a})\ S_c}{\sqrt{n}} \tag{13}$$

The precision in a trace element analysis is equal to $C_A/C_{DL}$ and approaches $\pm 100$ percent as $C_A$ approaches $C_{DL}$.

Ziebold [83] has shown the trace element sensitivity to be

$$C_{DL} \geqslant 3.29a/(n\ \tau\ I\ R)^{1/2} \tag{14}$$

where

$\tau$  = time of each measurement taken,

$n$  = number of repetitions of each measurement,

$I$  = pure element counting rate,

$R$  = peak/background ratio of the pure element (it is the ratio of the counting rate of the pure element to the background counting rate of the pure element), and

$a$  = relation of composition and intensity of element $A$ through the Ziebold and Ogilvie [87] empirical relation.

To illustrate the use of this relation, the following values were used for calculating the detectability limit for germanium in iron meteorites [88]. The operating conditions were:

high voltage, 35 kV

specimen current, 0.2 $\mu$A

$I$  = 150 000 counts/s

$R$  = 200

$\tau$  = 100 s

$n$  = 16

$a$  = 1

Using these numbers, $C_{DL} \geqslant 15$ ppm. The actual detectability limit after calculation of $S_c$ and Eq 12 was 20 ppm. Equation 14 is very useful for determining the operating conditions for trace analysis before the actual data are taken.

Therefore, to do trace element analysis one needs to employ long counting times, high peak intensities, and a high peak to background ratio $(R)$. Because of instrumental drift, and specimen contamination, a practical limit on the counting time is 15 to 30 min. The peak intensities can be raised by increasing the beam current. However, beam currents over 0.2 $\mu$A tend to heat the specimen locally and increase the size of the electron beam. Unfortunately, the peak to background ratio cannot be reduced below a certain limit since continuum X-ray radiation is always present and very small peaks from trace elements are difficult to separate statistically from the background continuum.

Trace element measurements have been made by various authors. Heidel

[89] measured $C_{DL}$ for metallic elements in a silicate glass. Using ±3 $\sigma_c$ above background as $\bar{N}_A - \bar{N}_B$, he found a detectability limit of 150 to 350 ppm for 20 kV, 2 x $10^{-8}$A specimen current and 10-s counting times. If 2 x $10^{-7}$A specimen current and 100-s counting times were used, a detectability limit of 15 to 35 ppm could have been achieved. Buseck and Goldstein [85] made trace element measurements of manganese, nickel, titanium, and calcium in olivine crystals. Operating at 30 kV, 2 x $10^{-7}$A specimen current and taking four 100-s counts per crystal, the detectability limits according to Eq 13 were 40 ppm for manganese, 20 ppm for nickel, 10 ppm for titanium, and 15 ppm for calcium. In practice, therefore, it is very difficult to obtain measurements below a detectability limit of 10 ppm.

Trace element measurements are almost always made in the EMP using X-ray crystal spectrometers. The peak to background ratio $(R)$ is quite high (> 100) and at the specimen currents typically used, the peak intensity is also quite high, $>10^4$ to $10^5$ counts/s from the pure elements. The background intensity $(\bar{N}_B)$ must be obtained to determine $(C_A)$ the unknown composition, Eq 12. As discussed the previous section of this paper, with careful usage, the background intensity can be obtained by going off the wavelength peak on the specimen itself.

It would be of great advantage to obtain trace analysis measurements at low beam currents, $\leqslant 10^{-9}$ A, where it might be possible to have a smaller X-ray excitation area. The solid state detector might be a logical instrument to use in this case. The peak intensity $(I)$ is high at these specimen currents although the peak to background ratio $(R)$ is much poorer than that obtained with the crystal spectrometer. According to Eq 12, $C_{DL}$ would approach 100 ppm in the best cases. However, detectability limits of <1000 ppm (0.1 percent) are difficult to achieve in practice since it is difficult to measure the background continuum intensity accurately.

## EMP Analysis of Phases

The application of the EMP to phase analysis is practically unlimited. Several typical examples of applications will be given here. Phosphides and sulfides are common nonmetallic inclusions found in metallic and nonmetallic (stony) meteorites. Figure 15 shows the distribution of cobalt, iron, and nickel across a phosphide found in the kamacite ($\alpha$-FeNi) phase of the Breece iron meteorite [90]. The data are taken by attaching a motor to the X- or Y-drive of the specimen stage and recording the X-ray output for cobalt, iron, and nickel on a chart recorder. The data are taken in a matter of minutes. Even though it is qualitative in nature, it shows the relative homogeneity of the phosphide, the nickel gradients in the surrounding kamacite, and the effect of the cracks which were present in the phosphide. Calculations reveal that the phosphide is a complex $(FeCoNi)_3P$ mineral.

Quantitative EMP analyses can be carried out by either moving the specimen automatically in micron-sized steps under the electron beam or moving the electron beam itself. In this way, the phase is covered by rows of analyses. An

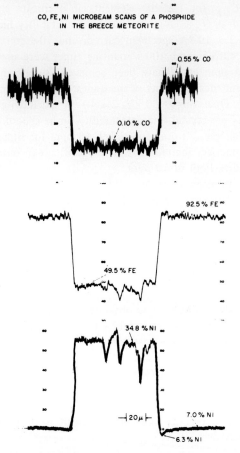

FIG. 15—*Distribution of cobalt, iron, and nickel across a phosphide inclusion in the kamacite (α) phase of the Breece iron meteorite.*

example of such a concentration-distance plot for a sinoite ($Si_2N_2O$) grain in the Jajh deh Kot Lalu enstatite chondrite is given in Fig. 16 [*91*]. The matrix surrounding sinoite is enstatite. The data were obtained by moving the section after every analysis in steps of 3 $\mu$m. Quantitative analyses were obtained using appropriate standards and the *ZAF* corrections, Eq 4.

Many phases have chemical gradients caused by various phenomenon. Figure 13 showed the *C* concentration which developed in the austenite phase of a steel due to the growth of ferrite. Figure 17 shows the effects of solidification on the phase compositions of the dendrites in a *M*2-tool steel (Fig. 13) [*92*]. The concentration profile of tungsten, molybdenum, chromium, and vanadium across the primary dendrite axis is given. These results indicate a slight alloy enrichment at the dendrite core and a relatively uniform distribution of chromium in comparison with more pronounced segregation of tungsten, molybdenum, and vanadium. Figure 18 shows the diffusion profile developed

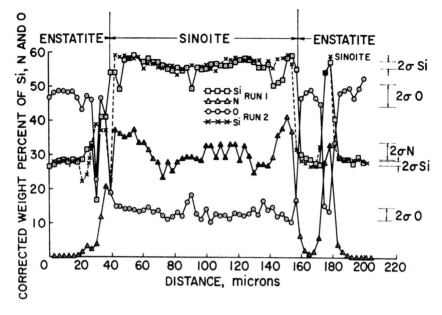

FIG. 16 – *Concentration distance plot for silicon, nickel, and oxygen across a sinoite ($Si_2N_2O$) grain in the Jajh deh kot Lalu enstatite chondrite. The analyses are point-by-point measurements obtained by moving the section after every analysis in steps of 3 μm under the fixed electron beam.*

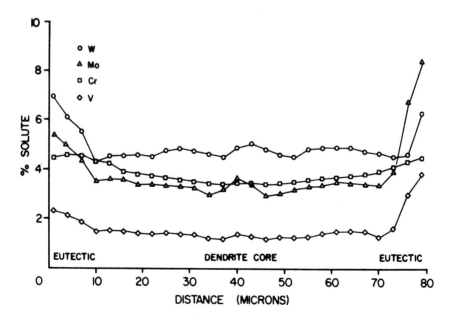

FIG. 17 – *Concentration profiles of tungsten, molybdenum, chromium, and vanadium across a primary dendrite axis in a unidirectionally solidified M2 steel.*

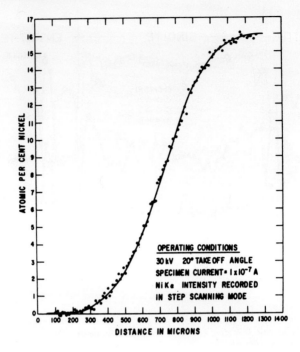

FIG. 18–*Diffusion profile developed when a gold versus a Au-6.1Ni couple was heated for one week at 875°C.*

when a gold versus a Au-6.1Ni couple diffused for one week at 875°C. The couple was one phase face centered cubic (fcc), and the gradient was controlled by the diffusivity at 875°C. The concentration profile was taken by moving the specimen under the electron beam and the concentration was determined by comparison with well characterized gold-nickel alloys [93]. Many other examples of electron beam X-ray phase analyses can be found in the literature.

In many investigations, it is of interest to know more than the chemical composition of the various phases present in the microstructure. The EMP can be used to obtain quantitative metallographic information such as volume fraction, mean particle size, surface area, and particle size distribution for the various phases. Many different systems have been developed for quantitative metallography with the EMP. Melford and Whittington [94] have developed a lineal scanning technique using a special purpose computer to handle the scanning probe data. For example, the aluminum $K_\alpha$-, sulfur $K_\alpha$-, and manganese $K_\alpha$- intensities are obtained from a line scan through inclusions of manganese sulfide (MnS), manganese oxide (MnO), and aluminum oxide ($Al_2O_3$). Using the two X-ray signals, logic circuitry compares them in such a way that the inclusions can be recognized. An oxide particle might be recognized by the fact that it contained either (*a*) aluminum, (*b*) manganese +

aluminum, or (c) manganese but not sulfur. The size of the inclusion can also be determined from the line scan and the information stored. To avoid double counting due to the beam crossing the same inclusion on more than one successive line, the signal obtained along one line is stored for comparison with the signal obtained along the subsequent line. Signals are counted only if they are not inhibited by a similar signal in the previous line. The inclusion type, size range, and volume percent can be determined.

Dörfler and Plöckinger [95] have developed a lineal analysis technique for quantitative metallography of phases containing the same elements but in varying concentrations. The various phases are delineated by measuring the voltage output of the ratemeter as the beam is moved across the specimen. A voltage band (corresponding to a certain concentration range of a character-istic element for the one phase) is selected by two variable thresholds. One phase is identified by being within the voltage band, and the other phase is identified as located outside the band. The ratio of the measured time for one phase to that of the entire analysis gives the fraction of that particular phase. Further development of this basic system [96] has lead to a procedure where the various quantitative metallographic information can be calculated. An automatic lineal analysis is accomplished by the scanning system. Two or more signals are measured and the phase integrator, which is similar to the system previously described, determines which phase is present and stores this information. A small special purpose computer is responsible for calculating the stereometric (quantitative metallographic) analyses.

White et al [97] have developed techniques for computer processing of SEM images to yield quantitative metallographic parameters. The same method can be applied to EMP scanning images. The fundamental characteristic of the computer approach is that the entire image is recorded on digital magnetic tape and all data reduction are left to the computer. Two methods can be used to process the data in the computer. (1) The intensity of each data point, corresponding to the brightness level at a given coordinate position on the scanning image, is reduced to a simple binary code that indicates whether the intensity was above or below a preselected value. The program analyzed the resultant binary coded map to extract the quantitative metallographic parameters. (2) The computer generates contour maps at selected intensity levels and then calculates the characteristics of each closed contour to yield size, shape, and orientation information. McMillan et al [98] have discussed various methods of handling the data produced from the scanning instrument and Gortz et al [99] discusses the inclusion of X-ray analysis to the method.

Another method of attack [100] involves the use of special hardware to perform analysis within the scanning time. The approach allows a more rapid analysis because little data storage is involved. The data, however, must first be displayed as video signals. For X-ray signals this necessitates a very slow scan. Detection is accomplished by extracting information on preselected grey levels in the signal and converting it into a digital signal for computation. If the X-ray and specimen current signals are mixed [101], using the X-ray signal as discrete pulses, the specimen current can be used to define the outline of the phases and the X-rays to identify the phases themselves. It is apparent that quantitative metallography can be accomplished using the EMP and commercial units are now becoming available.

### Extension of Instrument Capability

#### Inclusion-Particle Analysis

Accurate analyses of inclusions are subject to several subtle sources of error. When an inclusion is analyzed, one takes great pains to analyze particles larger than the excitation volume produced by the electron beam. However, because the electron beam penetrates beneath the specimen surface, it is possible for part of the beam to penetrate to the matrix (Fig. 19a). It is also possible that inclusion particles lying just below the specimen surface may contribute to the analysis of the matrix (Fig. 19b). Consequently, it is necessary to repeat measurements on several inclusions to be assured that these effects are minimized. Another subtle source of error can be caused by X-ray fluorescence. Even if the inclusion is larger than the X-ray excitation volume, the characteristic and continuous spectrum produced in the inclusion may penetrate into the matrix. In certain cases fluorescence of the matrix by characteristic or continuum radiation may then occur. This radiation will be measured, in addition to the X-ray intensity from the inclusion, if specimen absorption is low and the area fluoresced is still on the X-ray focusing circle. A practical consequence of such an effect was discussed by Duke and Brett [102] in their study of metallic copper inclusions in meteorites.

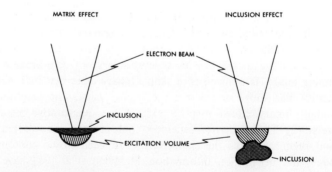

FIG. 19–*Inclusion analysis,* (a) *matrix effect,* (b) *inclusion effect. Direct excitation by the ectron beam.*

There are several ways to overcome the problems associated with the fact that the X-ray excitation volume under normal operating conditions may be the same size or larger than the particle of interest. One method is to isolate the particles and treat them essentially as thin films rather than as bulk samples. In this situation, the amount of elastic scattering in the thin specimen is minimized and X-ray resolution approaches that of the electron beam.

Submicron precipitates and inclusions have been studied by a combination of electron microscopy and EMP analysis. Fleetwood [103] identified precipitates smaller than 0.1 μm in maraging steels, and carbon extraction replicas were stripped from specimens of heat treated steel. Electron diffraction patterns were taken first in the transmission electron microscope (TEM). Subsequently, electron probe analysis of the same precipitates for nickel, iron, molybdenum, titanium, and cobalt were made. Since the precipitates were essentially thin films, some of the electron beam passed completely through the specimen and the amount of X-ray intensities were only used as a measure of the relative proportions of the elements present in the precipitates. Absorption corrections were applied to the thin films to more accurately determine the iron/molybdenum ratio in the precipitates. Ancey et al have also analyzed precipitates on extraction replicas in the EMP [104]. If characteristic X-rays from two elements are measured simultaneously, the concentration ratios could be calculated accurately despite the fact that the precipitates themselves varied greatly in thickness.

A combined electron microscope-electron probe (EMMA) has been designed by Duncumb [105]. In this instrument, the specimen can be studied by electron microscopy, electron diffraction, and either point or scanning electron probe analysis without altering the field of view. The electron beam can be focused down to a spot of 0.1 μm, and the maximum magnification from the objective and projector lenses is about X12 000 at 60 kV. To obtain structural information, the intermediate lens is adjusted to image the diffraction pattern from the particle; for chemical information, the characteristic X-ray emission is analyzed by means of a crystal spectrometer and proportional counter. The chief requirement of the X-ray spectrometer is that it should have as high a collection efficiency as possible since the X-ray intensity emitted from the submicron particles is very weak. Because of the rapid decrease of counting rate with particle size and contamination difficulties, the smallest sized particle that can be analyzed using a focusing spectrometer appears to be a particle of about 0.1 μm in size. A similar type of instrument was also used by Ancey et al [104] to study inclusion particles extracted from a fracture surface.

A new combined instrument has been developed [106,107] which allows a TEM resolution of 3Au at 100 kV. A minilens is also used to achieve a 0.2 to 0.3-μm probe. In an instrument of this type, particles down to 0.1 μm can be analyzed; it is relatively easy to locate regions for analysis in a transmission image, and selected area diffraction (SAD) can be accomplished. It should be possible now to analyze even smaller particles by means of the solid state detector.

In solid specimens one can attempt to reduce the finite size of the X-ray excitation volume below the normal resolution of 1 to 2 μm. The method of reducing the X-ray range $(R(X))$ in Eq 3 has been discussed previously. Since the total X-ray spatial resolution $(R_x)$ is equal to the sum of the X-ray range $(R(X))$ and the size of the electron beam $(d_p)$, there is no advantage in reducing the beam diameter below 0.2 μm, (2000Å) if the X-ray range $(R(X))$

is greater than about 0.5 $\mu$m. For example, if one is analyzing MnS inclusions in a steel at the normal operating potential of 20 kV, the X-ray range is about 2 $\mu$ for both manganese $K$- and sulfur $K$-radiation. At 10 kV operating potential the X-ray range is improved, 0.4 $\mu$m for manganese $K$ and 0.6 $\mu$m for sulfur $K$. However, in neither case is there any real point in reducing the beam current and, subsequently, decreasing X-ray intensity in order to produce a beam size below 0.2 $\mu$m.

In a study of (manganese-iron)sulfur inclusions in steel a matrix effect was observed [108]. The electron beam at 25 kV potential passed partially through the inclusion exciting the iron matrix even if the particles had a visible diameter greater than 5 $\mu$m. Obviously the thickness of the particles was not sufficient to contain the electron beam, see Fig. 21a. In this study an empirical technique was developed on the basis that the sulfur $K$-intensity was decreased in proportion to the additional iron $K$-intensity generated from the matrix effect.

Bolon and Lifshin [109] have attempted to study the effect of reducing the electron probe size in order to increase X-ray spatial resolution. Their test system was that of unidirectionally solidified alloy containing 1.5-$\mu$m tantalum carbide (TaC) rods in a nickel-chromium matrix. The calculation of X-ray source size was accomplished by using a modification of the Monte Carlo method proposed by Curgenven and Duncumb [110]. X-ray data were collected with both 0.25 and 1.0-$\mu$m-diameter beams at 20 kV voltage. The Monte Carlo plots of simulated electron trajectories are shown in Fig. 20. The calculations show that the direct X-ray excited volume should be contained within the TaC rods in the case of the 0.25-$\mu$m beam but not for a 1.0-$\mu$m beam. The data obtained showed that the Monte Carlo calculations correctly predicted the dimensions of the X-ray excited volume.

Calculations using Eq 3 show that $R(X)$ is 0.45 $\mu$m for tantalum $L$- and 0.65 $\mu$m for tantalum $M$-radiation. Therefore, for $d_p$ = 0.25 $\mu$m, the calculated spatial resolution is about 0.8 $\mu$m in agreement with this study [109]. If $d_p$ was 1 $\mu$m, the X-ray source would be slightly larger than the TaC rods. It is clear that Monte Carlo calculations will be valuable in predicting the X-ray excited volume and the intensity generated from that volume provided that the shapes of these structures and the diameter of the electron beam are accurately known. A treatment of a similar problem, for lamellar Al-CuAl$_2$ eutectic plates of varying sizes, was given by Jackson et al [111].

*Measurements Near Interfaces*

One of the major applications of quantitative EMP analysis is the determination of compositions at phase interfaces. These measurements may indicate the last temperature of equilibration of a given system, the composition of various phases in an equilibrium phase diagram, or the discontinuous change of the composition of a component near an interface. As discussed by Reed and Long [112] there are three major effects which must be considered when

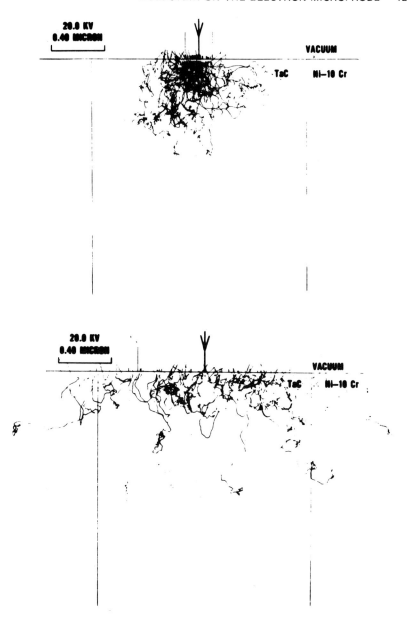

FIG. 20–*Monte Carlo calculations of electron trajectories in 1.5 μm tantalum carbide rods at 20 kV operating voltage. Electron trajectories are contained in the rods in the case where* $d_p = 0.25$ *μm (upper) but not in the case where* $d_p = 1.0$ *μm (bottom).*

making measurements at or near interfaces:

(1) *Electron Diffusion-X-ray Excitation Volume*–If there are variations in the concentration of the analyzed element within the volume excited by the electrons, the apparent concentration will be an average of the concentration within that volume. Therefore, measurements at phase boundaries where part of the beam is in both phases is quite difficult to make. If one knows the distribution of X-ray production within the analyzed volume, it should be possible to improve the effective resolution of the probe.

2. *X-ray Absorption*–The *A* correction for absorption can only be calculated for homogeneous specimens. An error may be introduced when the region through which the generated X-rays pass is of a different composition from the analyzed area. Such errors can be minimized by having a high takeoff angle and by choosing the orientation of the specimen so that the X-rays leave parallel to the phase interface in material of similar composition.

3. *X-ray Fluorescence*–When measurements are made near interfaces, not only may part of the electron beam excite X-ray radiation, continuum and characteristic, in the major phase, but the X-ray radiation produced could cause secondary fluorescence of elements across the boundary in the second phase. The measured X-ray intensity may, therefore, be modified by such a fluorescent effect.

The most important of these three effects is fluorescence since the errors may be large. The effect is most serious when the analyzed element is present in a large concentration in the adjacent phase, as in Fig. 21. In this figure an

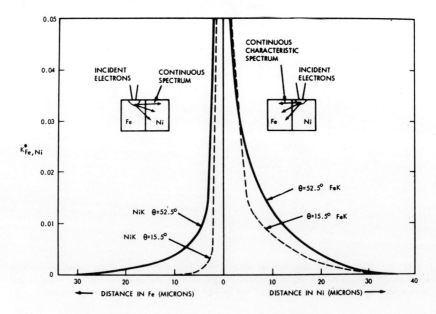

FIG. 21–*Effect of finite beam size in the Fe-Ni system. Nickel* $K_\alpha$ *and iron* $K_\alpha$ *intensity from an undiffused Fe-Ni couple.*

undiffused couple of pure iron versus pure nickel was polished and a micro-probe trace was taken at two takeoff angles 15.5 and 52.5 deg for iron $K$- and nickel $K$-radiation across the interface [113]. The nickel $K_\alpha$-radiation will produce secondary fluorescence of iron $K_\alpha$. Ideally, when the data are taken across the interface, a sharp gradient influenced only by the excitation volume should be observed. In this case when the electron beam is situated in pure nickel (Fig. 21), both the continuum radiation and the nickel $K$-characteristic radiation travel across the interface and produce, by secondary fluorescence, iron $K_\alpha$-radiation which is measured by the X-ray spectrometer. The effect extends up to 30 $\mu$m from the interface into the nickel. In some systems, zirconium-columbium (Zr-Cb), yttrium-molybdenum (Y-Mo), the apparent concentration is as high as 10 percent [114,115]. Calculations have been made [112,114] to account for the effect of secondary fluorescence by characteristic radiation near phase boundaries and have met with good success. When the electron beam is situated in the iron (Fig. 21), the continuum radiation travels across the iron-nickel interface and produces some nickel $K_\alpha$-secondary fluorescent radiation which is also measured by the spectro-meter. This effect is more difficult to calculate although a few attempts have been made [112,115]. It is clear, however, that if one is to attempt measure-ments of compositions near interfaces, calculations of the possible fluorescent effect should be made. Since it is not difficult to make undiffused couples, in some cases experimental measurements are justified.

When steep concentration profiles are encountered, the finite volume from which X-rays are excited in a specimen causes the true concentration profile to be smeared. A schematic representation of this process is shown in Fig. 22 as modified from Rapperport [116]. The X-ray excitation volume is described by a triangular-shaped function ($f(x)$), while the true concentration profile is in the form of a step function ($g(x)$). The curve ($h(x)$) represents the observed profile as the beam passes over the concentration step. A mathematical expression describes the relationship between these functions and is of the form [116]

$$h(x) = \int_{-\infty}^{\infty} g(x - x_o) \, f(x) \, dx \qquad (15)$$

The observed profile ($h(x)$) is, therefore, the mathematical convolution of the probe function and true concentration profile function.

One way in which the probe function can be experimentally determined is by passing the electron beam across a known concentration step and plotting the observed profile. By assuming a probe function which is Gaussian [117], the resulting probe trace should be an error function. Figure 23 shows the results of a step scan for nickel $K_\alpha$ taken at 1/4-$\mu$m intervals across an $\alpha$-phosphide interface in the Tucson meteorite [118]. The Gaussian probe function is described by [119]

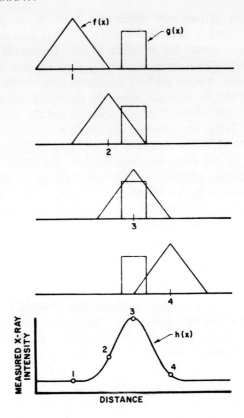

FIG. 22–*Convolution of the probe function* f(x) *with the true concentration profile* g(x). *The resultant curve* h(x) *is the mathematical convolution of* f(x) *and* g(x).

$$f(x) = \frac{1}{d} \exp \left[ -\frac{\pi}{4} \left( \frac{x}{d} \right) \right]^2 \qquad (16)$$

The parameter $d$ can be determined by drawing a tangent to the curve at the midpoint and measuring the intercept on the distance axis (Fig. 23). Once the probe function is known, it can be generated across a predicted true concentration profile to give an expected probe result, which can be compared with experimental data. The value of $d$ varies with the composition step, so the experiment must be done for each system. An estimate of the true profile is attained, when a set of experiment points lies on the observed profile resulting from the convolution of the true profile and probe function. Operating at 20 kV and 0.01 $\mu$A, an average $d$ value of 0.45 $\mu$m was measured for the $\alpha$-phosphide combination. The value of $2d$ (0.9 $\mu$m) is quite similar to the value of 1.0 $\mu$m for the X-ray spatial resolution $(R_x)$ predicted when $R(X) =$ 0.8 $\mu$m (Fig. 5) and $d_p \simeq 0.2$ $\mu$m.

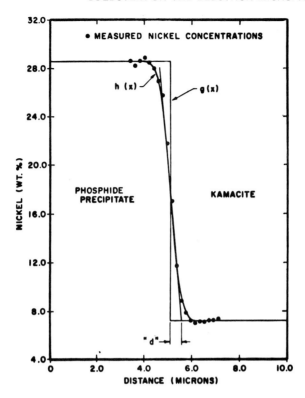

FIG. 23—*Step scan for nickel* K$_\alpha$ *across a kamacite (α)-phosphide interface in the Tucson meteorite.*

Deconvolution techniques have been used to determine the peak nickel concentrations in the γ-taenite phase at the α-γ interface in the Tucson meteorite [118]. This meteorite was cooled rapidly and the large nickel gradients developed due to the lack of time for diffusion of nickel in the taenite phase. Using a computer program, the probe function was generated across a predicted true concentration profile such as that illustrated in Fig. 24. The resulting convoluted profile is also shown, and indicated whether the predicted profile had been correct. In the analysis shown in Fig. 24, a peak nickel concentration of 21.7 percent was calculated for a true nickel value of 24.6 percent at the interface. Since the actual measured data points across the γ-α interface correspond closely to the calculated profile, it is reasonable to conclude that the true composition of taenite in equilibrium with kamacite is ~25Ni. In this example the interface equilibrium composition can be accurately determined. Effectively then, the deconvolution technique increases the spatial resolution of the electron microprobe. Interface compositions as well as steep compositional gradients can now be more effectively measured with the EMP. However this method can only be directly applied if the effect of fluorescence is unimportant.

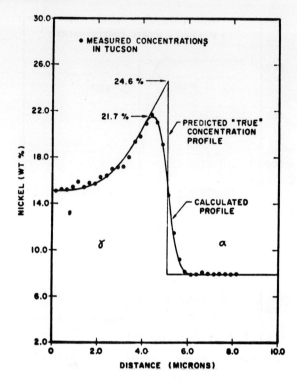

FIG. 24—*Deconvolution technique applied to the nickel concentration gradient in the taenite (γ) phase of the Tucson meteorite.*

## Chemical Bonding, Soft X-ray Spectra

For the very light elements, the X-ray emission spectra consists mainly of a single band produced by the transition of a valence electron to a vacancy in the $K$ shell. As pointed out by Fischer and Baun [120], the valence electrons are the ones most affected by chemical combination and the emission band can and does reflect the often large effects of changes in chemical bonding between atoms. These changes are signified by wavelength shifts, increases or decreases in the relative intensities of various lines or bands, and in their shape. This allows one to obtain an indication of how a particular element is combined chemically. Practical uses of the soft X-ray spectra analysis involve studies of corrosion layers on fracture and oxidized surfaces, thin films, and the formation of compounds with beryllium, boron, carbon, and nitrogen.

The determination of band shapes, relative intensities, and wavelength shifts and the changes which occur in them is not always a straight forward process. Self-absorption may seriously distort the true emission spectrum and can result in a false interpretation of the apparent spectral changes. The EMP with large $d$-spacing xtals such as KAP, lead stearate, and clinochlore has been used to obtain the emission spectra. Originally, data for spectral shape and peak positions were taken using a ratemeter and strip chart recorder. Such a technique requires careful calibration of the recorder, and the final evaluation is somewhat subjective. Currently, data are being handled and processed with the use of the computer. Several computer systems have been reported [121-123], and all of these lead to a significant improvement in the quality of the data.

Figure 25 shows the carbon $K$-band from carbon deposited by the electron beam compared to that of electrode grade graphite [124]. The wavelengths of

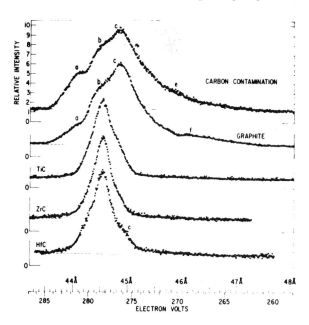

FIG. 25–*Carbon* K-*spectra from carbon deposited by the electron beam, electrode grade graphite, and various carbides. The target voltage was 4 kV.*

the peaks *a, b,* and *c,* as well as the general band shape, are the same for both forms of carbon. Possible reasons for the differences in intensity distribution of the carbon $K$-bands is that carbon deposited by the electron beam may be amorphous or impure resulting in somewhat different bonding than for graphite. The carbon $K$-spectra of various carbides are also shown in Fig. 25. The energy shift of the carbides relative to graphite is significant and can be used to identify, in some cases, the type of carbide present.

Krause et al [125] have shown that measurements of the shifts of the oxygen $K_\alpha$-X-ray peak, with respect to the oxygen $K_\alpha$-peak from α quartz, could be used to characterize structurally and chemically the thin, often amorphous, oxide layers that form when a metal corrodes. Experiments were performed to characterize oxide films on transition metals. They found that the magnitude of the shifts in the oxygen X-ray emission bands is a continuous function of the metal to oxygen ratio of the emitter. In the three series of transition metal oxides (titanium, manganese, and iron) studied, the peaks shift toward shorter wavelength with increasing oxidation. The cation valence of these transition metal oxides can be determined from measurements of the oxide $K_\alpha$-wavelength. As an example [125], the oxygen band shift technique was applied to a thin (0.5 μm) oxide layer prepared by heating an iron bar. The oxide was identified as $Fe_3O_4$ by X-ray diffraction and shows the wavelength of the oxide $K_\alpha$-band emitted in the oxide is essentially the same as that measured from iron oxide ($Fe_3O_4$). Oxide films thicker than 100 Å can be investigated by this technique free of interference from the metallic substrate. In addition, the oxide films need not be crystalline or of uniform thickness.

Another application to the study of oxides is the characterization of thin film and bulk silicon oxide (SiO). The silicon $K$-emission spectra in the 7 Å region can easily be measured. Figure 26 shows the silicon $K_\beta$-X-ray bands for elemental silicon dioxide ($SiO_2$), and SiO [126]. Significant changes in the spectrum are noted when going from silicon to $SiO_2$. Only a single asymmetrical band is obtained from elemental silicon in contrast to the spectrum from $SiO_2$ where two bands are recorded. In SiO, the main $K$-band is split and the energy of the three components corresponds to positions found for silicon and $SiO_2$. White and Roy [127] used this band splitting as evidence that SiO was a mixture of silicon and $SiO_2$. In addition, the silicon $K_\alpha$-satellites $K_{\alpha_3}$ and $K_{\alpha_4}$, and silicon $K_\beta'$ are very sensitive to chemical combination. Figure 26 shows the oxygen $K$-spectrum from SiO and $SiO_2$ [126]. The oxygen spec-

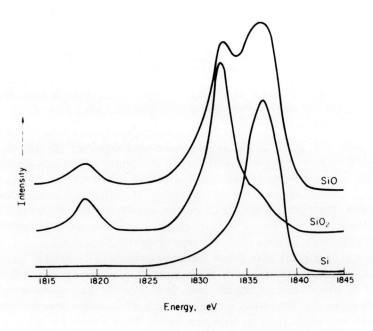

FIG. 26a—*Silicon K-X-ray bands from elemental silicon, SiO₂ and SiO.*

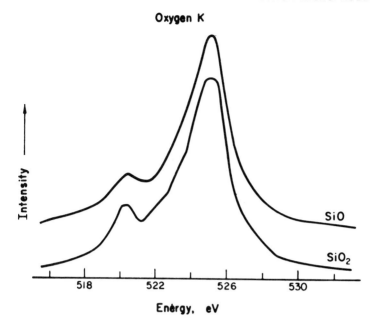

FIG. 26b—*Oxygen K-band for SiO and SiO₂ (α-quartz).*

trums are virtually identical indicating again that the condensed phase SiO consists of a variable mixture of silicon and $SiO_2$. Other studies have characterized films containing nitrogen [*128*]. In addition, combined EMP and ellipsometric study of thin $SiO_2$ films on silicon enabled data to be obtained on contamination films as well as the mass thickness and uniformity of the thin film [*129*]. Other examples of soft X-ray application to materials characterization have been reported in the literature [*130-132*] and give support for the use of this technique to microprobe analysis.

*Acknowledgments*

The author wishes to acknowledge research support from NASA under grant number NGR 39-007-043 and from NSF grant number GA 15349.

**References**

[*1*]  Castaing, R., *Advances in Electronics and Electron Physics,* L. Marton, Ed., Academic Press, New York, 1960, p. 317.
[*2*]  Heinrich, K.F.J., *Applied Spectroscopy,* Vol. 22, 1968, p. 395.
[*3*]  Beaman, D.R. and Isasi, J.A., *Materials Research and Standards,* Vol. 11, No. 11, 1971, p. 8.
[*4*]  Pease, R.F.W. and Nixon, W.C., *Journal of Scientific Instruments,* Vol. 42, 1965, p. 81.
[*5*]  Duncumb, P. and Shields, P.K., *British Journal of Applied Physics,* Vol. 14, 1963, p. 617.
[*6*]  Kanaya, K. and Okayama, S., *Journal of Physics D, Applied Physics,* Vol. 5, 1972, p. 43.

[7]   Cosslett, V.E. and Thomas R.N., *British Journal of Applied Physics,* Vol. 15, 1964, p. 1283.
[8]   Heinrich, K.F.J. in *X-ray Optics and Microanalysis,* Fourth International Congress on X-ray Optics and Microanalysis, Orsay, 1965, R. Castaing, P. Deschamps, and J. Philibert, Eds., Hermann, Paris, 1966, p. 159.
[9]   Bishop, H.E. in *X-ray Optics and Microanalysis,* Fourth International Congress on X-ray Optics and Microanalysis, Orsay, 1965, R. Castaing, P. Deschamps, and J. Philibert, Eds., Hermann, Paris, 1966, p. 153.
[10]  Cosslett, V.E. and Thomas, R.N., *British Journal of Applied Physics,* Vol. 16, 1965, p. 779.
[11]  Shimizu, R. and Murata, K., *Japanese Journal of Applied Physics,* Vol. 42, 1971, p. 387.
[12]  Duncumb, P. in *Proceedings,* Second International Symposium on X-ray Microscopy and X-ray Microanalysis, Stockholm, 1959, A. Engström, V.E. Cosslett, and H. Pattee, Eds., Elsevier, Amsterdam, 1960, p. 365.
[13]  Anderson, C.A. and Hasler, M.F. in *X-ray Optics and Microanalysis,* Fourth International Congress on X-ray Optics and Microanalysis, Orsay, 1965, R. Castaing, P. Deschamps, and J. Philibert, Eds., Herman, Paris, 1966, p. 310.
[14]  Reed, S.J.B. in *X-ray Optics and Microanalysis,* Fourth International Congress on X-ray Optics and Microanalysis, Orsay, 1965, R. Castaing, P. Deschamps, and J. Philibert, Eds., Herman, Paris, 1966, p. 339.
[15]  Moll, S.H., *Norelco Reporter,* Vol. 11, 1964, p. 55.
[16]  Kimoto, S., Hashimoto, H., and Tagata, S. in *Proceedings,* Fifth National Conference on Electron Probe Analysis, New York, July 1970, Paper No. 51.
[17]  Fitzgerald, R., Keil, K., and Heinrich, K.F.J., *Science,* Vol. 159, 1968, p. 528.
[18]  Frankel, R.S. and Aitken, D.W., *Applied Spectroscopy,* Vol. 24, 1970, p. 557.
[19]  *Energy Dispersive X-ray Analysis: X-ray and Electron Probe Analysis, ASTM STP 485,* American Society for Testing and Materials, 1971.
[20]  Lifshin, E. in *Summer Course Notes,* Electron Probe Microanalysis and Scanning Electron Microscopy, Lehigh University, June 1972.
[21]  Jaklevic, J.M. and Goulding, F.S. in *Proceedings,* Sixth National Conference on Electron Probe Analysis, Pittsburgh, July 1971, paper No. 1.
[22]  Castaing, R., Ph.D. thesis, University of Paris, 1951.
[23]  *Quantitative Electron Probe Microanalysis,* National Bureau of Standards Special Publication 298, K.F.J. Heinrich, Ed. 1968.
[24]  Martin, P.M. and Poole, D.M., *Metallurgical Reviews,* Vol. 16, 1971, p. 19.
[25]  Heinrich, K.F.J., *Analytical Chemistry,* Vol. 44, 1972, p. 350.
[26]  Goldstein, J.I. in *Electron Probe Microanalysis,* A.J. Tousimis and L. Marton, Eds., Academic Press, New York, 1969, p. 245.
[27]  Keil, K., *Fortschritte der Mineralogie,* Vol. 44, No. 1, Stuttgart, Jan. 1967, p. 4.
[28]  Varshneya, A.K., Cooper, A.R., and Cable, M., *Journal Applied Physics,* Vol. 37, 1966, p. 2199.
[29]  Borom, M.P. and Hanneman, R.E., *Journal Applied Physics,* Vol. 38, 1967, p. 2406.
[30]  Scholes, S. and Wilkinson, F.C.F. in *Fifth International Congress on X-ray Optics and Microanalysis,* Tübingen, 1968, G. Möllenstedt and K.H. Gaukler, Eds., Springer Verlag, Berlin, 1969, p. 438.
[31]  Bence, A.E. and Albee, A.L., *Journal of Geology,* Vol. 76, 1968, p. 382.
[32]  Myklebust, R.L. and Heinrich, K.F.J. in *Energy Dispersion X-ray Analysis: X-ray and Electron Probe Analysis, ASTM STP 485,* American Society for Testing and Materials, 1971, p. 232.
[33]  Russ, J.C. in *Energy Dispersion X-ray Analysis: X-ray and Electron Probe Analysis, ASTM STP 485,* American Society for Testing and Materials, 1971, p. 154.
[34]  Henoc, J., Heinrich, K.F.J., and Myklebust, R., *Technical Note,* National Bureau of Standards, 1972, in press.
[35]  Colby, J.W. in *Thin Film Dielectrics,* Electrochemical Society, Inc., F. Vratny, Ed., 1968, p. 491.
[36]  Goldstein, J.I. and Comella, P., *Goddard Space Flight Center Publication,* X-642-69-115, 1969.

[37] Chambers, W.F. in *Proceedings,* Fifth National Conference on Electron Probe Analysis, New York, July 1970, Paper No. 7.

[38] Wolf, R. and Saffir, A.J. in *Proceedings,* Fifth National Conference on Electron Probe Analysis, New York, July 1970, Paper No. 6.

[39] Kunz, F., Eichen, E., Matthews, H., and Francis, J. in *Advances in X-ray Analysis,* Vol. 15, K.F.J. Heinrich, C.S. Barrett, J.B. Newkirk, and C.O. Rudd, Eds., Plenum, 1972, p. 148.

[40] Colby, J.W. in *Proceedings,* Seventh National Conference on Electron Probe Analysis, San Francisco, July 1972, Paper No. 68.

[41] Shiraiwa, T. and Fujino, N. in *Fifth International Congress on X-ray Optics and Microanalysis,* Tübingen, 1968, G. Möllenstedt and K.H. Gaukler, Eds., Springer Verlag, Berlin, 1969, p. 365.

[42] Shiraiwa, T. and Fujino, N., *Japanese Journal of Applied Physics,* Vol. 9, 1970, p. 976.

[43] Duncumb, P. and Melford, D.A. in *X-ray Optics and Microanalysis,* Fourth International Congress on X-ray Optics and Microanalysis, Orsay, 1965, R. Castaing, P. Deschamps, and J. Philibert, Eds., Hermann, Paris, 1966, p. 240.

[44] Shiraiwa, T., Fujino, N., and Murayama, J., *Transactions,* Iron and Steel Institute of Japan, Vol. 10, 1970, p. 406.

[45] Castaing, R. and Descamps, J., *Comptes Rendus,* Vol. 238, 1954, p. 1506.

[46] Duerr, J.S., Adario, J., and Ogilvie, R.E. in *Proceedings,* Fourth National Conference on Electron Microprobe Analysis, Pasadena, Calif., July 1969, Paper No. 31.

[47] Moll, S.H. and Bruno, G.W. in *Second National Conference on Electron Microprobe Analysis,* Boston, Mass., June 1967.

[48] Galda, E. and Goldstein, J.I., private communication, Lehigh University.

[49] Eichen, E., Tabock, J., and Kinsman, K.R., "An Electron Microprobe Technique for Detecting Low Carbon Concentrations in Iron," Publication Preprint, Scientific Research Staff, Ford Motor Company, 1971.

[50] Renzetta, G.V.T. and Scott, V.D. in *X-ray Optics and Microanalysis,* Fourth International Congress on X-ray Optics and Microanalysis, Orsay, 1965, R. Castaing, P. Deschamps, and J. Philibert, Eds., Hermann, Paris, 1966, p. 254.

[51] Ong, P.S. in *X-ray Optics and Microanalysis,* Fourth International Congress on X-ray Optics and Microanalysis, Orsay, 1965, R. Castaing, P. Deschamps, and J. Philibert, Eds., Hermann, Paris, 1966, p. 181.

[52] Kimoto, S., Hashimoto, H., and Uchiyama, H. in *Fifth International Congress on X-ray Optics and Microanalysis,* Tübingen, 1968, G. Möllenstedt and K.H. Gaukler, Eds., Springer Verlag, Berlin, 1969, p. 369.

[53] Kohlhaas, V.E. and Scheiding, F., *Archiv für das Eisenhüttenwesen,* Vol. 40, 1969, p. 1.

[54] Cosslett, V.E. and Dumcumb, P., *Nature,* Vol. 177, 1956, p. 1172.

[55] Heinrich, K.F.J. in *Fifty Years of Progress in Metallographic Techniques, ASTM STP 430,* American Society for Testing and Materials, 1968, p. 315.

[56] Barkalow, R.H., Kraft, R.W., and Goldstein, J.I., *Metallurgical Transactions,* Vol. 3, 1972, p. 919., Barkalow, R.H., "Solidification Structures and Phase Relationships in M2 High Speed Steel," Ph.D. dissertation, Lehigh University, 1971.

[57] Eichen, E., Kunz, F., and Tabock, J. in *Applications of Modern Metallographic Techniques, ASTM STP 480,* American Society for Testing and Materials, 1970, p. 183.

[58] Ingram, M.J. and Hogben, C.A.M. in *Developments in Applied Spectroscopy,* W.D. Ash, Ed., Plenum Press, Vol. 6, 1968, p. 43.

[59] Rasmussen, H.P., Shull, V.E., and Dryer, H.T. in *Developments in Applied Spectroscopy,* W.D. Ash, Ed., Plenum Press, Vol. 6, 1968, p. 29.

[60] Tousimis, A.J., in *Scanning Electron Microscopy/1969, Proceedings,* Second Annual Scanning Electron Microscopy Symposium, April 1969, IIT Research Institute, Chicago, Ill., p. 217.

[61] Yakowitz, H. and Heinrich, K.F.J., *Journal of Research of the National Bureau of Standards — A., Physics and Chemistry,* Vol. 73A, 1969, p. 113.

[62] Melford, D.A., *Journal of the Institute of Metals,* Vol. 90, 1962, p. 217.

[63] Wells, O.C. in *Scanning Electron Microscopy/1972 (Part I), Proceedings,* Fifth Annual Scanning Electron Microscope Symposium, April 1972, IIT Research

Institute, Chicago, Ill., p. 169.

[64]  Heinrich, K.F.J., Fiori, C., and Yakowitz, H., *Science*, Vol. 167, 1970, p. 1129.

[65]  Long, J.V.P. and Angrell, S.O., *Mineralogical Magazine*, Vol. 34, 1965, p. 318.

[66]  Kyser, D.F. and Wittry, D.B. in *The Electron Microprobe*, T.D. McKinley, K.F.J. Heinrich, and D.B. Wittry, Eds., Wiley, New York, 1966.

[67]  Wittry, D.B., *Applied Physics Letters*, Vol. 8, 1966, p. 142.

[68]  Muir, M.D., Grant, P.R., Hubbard, G., and Mundell, J. in *Scanning Electron Microscopy/1971, Proceedings*, Fourth Annual Scanning Electron Microscope Symposium, April 1971, IIT Research Institute, Chicago, Ill., p. 403.

[69]  Kniseley, R.N., Laabs, F.C., and Fassel, V.A., *Analytical Chemistry*, Vol. 41, 1969, p. 50.

[70]  Smith, J.P. in *Transactions*, Third National Conference on Electron Microprobe Analysis, Chicago, Ill., July 1968, Paper No. 38.

[71]  Davey, J.P. in *X-ray Optics and Microanalysis*, Fourth International Congress on X-ray Optics and Microanalysis, Orsay, 1965, R. Castaing, P. Deschamps, and J. Philibert, Eds., Hermann, Paris, 1966, p. 566.

[72]  Bhalla, R.J.R.S.B. and White, E.W. in *Proceedings*, Fifth National Conference on Electron Probe Analysis, New York, July 1970, Paper No. 30.

[73]  Yakowitz, H. in *Fifty Years of Progress in Metallographic Techniques, ASTM STP 430*, American Society for Testing Materials, 1968, p. 383.

[74]  Ohmae, K. and Ziebold, T.O., *Journal of Nuclear Materials*, Vol. 43, 1972, p. 245.

[75]  Liebhafsky, H.A., Pfeiffer, H.G., and Zemany, P.D., *Analytical Chemistry*, Vol. 27, 1955, p. 1257.

[76]  Ziebold, T.O., *Analytical Chemistry*, Vol. 39, 1967, p. 858.

[77]  Michaelis, R.E., Yakowitz, H., and Moore, G.A., *Journal of Research of the National Bureau of Standards*, Vol. A68, 1964, p. 343.

[78]  Yakowitz, H., Vieth, D.L., Heinrich, K.F.J., and Michaelis, R.E., *Special Publication 260-10*, National Bureau of Standards, 1965.

[79]  Goldstein, J.I., Majeske, F.J. and Yakowitz, H. in *Application of X-ray Analysis*, Vol. 10, J.B. Newkirk and G.R. Mallett, Eds., Plenum Press, 1967, p. 431.

[80]  Yakowitz, H., Ruff, A.W. and Michaelis, R.E., *Special Publication 260-43*, National Bureau of Standards, 1972.

[81]  Bauer, E.L., *A Statistical Manual for Chemists*, 2nd Edition, Academic Press, 1971.

[82]  Kunz, F., Eichen, E., and Varshneya, A. in *Proceedings*, Sixth National Conference on Electron Probe Analysis, Pittsburgh, Pa., July, 1971, Paper No. 20.

[83]  Ziebold, T.O., *Analytical Chemistry*, Vol. 39, 1967, p. 858.

[84]  Shastry, C.R. and Judd, G., *Metallurgical Transactions*, Vol. 3, 1972, p. 779.

[85]  Buseck, P.R. and Goldstein, J.I., *Geological Society of America Bulletin*, Vol. 80, 1969, p. 2141.

[86]  Theisen, R., *Quantitative Electron Microprobe Analysis*, Springer-Verlag, 1965.

[87]  Ziebold, T.O. and Ogilvie, R.E., *Analytical Chemistry*, Vol. 36, 1964, p. 322.

[88]  Goldstein, J.I., *Journal Geophysical Research*, Vol. 72, 1967, p. 4689.

[89]  Heindel, R.H., *Analytical Chemistry*, Vol. 43, 1971, p. 1907.

[90]  Goldstein, J.I. and Ogilvie, R.E., *Geochimica et Cosmochimica Acta*, Vol. 27, 1963, p. 623.

[91]  Keil, K. and Anderson, C.A., *Geochimica et Cosmochimica Acta*, Vol. 29, 1965, p. 621.

[92]  Barkalow, R.H., Kraft, R.W., and Goldstein, J.I., *Metallurgical Transactions*, Vol. 3, 1972, p. 919.

[93]  Lifshin, E. and Hanneman, R.E., "General Electric Research Laboratory Reports 65-RL-3944M," 1965 and 66-C-250, 1966.

[94]  Melford, D.A. and Whittington, K.R. in *X-ray Optics and Microanalysis*, Fourth International Congress on X-ray Optics and Microanalysis, Orsay, 1965, R. Castaing, P. Deschamps, and J. Philibert, Eds., Hermann, Paris, 1966, p. 497.

[95]  Dörfler, G. and Plöckinger, E. in *X-ray Optics and Microanalysis*, Fourth International Congress on X-ray Optics and Microanalysis, Orsay, 1965, R. Castaing, P. Deschamps, and J. Philibert, Eds., Hermann, Paris, 1966, p. 506.

[96] Dörfler, G. and Russ, J.C. in *Scanning Electron Microscopy/1970, Proceedings,* Third Annual Scanning Electron Microscope Symposium, April 1970, IIT Research Institute, Chicago, Ill., p. 67.

[97] White, E.W., Johnson, G.G., and McKinstry, H.A. in *Scanning Electron Microscopy/1968, Proceedings,* First Annual Scanning Electron Microscope Symposium, April 1968, IIT Research Institute, Chicago, Ill., p. 95.

[98] McMillan, R.E., Johnson, G.G., and White, E.W. in *Scanning Electron Microscopy/1969, Proceedings,* Second Annual Scanning Electron Microscope Symposium, April 1969, IIT Research Institute, Chicago, Ill., p. 439.

[99] Görz, H., White, E.W., McMillan, R.E., and Lebiedzik, J. in *Proceedings,* Fifth National Conference on Electron Probe Analysis, New York, July 1970, Paper No. 10.

[100] Braggins, D.W., Gardner, G.M., and Gibbard, D.W. in *Scanning Electron Microscopy/1971, Proceedings,* Fourth Annual Scanning Electron Microscope Symposium, April 1971, IIT Research Institute, Chicago, Ill., p. 393.

[101] Fisher, C. and Gibbard, D.W. in *Proceedings,* Sixth National Conference on Electron Probe Analysis, Pittsburgh, Pa., July 1971, Paper No. 54.

[102] Duke, M.B. and Brett, R., *Geological Survey Research,* Vol. B101, 1965, p. 103.

[103] Fleetwood, M.J., Higginson, G.M., and Miller, G.P., *British Journal of Applied Physics,* Vol. 16, 1965, p. 645.

[104] Ancey, M., Henry, G., Philibert, J., and Tixier, R. in *Fifth International Congress on X-ray Optics and Microanalysis,* Tübingen, 1968, G. Möllenstedt and K.H. Gaukler, Eds., Springer-Verlag, Berlin, 1969, p. 509.

[105] Duncumb, P. in *The Electron Microprobe,* T.D. McKinley, K.F.J. Heinrich, and D.B. Wittry, Eds., Wiley, New York, 1966, p. 490.

[106] Cooke, C.J. and Duncumb, P. in *Fifth International Congress on X-ray Optics and Microanalysis,* Tübingen, 1968, G. Möllenstedt and K.H. Gaukler, Eds., Springer-Verlag, Berlin, 1969, p. 245.

[107] Cooke, C.J. and Openshaw, I.K. in *Proceedings,* Fourth National Conference on Electron Microprobe Analysis, Pasadena, Calif., July 1969, Paper No. 64.

[108] Ryder, P.L. and Jackel, G., *Zutschrift fuer Metallkunde,* Vol. 63, 1972, p. 187.

[109] Bolon, R.B. and Lifshin, E. in *Scanning Electron Microscopy/1973, Proceedings,* Sixth Annual Scanning Electron Microscope Symposium, April 1973, IIT Research Institute, Chicago, Ill., p. 287.

[110] Curgenven, L. and Duncumb, P., "Tube Investments Research Laboratory Report No. 303," July 1971.

[111] Jackson, M.R., Goldstein, J.I., and Kraft, R.W. in *Proceedings,* Sixth National Conference on Electron Microprobe Analysis, Pittsburgh, Pa., July 1971, Paper No. 22.

[112] Reed, S.J.B. and Long, J.V.P. in *X-ray Optics and X-ray Microanalysis,* Third International Symposium, Stanford University, Stanford, Calif., 1962, H.H. Pattee, V.E. Cosslett, and A. Engström, Eds., Academic Press, New York, 1963, p. 317.

[113] Goldstein, J.I. and Ogilvie, R.E. in *X-ray Optics and Microanalysis,* Fourth International Congress on X-ray Optics and Microanalysis, Orsay, 1965, R. Castaing, P. Deschamps, and J. Philibert, Eds., Hermann, Paris, 1966, p. 594.

[114] Maurice, F., Sequin, R., and Henoc, J. in *X-ray Optics and Microanalysis,* Fourth International Congress on X-ray Optics and Microanalysis, Orsay, 1965, R. Castaing, P. Deschamps, and J. Philibert, Eds., Hermann, Paris, 1966, p. 357.

[115] Henoc, M.J., Maurice, F., and Zemskoff, A. in *Fifth International Congress on X-ray Optics and Microanalysis,* Tübingen, 1968, G. Möllenstedt and K.H. Gaukler, Eds., Springer-Verlag, Berlin, 1969, p. 187.

[116] Rapperport, E.J. in *Electron Probe Microanalysis,* A.J. Tousimis and L. Marton, Eds., Academic Press, New York, 1969, p. 117.

[117] Gupta, P.K., *Journal of Physics D: Applied Physics,* Vol. 3, 1970, p. 1919.

[118] Miyake, G.T. and Goldstein, J.I. to be published in *Geochimica et Cosmochimica Acta,* 1974. Miyake, G.T., "The Shock and Thermal History of Two Unusual Iron Meteorites," M.S. thesis, Lehigh University, 1973.

[119] Gilmour, J.B., Purdy, G.R., and Kirkaldy, J.S., *Metallurgical Transactions,* Vol. 3,

1972, p. 3213.
[120] Fischer, D.W. and Baun, W.L., *Norelco Reporter,* Vol. 14, 1967, p. 92.
[121] Solomon, J.S. and Baun, W.L., *Applied Spectroscopy,* Vol. 25, 1971, p. 518.
[122] Colby, J.W., Wonsidler, D.R., and Androshuk, A. in *Proceedings,* Fourth National Conference on Electron Probe Analysis, Pasadena, Calif., July 1969, Paper No. 26.
[123] Colby, J.W. in *Proceedings,* Sixth International Conference on X-ray Optics and Microanalysis, G. Shinoda, K. Kohra and T. Ichiokawa, Eds., University of Tokyo Press, 1972, p. 247.
[124] Holliday, J.E., *Norelco Reporter,* Vol. 14, 1967, p. 84.
[125] Krause, H.B., Savanick, G.A., and White, E.W., *Journal of the Electrochemical Society,* Solid State Science, Vol. 177, 1970, p. 557.
[126] Baun, W.L. and Solomon, J.S., *Vacuum,* Vol. 21, 1971, p. 165.
[127] White, E.W. and Roy, R., *Solid State Communications,* Vol. 2, 1964, p. 151.
[128] Colby, J.W. in *Thin Film Dielectrics,* F. Vratny, Ed., Electrochemical Society, New York, 1969, p. 491.
[129] Knausenberger, W.H., Vedam, K., White, E.W., and Zeigler, W., *Applied Physics Letters,* Vol. 14, 1969, p. 43.
[130] Solomon, J.S. and Baun, W.L. in *Proceedings,* Seventh National Conference on Electron Probe Analysis, San Francisco, Calif., July 1972, Paper No. 11.
[131] Baun, W.L. and Solomon, J.S., "Technical Report AFML-TR-70-80," Air Force Materials Laboratory, 1970.
[132] Solomon, J.S. and Baun, W.L., "Technical Report AFML-TR-70-253," Air Force Materials Laboratory, 1970.

*M.G.H. Wells[1] and J.M. Capenos[1]*

# Transmission Electron Microscopy in Materials Research

REFERENCE: Wells, M.G.H. and Capenos, J.M., "Transmission Electron Microscopy in Materials Research," *Metallography—A Practical Tool for Correlating the Structure and Properties of Materials, ASTM STP 557,* American Society for Testing and Materials, 1974, pp. 137–168.

ABSTRACT: This paper very briefly reviews the development of transmission electron microscopy (TEM) including instrumentation and specimen preparation techniques, and generally describes typical examples of the use of TEM today in the study and understanding of the structure of materials. New observation techniques such as energy loss analysis, dark field imaging, the weak beam technique, Kikuchi line analysis, and computer generation of dislocation images are discussed. In addition to forefront work, many illustrations are given where TEM has greatly contributed to the optimization of properties and general improvement of many commercially important materials.

KEY WORDS: metallography, electron microscopy, energy loss analysis, electron diffraction, martensite, decomposition

Twenty-three years ago, Subcommittee 11 on Microscopy and Diffraction (Committee E-4 on Metallography) presented to the American Society of Testing and Materials (ASTM) a report which chronicled the first systematic study of steel structures using the electron microscope [1].[2] A collection of replica micrographs was presented showing details of pearlite and martensitic structures which had never before been seen. This historic work served as a foundation and spur for the metals and materials research community as it unmistakably demonstrated the usefulness and potential of the electron microscope in structure studies at higher magnifications and resolutions than was previously possible. In fact, the full potential of the electron microscope was little understood at that time by most workers and is only being realized today, 30 years after the appearance of the first commercial microscopes. In some respects, this has been extremely rapid progress.

This paper will briefly review specimen preparation techniques and generally describe some typical examples of the use of transmission electron microscopy (TEM) today, in the study and understanding of the structure of materials. Illustrations are given where the use of TEM has benefited technology by helping to optimize properties and generally improve materials.

[1] Technical director and staff microscopist, respectively, Crucible Materials Research Center, Colt Industries, Pittsburgh, Pa. 15230.
[2] The italic numbers in brackets refer to the list of references appended to this paper.

Most of the recent advances in TEM have come about as a result of increased resolution of the instrument, improved specimen preparation techniques, and further sophistication in image analysis.

Greatly increased magnification and resolving power of the TEM over those of the optical microscope were, of course, the main features of electron microscopy exploited during the early years; materials and techniques for surface replica preparations improved rapidly, and a number of convenient, reliable surface replica techniques were developed which afforded good high magnification images of specimen topography.

Figure 1, a typical shadowed surface replica from a polished and etched martensitic steel specimen, illustrates the fine detail reproduced by this technique.

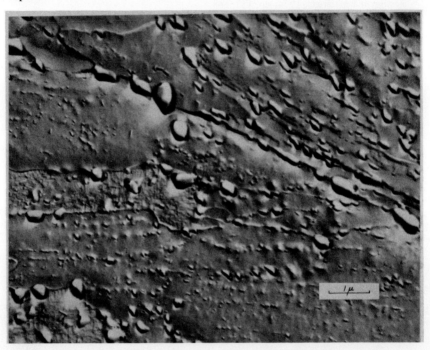

FIG. 1—*Shadowed surface replica electron micrograph of polished and etched martensitic T-410 stainless steel. The size and distribution of carbides within the martensite can be clearly seen.*

The extraction replica technique, first described by Fisher [2], made possible the direct examination and identification by electron diffraction of inclusions and precipitate phases removed from bulk specimens by the replicating process. Figure 2 illustrates extraction replica preparations of (a) coarse $M_{23}C_6$ grain boundary precipitates from T-446 stainless steel and (b) fine intragranular nickel titanium ($Ni_3Ti$) precipitates from an 18Ni maraging steel.

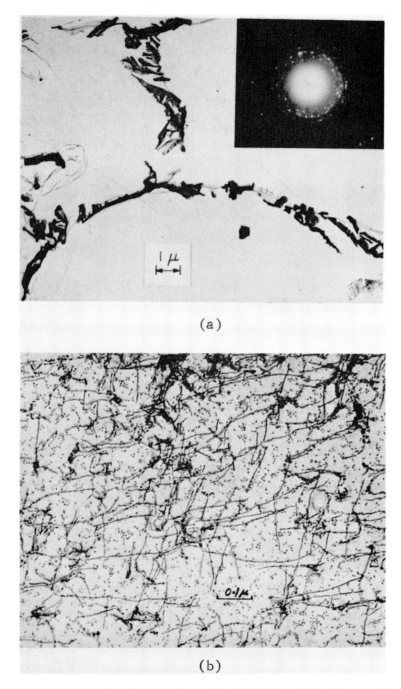

FIG. 2–*Extraction replica electron micrographs,* (a) $M_{23}C_6$ *grain boundary precipitates and the corresponding diffraction pattern from T-446 stainless steel and* (b) *ultrafine $Ni_3Ti$ precipitates from 18Ni maraging steel.*

Direct examination of thin metal foils, first accomplished by Heidenrich [3], gained popularity in the mid-1950's with the development of reproducible electrolytic thinning techniques. In 1956, Hirsch et al [4] and Bollman [5] published the first detailed studies of thin foil preparation and examination. Figure 3 illustrates the variety of details seen in a thin foil specimen of T-410 stainless steel heated at 1400°F for 2 h. This micrograph was prepared as part of a study of tempering reactions in this commercially important stainless steel [6]. Details of all of these techniques have been given in several excellent reviews [7-9].

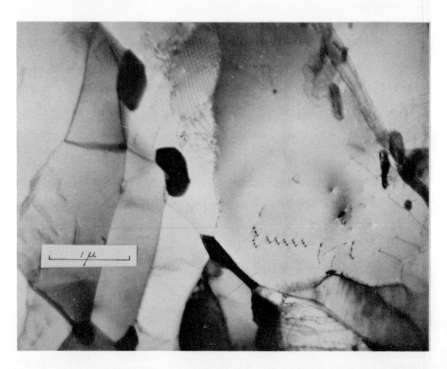

FIG. 3–*Thin foil electron micrograph of T-410 stainless steel heated 2 h at 1400°F. Note the variety of substructural detail revealed by this technique.*

In this period, the use of selected area diffraction (SAD) to determine the structure, orientation, and orientation relationships of metal foils was rapidly being developed. Researchers at the forefront of this field were advocating that a diffraction pattern be taken each time a micrograph was taken to gain the maximum information from the specimen. Thomas [10] helped to bring fundamentals to a large number of newcomers to the field. The kinematical theory of electron diffraction contrast had been developing for many years, and the more comprehensive dynamical theory of contrast was developed about this time. This theory, reviewed in detail by Hirsch et al [11], has proved invaluable in interpreting TEM images.

## Instrument Design Improvements

Instrument design improvements over the past decade have resulted in a number of very sophisticated electron microscopes offering a combination of high performance, versatility, and ease of operation. Resolutions of the order of 5 to 10 Å units are routinely obtained with most newer instruments using conventional imaging techniques. The double condenser lens system, now standard equipment on most instruments, permits a wide range of illumination conditions as well as better penetration of thin foil specimens. Other basic design improvements and additions include beam (gun) tilting devices for high resolution dark field studies, refined electromagnetic stigmators for better astigmatism correction, specimen anticontamination devices, high performance automatic vacuum systems, improved airlocking of various sections of the column, and greatly improved, high stability, solid state electronic circuitry.

In addition to these basic instrument design improvements, a variety of accessories are available which further extend the versatility of the TEM. Of particular interest to the materials scientist are the special stages and specimen holders permitting tilt, rotation, heating, cooling, and tension testing of specimens in the microscope. Recording and display capabilities are extended by optional video tape recorder attachments and TV monitors. Most recently, X-ray analyzer attachments have become available permitting both wavelength and energy dispersive chemical analysis of microareas of electron microscope specimens.

## New Observation Techniques

Recent developments and improvements in observation techniques in electron microscopy include energy loss analysis, dark field imaging, and the weak beam technique, among others. These techniques, coupled with advances in the knowledge of diffraction theory, have greatly expanded the use of TEM in materials research.

When electrons pass through specimens in the electron microscope they lose energy. These electrons have energy distributions that are characteristic of the element(s) comprising the specimen. Knowledge of this phenomenon has prompted a number of workers to develop energy analyzers to obtain a measure of the chemical composition of extremely small regions. These analyzers show the energy spectrum of transmitted electrons after they pass through a narrow slit beneath the specimen. Klemperer [12] has reviewed the development work up to 1965, and, more recently, Curtis and Silcox [13] have described a Wien-type focusing spectrometer for energy loss analysis in an electron microscope. However, not a great deal of experimental data has yet been obtained with this technique.

Ever since the first electron microscopes became available, work has continued to improve their resolving power by design improvements. However, commensurately with instrument improvements, new techniques have been continually devised to utilize the improved resolving power. Menter [14] first resolved individual lattice planes using the $(20\bar{1})$ planes of platinum phthalocyanine with a spacing of 11.9 Å. A high density of platinum ions along those planes provides higher electron scattering and image formation results from a recombination of the direct beam and the 20$\bar{1}$ diffracted beam. An example of lattice imaging is shown in Fig. 4, in which lattice planes in a pyrophyllite crystal with a spacing of 4.45 Å are clearly resolved [15]. Progress has

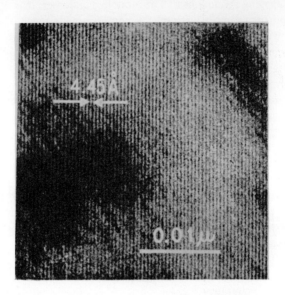

FIG. 4–*Pyrophyllite crystal showing 4.45 Å resolution of lattice planes [15].*

continued to be rapid to the point where Hugo and Phillips [16] have resolved the 110 atomic planes of tungsten having a spacing of 2.23 Å. Recently, Hashimoto [17] has been able to obtain an image of individual atoms. Thorium atoms in specimens of thorium-benzene tetracarboxylic acid supported on a graphite crystal were observed in dark field used to minimize image interference from the supporting material. Of course, the principal reason for wanting improvements in resolving power is to progressively study the very fine structure and substructure of materials. This high resolution is necessary for the examination of precipitate particles, but, in general, has not proved necessary for the study of dislocations. Dislocations may be imaged in the electron microscope when the crystal is set close to a Bragg reflecting angle. For most metals, dislocation images produced in this manner are of the order of 80 to 100 Å wide, and a vast amount of analysis of dislocation configuration, interaction, movement, etc., has been done using this method (examples are given later in the paper).

Recently, however, the weak beam technique has been used to obtain dislocation images an order of magnitude smaller than those produced under normal conditions. In the weak beam technique, which was first effectively developed by Cockayne et al [*18*], a high resolution dark field micrograph is obtained by setting the crystal to an operating vector ($g$) which is far removed from the Bragg condition. Only the region near the dislocation core, where the planes are bent locally into the reflecting position, contribute to the image contrast. As pointed out by Hirsch [*19*], the method is suitable for accurate determination of the width of dissociated dislocations because the width of the individual images is very small. Figure 5 from Hirsch shows the effectiveness of this technique to more clearly define dislocations. Perhaps the major drawback to the weak beam technique is that rather time-consuming and tedious procedures are necessary to obtain the micrographs.

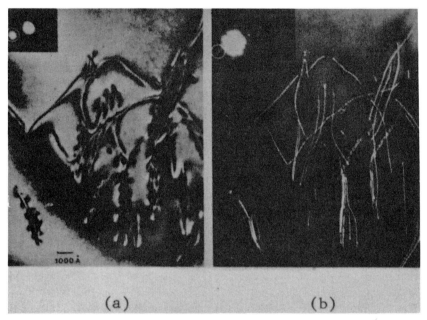

FIG. 5–(a) *Strong beam and* (b) *weak beam images of dislocation array made with the 220 reflection in deformed silicon. (Micrographs by I.L.F. Ray and D.J.H. Cockayne, Courtesy of P.B. Hirsch, [19].)*

Another useful technique becoming more widely used in electron microscopy is Kikuchi line analysis. Kikuchi lines, named after their discoverer [*20*], are formed by electron diffraction. An electron beam on entering a crystal specimen interacts with the atoms and is scattered inelastically and incoherently. These electrons may then be rescattered coherently when Bragg's law is satisfied for a particular set of reflecting planes. Cones of radiation are then emitted which intersect the screen in hyperbolae. However, since the wavelength of electrons is very small, the Kikuchi lines in the image are very nearly straight. Although Kikuchi lines are present in thin crystals, they are only observed in thicker foils when the Kikuchi cone is sufficiently intense. In addition, the foil must be generally quite free of internal strains, such as a high dislocation density or elastic buckling, or the Kikuchi lines will be too diffuse to be readily observed. Thomas [10,21] has given a good account of the geometric formation of Kikuchi patterns which is adequate for most purposes. As Thomas points out,

"The Kikuchi origin is fixed in the crystal so that the crystal is tilted, the cones sweep across the pattern as if rigidly "fixed" to the specimen. Thus, the Kikuchi pattern is extremely useful in determining the precise orientation, as well as for calibrating tilt angles etc. . . . Furthermore, the Kikuchi pattern represents the traces of all reflecting planes in the crystal and can thus be directly compared to the appropriate stereographic projection." [21].

Thus, Kikuchi line analysis may be used in orientation determinations and the study of phase transformations [22], as well as in the indexing of diffraction patterns. This analytical method has been discussed by several authors [23-26]. An example of a Kikuchi map is given in Fig. 6, in which a composite pattern (many individual exposures) made from hexagonal close packed (hcp) crystals of silver aluminum ($Ag_2Al$) is shown together with the indexed schematic [24]. In a precise study of orientation relations using Kikuchi analysis, a good double-tilting stage is essential.

Since Howie and Whelan [27] introduced the two-beam approximation of electron diffraction, there have been many calculations of the theoretical electron microscope images of various defects in thin foils. For dislocations the results are usually presented as a profile showing the variation of intensity along a line crossing the dislocation image. Head [28] has pointed out that the theoretical profiles are often mentally compared with the visual image or micrograph, and that a more valuable approach would be to present the theoretical images as pictures rather than as profiles. By computer integration of the Howie-Whelan differential equations describing image formation in the electron microscope and a suitable printout, various simple dislocations images have been generated. A more comprehensive discussion of such image formation has recently been given [29]. Figure 7 is of a dislocation dipole where the individual dislocations are not really resolved. This example shows the advantage of a pictorial rather than a graphical presentation of the theoretical prediction. While not a great deal of application of this technique has yet been used, it does appear that computer generation and pictorial presentation of defects observed in thin foils in the electron microscope will considerably increase our knowledge of the subject.

## Use of TEM in Structure-Property Relationships

For most materials scientists and engineers, electron microscopy is a tool, albeit a very powerful tool, to be used in developing an understanding of structure-property relationships. Electron microscopy has greatly helped workers to improve and optimize the properties of engineering materials. As discussed previously, TEM has shown a very, very rapid growth in the last ten years because of its unique value in this area. Of particular importance is the

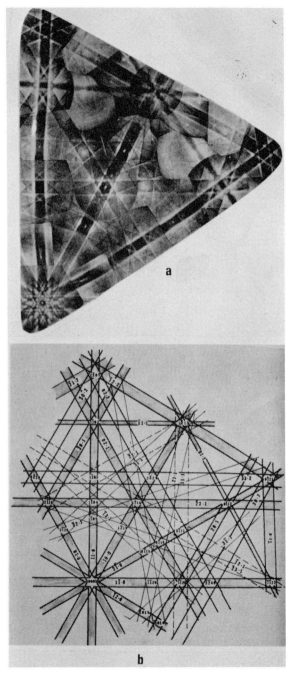

FIG. 6 – (a) *Composite Kikuchi map of hcp* $Ag_2Al$, $C/a = 1.588$, *showing all reciprocal lattice sections and traces lying within* $35°$ *of the [0001] zone axis.* (b) *Fully indexed, distortion-free schematic of* (a) *[24]*.

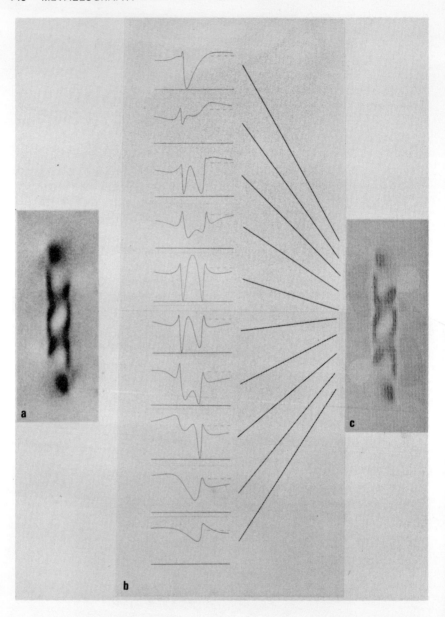

FIG. 7–(a) *Experimental micrograph of a dislocation dipole in nickel compared with* (b) *a set of computed intensity profiles and* (c) *a matching theoretical micrograph. The profiles and the theoretical micrograph were computed using the data corresponding to the particular circumstances of* (a) *[29].*

improvement in microscopes themselves and the advances in the theory of diffraction contrast. This has led to both better images and a much greater understanding in the interpretation of images.

In this section we will show some examples where TEM has greatly contributed to our understanding of structures and their relationships with properties. In particular, the technique has proved useful in the study of phase transformation and deformation mechanisms.

The development of superalloys has contributed greatly to man's technological advance in the last 30 years. The precipitation hardenable alloys really began during the early years of World War II with the development of the Nimonic nickel-base superalloys [30]. These creep resistant, high temperature materials designed for the early jet engines have been greatly improved in recent years and are essential to the aerospace industry today. Some early studies of the nickel-aluminum system had established by X-ray the presence of the $Ni_3Al$ phase [31]. However, although these nickel-base alloys were used extensively in this period it was not until 1950 in a study of the constitution of the nickel-chromium-aluminum system that the precipitate responsible for hardening in these alloys was identified by X-ray diffraction as ordered $\gamma^1$ [32]. Electron metallography was first used about that time and helped in the early identification of $\gamma^1$ [33]. Since that time, electron microscopy has played a large part in the further understanding and development of these alloys. For example, it is now known that the precipitate particles, which are very small and cannot be resolved by normal optical microscopy, are coherent and coplanar with the face centered cubic (fcc) $\gamma$ austenitic matrix. In addition, TEM of thin foils has helped in the elucidation of deformation mechanisms. An excellent summary of studies of $\gamma^1$ particles and the nature of dislocation interactions with these particles is given by Oblak and Kear [34]. To ensure correct interpretation of the complex microstructures, a thorough understanding of the dynamical theory of electron diffraction is necessary. An example of the cuboidal $\gamma^1$ particles in the commercial alloy Udimet 700 is shown in Fig. 8a. The misfit between the coherent particles and the matrix (for example, the difference in lattice parameters of the two phases) is only $\sim 0.1$ percent and little or no strain contrast is observed. The $\gamma/\gamma^1$ misfit is much greater for the alloy in Fig. 8b (Ni-8.2Al-3.3Cb), and results in considerable strain contrast.

The TEM has greatly helped in the development of dislocation theory because dislocations can be readily observed directly, and thus has also contributed immeasureably to our understanding of deformation mechanisms. In addition to dislocation configurations, the Burgers vector of dislocations may be determined by TEM, and the nature of stacking faults and the measurement of stacking fault energy may be determined.

Lattice dislocations are out of contrast in a bright field image when the dot product of the operating vector (in a two-beam image) and the Burgers vector of the dislocation is equal to zero. Thus, by two different operating vectors in which the dislocation is out of contrast, the Burgers vector may be obtained.

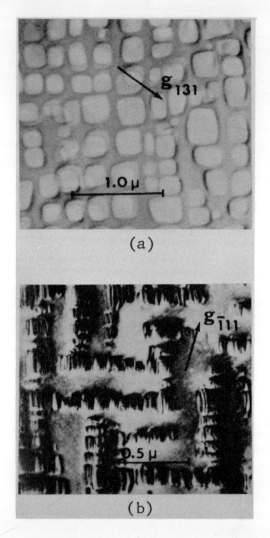

FIG. 8–(a) *Cuboid coherent particles of $\gamma^1$ in a $\gamma$ (austenite) matrix in Udimet 700 showing virtually no strain contrast, (b) $\gamma^1$ particles in a Ni-8.2Al-3.3Cb alloy showing the strain contrast resulting from a much larger $\gamma/\gamma^1$ lattice mismatch [34].*

The conditions for determining the Burgers vector of partial dislocation are different, but may also be calculated [*11*].

An example of the varying visibility of partial dislocations in graphite as a function of the operating vector is shown in Fig. 9 due to Amelinckx and Delavignette [*35*]. In Fig. 9a, the extended and contracted stacking fault nodes bounded by partials can be readily observed. In the other three micrographs each of the three sets of partial dislocations are respectively out of contrast when different strong operating reflections are imaged. An esti-

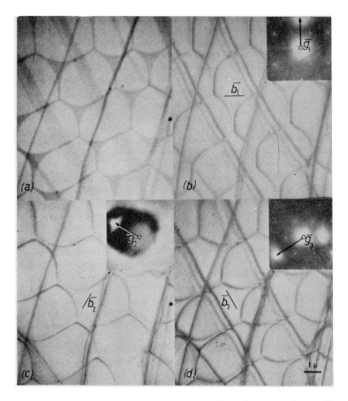

FIG. 9—(a) *Extended and contracted stacking fault nodes in graphite. The nodes are bounded by partial dislocations which are respectively out of contrast in* (b), (c), *and* (d) *taken with three different operating reflections [35].*

mate of the stacking fault energy may be made by measuring the radius of curvature of the partials bounding an extended node. Howie and Swann [36] used this technique to measure stacking fault energy in a number of copper and silver-based alloys.

Stacking faults in crystals may be made visible in the TEM under suitable diffraction conditions. In bright field imaging the stacking fault appears as fringes as shown in Fig. 10a [34]. In dark field the fringes at the extreme edge on one side (for example, at one edge of the thin foil) of the fault change contrast. With a knowledge of the operating reflection, the nature of the stacking fault can be determined. In Fig. 10b, for example, extrinsic stacking faults in MAR-M200 superalloy can be seen, where the fringe at the bottom is now white in dark field compared with the black fringe seen in the bright field micrograph (Fig. 10a).

The methods of TEM are particularly suited to the study of alloy systems exhibiting precipitation reactions. Age hardening was first discovered serendipitously more than 60 years ago in an aluminum alloy, and although a considerable amount of work was done, subsequently, many years passed

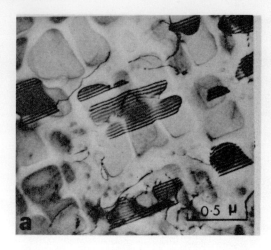

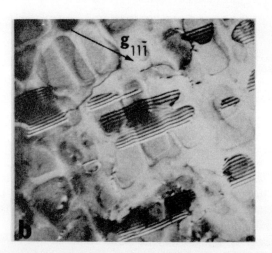

FIG. 10–(a) *Bright field micrograph of stacking faults in the superalloy MAR M200,* (b) *dark field micrograph using the operating reflection g = 11Ī reveals the extrinsic nature of the faults [34].*

before the hardening mechanism was clarified by Guinier, Preston, and Wassermann, principally by single crystal X-ray studies. In 1954, Hardy and Heal [37] published a review of precipitation, including a discussion of the structure of systems undergoing precipitation hardening mainly determined by X-ray diffraction techniques.

Soon after this, as noted previously, electron metallographic techniques [4,5] began to be developed, and with the direct study of precipitates and dislocation interactions in thin foils, began to greatly increase our understanding of the mechanism of age hardening. As pointed out by Kelly and Nicholson [38] in an extensive review, the main advantage of electron micros-copy is that it directly reveals the microstructure of an alloy, that is, information on the number, size, shape, distribution, and orientation relation-ships of precipitate particles can be obtained. It should be stressed at this point that while TEM is an extremely useful tool in the study of material structures, other techniques (such as X-ray diffraction and electrical resistivity measurements) should often be used in conjunction with TEM for a complete characterization of the microstructure.

Much work has been done on the dislocation configurations resulting from the annihilation of quenched-in vacancies, since these have been shown to play an important part in the nucleation process. Figure 11 is an example showing dislocation loops in polycrystalline pure aluminum quenched from 600°C [39]. The metallography of precipitation in an aluminum-silver alloy has been

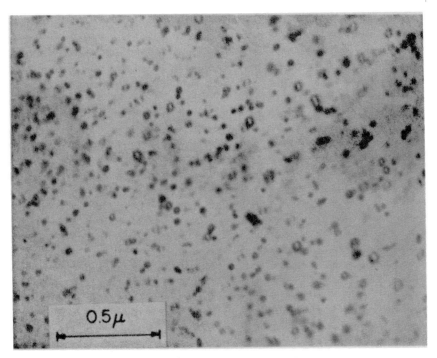

FIG. 11–*TEM of pure aluminum quenched from 600°C showing dislocation loops formed by the condensation of vacancies [39].*

studied extensively by Nicholson and Nutting [40]. Figure 12 shows the structure in the overaged condition in which precipitates of $\gamma^1$ have spread over almost the whole crystal, although Guinier-Preston (GP) zones are still present between the $\gamma^1$ platelets. Many aspects of the nucleation and growth of GP zones, $\gamma^1$ and $\gamma$ in various aluminum-based alloys, with and without

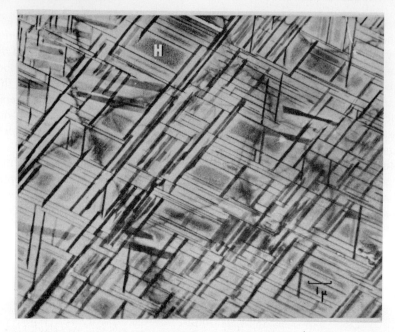

FIG. 12–*Electron micrograph of a thin foil of Al-4.4Ag alloy, water quenched from 525°C, and aged 100 days at 100°C showing the extensive heterogeneous precipitates of* $\gamma^1$. *Some* GP *zones,* ~ 200 Å *diameter are still present in regions such as* H *which are isolated from* $\gamma^1$ *particles [40].*

small additions of other elements, have been studied with TEM and the literature is voluminous on this subject. Thus, TEM has greatly enhanced our understanding of precipitation in aluminum alloys which, of course, are widely used commercially.

There are also many other systems that exhibit age hardening, and TEM has helped in the solution of problems and the development of new alloys in steels. Strain aging and quench aging of iron-carbon alloys while being useful, in some cases have caused problems in the steel industry. These phenomena have been studied for many years, often producing conflicting results. However, with the use of TEM the two stage precipitation of $\epsilon$-carbide and cementite could be followed directly and correlated with other observations [41]. An example of $\epsilon$-carbide precipitation in an Fe-0.035C alloy is shown in Fig. 13. In this micrograph the beginnings of cementite precipitation may be observed. Extensive studies have also been made of precipitation reactions in the iron-nitrogen system, and of dislocation-precipitate interactions in these systems [42]. In all these studies, SAD was used extensively to determine the habit planes of precipitate particles.

More recently, there has been considerable activity on titanium-based alloys stimulated by the increased usage and demands of the aerospace industry. In many high-strength, heat-treatable $\beta$-phase titanium alloys, the $\omega$ phase may precipitate under certain conditions [43]. Considerable hardening also accom-

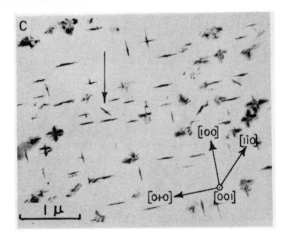

FIG. 13—$\epsilon$-carbide particles precipitated on    100    planes in a quenched and aged Fe-0.035C alloy. Note the beginning of cementite precipitation on $\{110\}$ planes (see arrow).

panied by embrittlement occurs as a result of $\omega$ formation, so that the presence of this phase is generally undesirable. However, knowledge concerning the kinetics of precipitation, morphology, nucleation, etc., are essential to the design of new alloys and optimum heat treatments of current titanium grades. While much was known about the $\omega$ phase from studies using other techniques, principally X-ray diffraction, TEM provided a method to directly "see" the particles [44]. The $\omega$ phase forms on $\{111\}_\beta$ planes of the body centered cubic (bcc) matrix with four variants. In studies of $\omega$, dark field techniques are very useful, so that only variants may be observed independently. In studies of phase transformations [45] in Beta III, athermal $\omega$ formed during the water quench may be seen in Fig. 14. The total volume percentage of all four variants in this case is less than 10 percent. $\omega$ may reach quite a high volume percentage in some instances, for example, in Fig. 15 only one variant is shown in the dark field micrograph, and the total volume percentage of $\omega$ is of the order of 50 percent or more.

Another example of the use of dark field microscopy is shown in Fig. 16, where the $\alpha$ precipitation on the dislocations may be clearly seen [45].

The study and understanding of martensitic transformations have far reaching practical implications because the resulting structures form the basis for hardened steels and are important in many nonferrous alloy systems. The existence of martensite has been known for many years, and although martensite was known to form by a shear mechanism (in which each atom moves less than one atomic distance during transformation) details of the fine structure remained obscured up to about 1960. In the 1950's, the phenomenological generalized theories were published that describe the crystallography of the transformation with respect to the parent and martensite phases [46,47]. Perhaps the first TEM work was that of Pitsch [48], who

FIG. 14—*Bright field electron micrograph showing the four variants of ω precipitation on {111} planes in Ti-11.5Mo-6Zr-4.5Sn (Beta III) alloy. Courtesy of J.C. Williams [45].*

studied transformed thin foils of iron-carbon, iron-nitrogen, and iron-nickel alloys. The orientation relationship he found was quite different from that found in bulk material. Evidently, the transformation constraints are less than in a massive specimen. At this point it seems appropriate to emphasize that special care should be exercised in the interpretation of thin foil experiments made directly in the electron microscope. Because of the much smaller restraint in a thin foil, the nature and kinetics of transformations can be considerably changed, particularly those of strain-induced transformations such as occur in martensite. Kelly and Nutting [49] then showed that martensite in steels occurs in two main forms. In low carbon steels, the structure consists of needles containing a high dislocation density (Fig. 17), while in higher carbon and more highly alloyed materials the martensite occurs as plates which are internally twinned on a fine scale (see Fig. 18) [50]. Since that time there has been a considerable amount of work using TEM on the crystallography of various martensites, particularly by Wayman et al [51].

As mentioned previously, much work has also been done on nonferrous alloys exhibiting martensitic transformations. Some alloys with very small hysteresis between the forward and reverse transformations exhibit "rubber-like" behavior and thermoelastic properties. One interesting transformation occurs in the so-called "Marmem" alloys, in which a specimen (apparently) plastically deformed at a lower temperature will revert to its original shape on

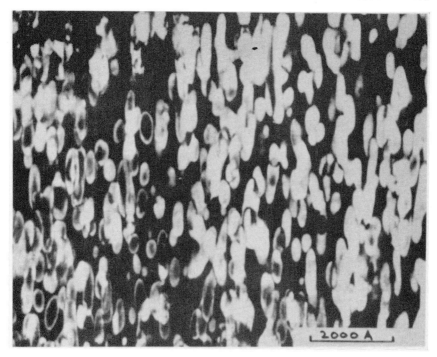

FIG. 15–*Dark field electron micrograph showing one of the ω phase variants in Beta III. In this case the total volume percentage of ω is high ( <50 percent). (Courtesy of J.C. Williams [45].*

heating to a higher temperature [52]. While this effect has been observed in a number of systems, it has been most publicized in the equiatomic nickel-titanium alloy. An antenna for use in space has been designed so that after initial fabrication in the austenite range, it is then crushed and so occupies a small volume at room temperature. Upon the application of heat the antenna deploys into the original configuration. Many other applications for these interesting alloys are envisaged in the future.

Notwithstanding all the study of martensite, a great deal is not yet fully understood, and TEM, while providing a much deeper insight, has only opened the door to further problem areas. These remarks particularly apply to ferrous martensites which are very complicated. The study of tempering reactions [6,50] is especially well suited to TEM methods, and much work has been done in this area. Also, an understanding of the structure-property relation-ships in steels with bainite and martensite structures is now being gained [53]. There has been a great deal of controversy in this respect, but it now appears that at the same strength level dislocated martensites are tougher than the internally twinned variety. Isothermally transformed lower bainite was found to have a toughness intermediate between the two kinds of martensite. These studies are now beginning to lead to the design of new steels (and heat treatments) with an optimum combination of properties.

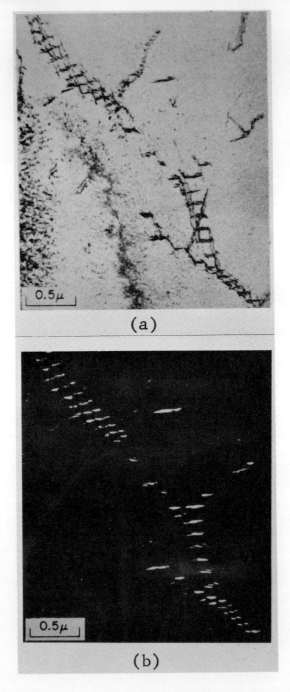

FIG. 16−(a) *Bright field micrograph showing precipitation of α-phase on dislocations in Beta III and* (b) *dark field micrograph showing the distribution of α particles much more clearly. (Courtesy of J.C. Williams, [45.)*

FIG. 17–*TEM of a quenched low carbon steel showing needles of martensite containing a high dislocation density.*

Considerable work has been done on the theoretical thermodynamic and kinetic aspects of spinodal decomposition during the last decade [54], but only recently has TEM been used to examine the microstructures. The spinodal transformation can occur in systems that have a miscibility gap in the solid state, and involves the separation of a single phase into two related coherent phases without the process of nucleation. The two phases have the same crystal structure but a different composition. The decomposition results from a thermodynamic instability, and occurs with a regular periodicity on a very fine scale, along elastically soft directions in the parent crystal. Weatherly and Nicholson [55] and Butler and Thomas [56] have studied the decomposition in copper-nickel-iron alloys in some detail and have shown that coherency is lost during continued aging when the wavelength of the composition fluctuations is about 1000 Å. At this point interfacial dislocations were observed and the coarsening rate was found to be increased. In this system decomposition takes place along $\{100\}$ planes. However, some tendency for the interface to rotate to $\{110\}$ planes was observed. A more detailed analysis of the boundary dislocations has been reported by Bouchard et al

FIG. 18—*Micrograph of fine twins on* $\{112\}$ *planes of martensite plates in a Fe-24Ni-0.5C alloy.*

[57]. An example of dislocation networks in stepped boundary particle interfaces may be seen in Fig. 19.

In the early stages of spinodal decomposition, structures in the electron microscope result primarily from matrix strain contrast produced by the periodic clustering of atoms [58]. (Some contrast has been thought to be caused by differences in thickness of the two phases that occurs during electropolishing [56].) Figure 20 shows a series of structures developed upon aging a Cu-4Ti alloy quenched from 900°C [59]. In Fig. 20a the structure is revealed by strain contrast of the periodic fluctuations which have a wavelength of about 65 Å. Upon aging at 500°C the structure gradually coarsens (see Fig. 20b and c) and individual interpenetrating rods growing along <100> may be readily seen. Upon continued aging the particles lose coherency with the matrix and the interfacial accommodation dislocations and Moire fringes can be seen in Fig. 20d.

Alloys that exhibit periodic microstructures are often called "sideband" alloys, because of "sidebands" or "satellite" reflections that occur next to the main lines or spots in X-ray or electron diffraction patterns. This effect is thought to result from periodic variations in the lattice spacing and scattering factor caused by modulation of the microstructure. An example of these extra

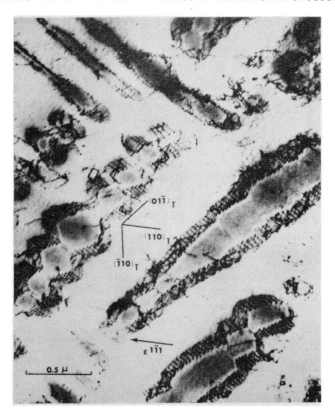

FIG. 19–*Thin foil electron micrograph of Cu-Ni-Fe alloy aged 200 h at 775°C showing stepped particle interfaces that may have resulted from dislocations gliding to the interfaces. Note that the interfaces tend to lie along* $\left\{ 110 \right\}$ *planes [57].*

reflections is given in the diffraction pattern by Datta [59] of a Cu-4Ti alloy (Fig. 21). The wavelength of the modulations can be calculated from a measurement of the distance of the satellite spots from the main reflection. As aging proceeds and the wavelength of the periodic microstructure increases, the sidebands move toward the matrix reflection and eventually become indistinguishable from the matrix spot.

Spinodal decomposition is homogeneous throughout an alloy. The regular nature of the microstructure occurs right up to the grain boundary as shown in Fig. 22a [59]. This structure is in direct contrast to that usually observed in most heterogeneously nucleated precipitation reactions [60]. Figure 22b clearly shows the denuded grain boundary zone. Precipitation is thought to nucleate at vacancy clusters, and thus particles do not form close to grain boundaries which act as vacancy sinks.

Because of the homogeneous and very fine nature of the structure, the possibilities for improved mechanical and physical properties is stimulating

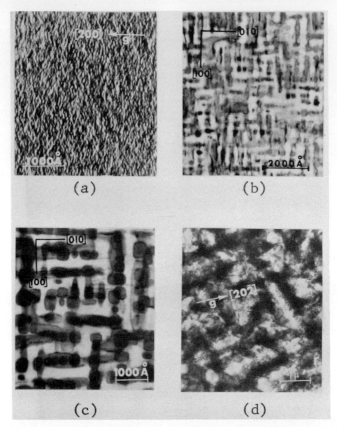

FIG. 20–*TEM series showing spinodal decomposition in Cu-4Ti alloy.* (a) *As quenched from 900°C, the structure shows periodic fluctuations of* λ ~ 65 Å. (b) *Aged 200 min at 500°C* λ @ 400 Å. (c) *Aged 1000 min at 500°C* λ ~ 700 Å. (d) *Aged 8000 min at 500°C shows Moiré fringes and interfacial dislocations at the semicoherent* β¹/ *matrix interfaces* [59].

more work on spinodal decomposition. Soffa et al are studying the decomposition in a number of alloy systems [58,59,61]. The copper-titanium alloys [58], for example, can attain very high strength upon aging and approach the properties of the well known copper-beryllium alloys.

The structures that develop by this mechanism also hold promise for the improvement of other properties. For example, the structure observed in the well known "Alnico" permanent magnets is thought to arise by spinodal decomposition [62,63]. In this case, if the composition is magnetic at the temperature when the fluctuations occur, then magnetostrictive and magnetostatic energy will combine with the elastic energy to affect the morphology of the resulting structure. The application of a magnetic field during the decomposition promote composition peaks along the field direction while decreasing the effect in perpendicular directions, contributing to the desirable magnetic anisotropy observed in oriented magnets.

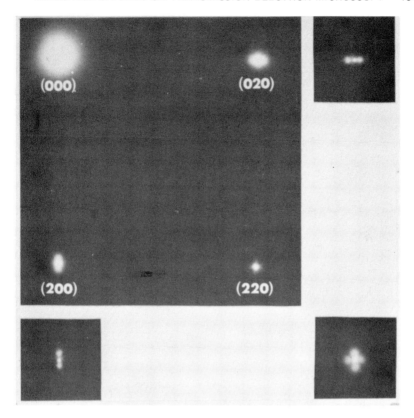

FIG. 21–*Diffraction pattern taken from a Cu-4Ti alloy in the early stages of spinodal decomposition. The satellite spots about the matrix spots along <100> can be clearly seen [59].*

Spinodal decomposition is also thought to occur in a Co-12Fe-6Ti alloy [*61*], which is a member of a new group of semihard permanent magnets used in memory devices and other electronic applications. In this case similar microstructures to those discussed are observed, and as aging occurs an increase in coercivity results from the formation of modulated microstructures. In fact, the similarity of microstructures that develop in alloys in a wide variety of systems undergoing spinodal decomposition is remarkable.

Other examples of spinodal structures in commercially useful materials occur in ceramics. A spinodal decomposition occurs in the sodium oxygen-silicon oxygen ($Na_2O$-$SiO_2$) system that forms the basis for many glass compositions [*64*]. In contrast to the structure developed in a crystalline material, in this amorphous system both phases are independently interconnected and are typified by irregular boundaries as seen in Fig. 23. These two phases have different compositions, and, therefore, different properties, and it is thought that the phase separation before the acid-leaching step used in the production of Vycor glass occurs by spinodal decomposition. Thus, interest in

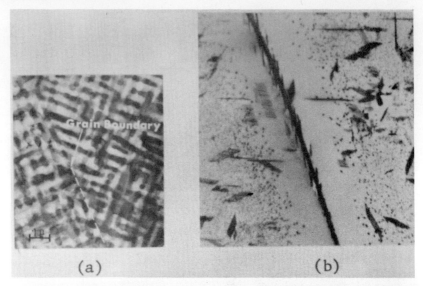

FIG. 22–(a) *Microstructure of spinodal decomposition in a Cu-4Ti alloy. Note the homogeneity of the structure in the vicinity of the grain boundary [59].* (b) *Precipitation of $M_{23}C_6$ carbides in an 18Cr-9Ni-4Mn austenitic stainless steel. In this case nucleation on vacancy clusters is heterogeneous. Note the precipitation-free-zone adjacent to the grain boundary [60].*

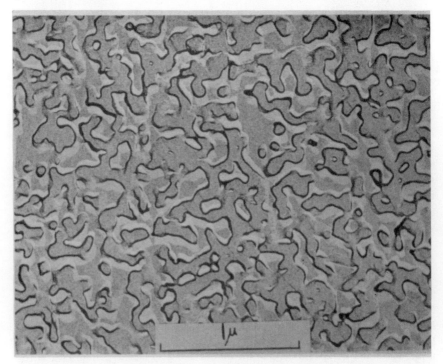

FIG. 23–*Shadowed replica electron micrograph showing amorphous phase decomposition in $Na_2O$-$SiO_2$ glass heat treated 72 h at 600°C [64].*

spinodal structures is increasing rapidly and we are likely to see expanded research by electron microscopists on such structures developed in both metallic materials and ceramics.

In other TEM work with ceramics and minerals, mechanical thinning techniques and more recently ion thinning have made possible the direct examination of mineral specimens, glasses, and ceramics in the electron microscope.

Doherty [65] has shown a number of ceramic microstructures prepared for TEM by mechanical thinning. Figure 24 shows an antimony oxide-opacified enamel; crystals 0.2 to 0.3 $\mu$m in diameter are seen in the glassy matrix.

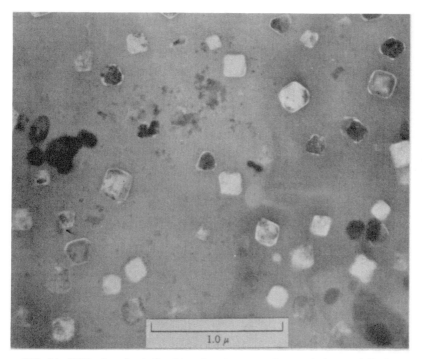

FIG. 24–*TEM of mechanically thinned antimony oxide-opacified enamel [65].*

Figure 25 shows lithium metasilicate crystals in a specimen of Fotoceram, a photosensitive glass manufactured by Corning Glass Works. Using these techniques, the TEM is unexcelled in revealing microstructural details of glass ceramics and, as such, is yielding important information about the control of nucleation and growth processes within these systems.

Cullen et al [66,67] used ion-thinning to study dislocation substructures in two-phase mineral systems. Figure 26 shows misfit dislocations at the interface of hematite and the ilmenite matrix and Fig. 27 showing an exsolution lamella in an augite matrix further illustrates the excellent results obtainable by the ion-thinning technique.

Geological studies have been similarly aided by the use of TEM; substructures observed by TEM offer clues to the thermal-mechanical history of

FIG. 25–*TEM of mechanically thinned specimen of Fotoceram (Corning Glass Works)
showing lithium metasilicate crystals [65].*

mineral specimens. Intense interest in this area of research was generated by
the recent retrieval of numerous rock fragments from the lunar surface in the
course of the Apollo manned space program.

In particular, Christie et al [68] and Champness et al [69] have published
results of TEM comparison of several lunar and terrestrial mineral specimens
prepared by ion thinning. The results of these and similar investigations will,
no doubt, lead to a fuller understanding of the earth's and the moon's
geological history.

In summary, TEM is a very powerful tool being used in the field of
materials research. Improvements in instrument design and specimen preparation techniques together with further sophistication in image analysis have
greatly advanced the usefulness of TEM in the study and understanding of
materials systems. Many significant contributions are being made by TEM
toward the development of new materials and improvements in properties of
existing ones.

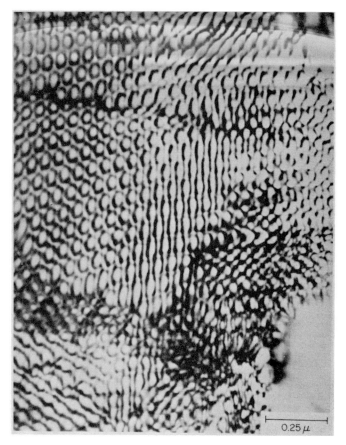

FIG. 26–*Ion-thinned specimen of ilmenite showing misfit dislocation networks at exsolved hematite plate boundary [66].*

## Acknowledgments

We wish to express our appreciation to the many people who were kind enough to provide micrographs, reprints, and details of new work and, in particular, to J.P. Hirth, F.H. Froes, and W.A. Soffa for their many helpful suggestions.

Figures 5, 8, and 10 were originally published by the University of California Press and reprinted by permission of the Regents of the University of California.

## References

[*1*]    "Electron Microstructure of Steel," First Progress Report, Subcommittee 11 on Electron Microscopy and Diffraction, ASTM Committee E-4 on Metallography, *Proceedings,* American Society for Testing and Materials, Vol. 50, 1950, p. 444.

[2]    Fisher, R.M. in *Techniques for Electron Metallography,* ASTM STP 155, American Society for Testing and Materials, 1954, p. 49.

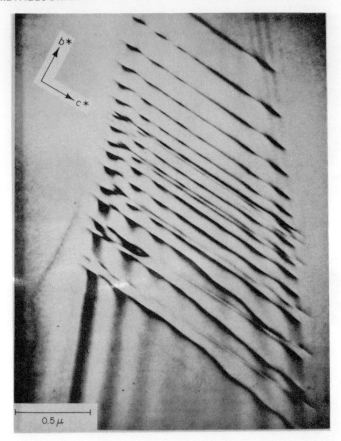

FIG. 27–*Ion-thinned specimen of augite showing an exsolution lamella thought to be orthopyroxene. Note the misfit dislocations at the two-phase interface [67].*

[3]    Heidenreich, R.D., *Journal of Applied Physics,* Vol. 20, 1949, p. 993.

[4]    Hirsch, P.B., Horne, R.W., and Whelan, M.J., *Philosophical Magazine,* Vol. 1, 1956, p. 677.

[5]    Bollman, W., *Physical Review,* Vol. 103, 1956, p. 1588.

[6]    Capenos, J.M., Hauser, J.J., and Banerjee, B.R. in *Advances in Electron Metallography and Electron Probe Microanalysis, ASTM STP 317,* American Society for Testing and Materials, 1962, pp. 26-33.

[7]    Kelly, P.M. and Nutting, J., *Journal of the Institute of Metals,* Vol. 87, 1959, p. 385.

[8]    Bigelow, W.C. in *Advances in Electron Metallography and Electron Probe Microanalysis, ASTM STP 317,* American Society for Testing and Materials, 1962, p. 58.

[9]    Brammer, I.S. and Dewey, M.A.P., *Specimen Preparation for Electron Microscopy,* American Elsevier Publishing Co., New York, 1966.

[10]   Thomas, G., *Transmission Electron Microscopy of Metals,* Wiley, New York, 1962.

[11]   Hirsch, P.B., Howie, A., Nicholson, R.B., Pashley, D.W., and Whelan, M.J., *Electron Microscopy of Thin Crystals,* Butterworths, Washington, 1965.

[12]   Klemperer, O., *Reports on the Progress of Physics,* Vol. 28, 1965, p. 77.

[13] Curtis, G.H. and Silcox, J., *Review of Scientific Instruments,* Vol. 42, No. 5, 1971, p. 630.
[14] Menter, J.W., *Proceedings,* Royal Society of London, Vol. A236, 1956, p. 119.
[15] Sudoh, T., *JEOL News,* Japan Electron Optics Laboratory Co., Ltd., Vol. 3, No. 1, 1965, p. 2.
[16] Hugo, J.A. and Phillips, V.A., *Metallography,* Vol. 2, No. 4, 1969, p. 395.
[17] Hashimoto, H., paper presented at High Voltage Electron Microscopy Meeting, Stockholm, 1971.
[18] Cockayne, D.J.H., Ray, I.L.F., and Whelan, M.J., *Philosophical Magazine,* Vol. 20, 1969, p. 1265.
[19] Hirsch, P.B. in *Electron Microscopy and Structure of Materials,* G. Thomas, R.M. Fulrath, R.M. Fisher, Eds., University of California Press, Berkeley, Calif. 1972, pp. 1-22.
[20] Kikuchi, S., *Journal of Physics,* Vol. 5, 1928, p. 83.
[21] Thomas, G., "Kikuchi Electron Diffraction and Applications" in *Modern Diffraction and Imaging Techniques in Materials Science,* S. Amelinckx, R. Gevers, G. Remant, and I. Van Landuyt, Eds., North Holland Publishing Co., Amsterdam, Holland, 1970.
[22] Thomas, G., *Transactions,* Metallurgical Society, American Institute of Mining, Metallurgical, and Petroleum Engineers, Vol. 233, 1965, p. 1608.
[23] Levine, E., Bell, W.L., and Thomas, G., *Journal of Applied Physics,* Vol. 37, No. 5, 1966, p. 2141.
[24] Okamoto, P.R., Levine, E., and Thomas, G., *Journal of Applied Physics,* Vol. 38, No. 1, 1967, p. 289.
[25] Otte, H.M., Dash, J., and Schaake, H.F., *Physical Status Solidi,* Vol. 5, 1964, p. 527.
[26] Von Heimendahl, M., Bell, W., and Thomas, G., *Journal of Applied Physics,* Vol. 35, No. 12, 1964, p. 3614.
[27] Howie, A. and Whelan, M.J., *Proceedings,* Royal Society of Londc  Vol. A263, p. 217.
[28] Head, A.K., *Australian Journal of Physics,* Vol. 20, 1967, p. 557.
[29] Head, A.K., Humble, P., Clarebrough, L.M., Morton, A.J., and Forwood, C.T., *Computed Electron Micrographs and Defect Identification,* North Holland Publishing Co., Amsterdam, Holland, 1973.
[30] Betteridge, N., *The Nimonic Alloys,* E. Arnold Ltd., London, 1959.
[31] Bradley, A.J. and Taylor, A., *Proceedings,* Royal Society of London, Vol. A159, 1937, p. 56.
[32] Taylor, A. and Floyd, R.W., *Journal of the Institute of Metals,* Vol. 81, 1952-1953, p. 451.
[33] Hignett, H.W.G., *High Temperature Alloys in British Jet Engines,* International Nickel Co., New York, 1951.
[34] Oblak, J.M. and Kear, B.H. in Electron Microscopy and Structure of Materials, G. Thomas, R.M. Fulrath, and R.M. Fisher, Eds., University of California Press, Berkeley, Calif., 1972, pp. 566-616.
[35] Amelinckx, S. and Delavignette, P., *Journal of Applied Physics,* Vol. 31, 1960, p. 2126.
[36] Howie, A. and Swann, P.R., *Philosophical Magazine,* Vol. 6, 1961, p. 1215.
[37] Hardy, H.K. and Heal, T.J., *Progress in Metal Physics,* Vol. 5, 1954, p. 143.
[38] Kelly, A. and Nicholson, R.B., *Progress in Materials Science,* Vol. 10, No. 3, 1963, p. 151.
[39] Hirsch, P.B., Silcox, J., Smallman, R.E., and Westmacott, K.H., *Philosophical Magazine,* Vol. 3, 1958, p. 897.
[40] Nicholson, R.B. and Nutting, J., *Acta Metallurgica,* Vol. 9, 1961, p. 332.
[41] Wells, M.G.H. and Butler, J.F., *Transactions,* American Society for Metals, Vol. 59, 1966, p. 427.
[42] Keh, A.S., Leslie, W.C., and Sponseller, D.L., *AIME Metallurgical Society Transactions,* American Institute of Mining, Metallurgical, and Petroleum Engineers, Vol. 28, p. 281.
[43] Hickman, B.S., *AIME Metallurgical Society Transactions,* Vol. 249, 1969, p. 1329.

[44] Blackburn, M.J. and Williams, J.C., *AIME Metallurgical Society Transactions,* Vol. 242, 1968, p. 246.1

[45] Froes, F.H., Williams, J.C., Yolton, F.C., Capenos, J.M., and Wells, M.G.H., "Phase Transformations in Beta III Titanium," to be published.

[46] Weschler, M.S., Lieberman, D.S., and Read, T.A., *AIME Metallurgical Society Transactions,* Vol. 197, 1953, p. 1503.

[47] Bowles, J.S. and Mackenzie, J.K., *Acta Metallurgica,* Vol. 2, No. 129, 1954, pp. 138 and 224.

[48] Pitsch, W., *Journal of the Institute of Metals,* Vol. 87, 1958-1959, p. 444.

[49] Kelly, P.M. and Nutting, J., *Journal of the Iron and Steel Institute,* Vol. 197, 1961, p. 199.

[50] Wells, M.G.H., *Acta Metallurgica,* Vol. 12, 1964, p. 389.

[51] Wayman, C.M., "Martensitic Transformations" in *Modern Diffraction and Imaging Techniques in Material Science,* S. Amelinckx, R. Gevers, G. Remant, and I. Von Landuyt, Eds., North Holland Publishing Co., Amsterdam, Holland, 1970, p. 187.

[52] Wayman, C.M. and Shimizu, K., *Metal Science Journal,* Vol. 6, 1972, p. 175.

[53] Das, S.K. and Thomas, G., *Transactions,* American Society for Metals, Vol. 62, 1969, p. 659.

[54] Cahn, J.W., *AIME Metallurgical Society Transactions,* Vol. 242, 1968, p. 166.

[55] Weatherly, G.C. and Nicholson, R.B., *Philosophical Magazine,* Vol. 17, 1968, p. 801.

[56] Butler, E.P. and Thomas, G., *Acta Metallurgica,* Vol. 18, No. 3, 1970, p. 347.

[57] Bouchard, M. Livak, R.J., and Thomas, G., *Surface Science,* Vol. 31, 1972, p. 275.

[58] Cornie, J.A., Datta, A., and Soffa, W.A., *Metallurgical Transactions,* Vol. 4, 1973, p. 727.

[59] Datta, A., Ph.D. thesis, University of Pittsburgh.

[60] Froes, F.H., Wells, M.G.H., and Banerjee, B.R., *Metal Science Journal,* Vol. 2, 1968, p. 232.

[61] Shilling, J.W., Ph.D. thesis, University of Pittsburgh.

[62] Cahn, J.W., *Journal of Applied Physics,* Vol. 34, 1963, p. 3581.

[63] Gould, J.E., "Cobalt Alloy Permanent Magnets," Cobalt Monograph published by Cobalt Information Center, Brussels, Belgium, 1971.

[64] Redwine, R.H. and Conrad, M.A. in *Ceramic Microstructures,* R.M. Rulrath and J.A. Pask, Eds., Wiley, 1968, pp. 900-922.

[65] Doherty, P.E. in *Ceramic Microstructures,* R.M. Fulrath and J.A. Pask, Eds., Wiley, 1968, pp. 161-186.

[66] Cullen, W.H., Jr., Marcinkowski, M.J., and Das, E.S.P., *Surface Science,* Vol. 36, 1973, p. 395.

[67] Cullen, W.H., Jr., and Marcinkowski, M.J., "Study of Misfit Dislocations at Exsolution Boundaries in Augite," EMG Report No. XCVI, University of Maryland Center of Materials Research, College Park, Md.

[68] Christie, J.M., Griggs, D.T., Fisher, R.M., Lally, J.S., Heuer, A.H., and Radcliff, S.V. in *Electron Microscopy and Structure of Materials,* G. Thomas, R.M. Fulrath, and R.M. Fisher, Eds., University of California Press, 1972, pp. 1234-1244.

[69] Champness, P.E. and Lorimer, G.W. in *Electron Microscopy and Structure of Materials,* G. Thomas, R.M. Fulrath, and R.M. Fisher, Eds., University California Press, 1972, pp. 1245-1255.

*A. Szirmae[1] and R.M. Fisher[1]*

# High Voltage Electron Metallography
# — Achievements and Prospects

**REFERENCE:** Szirmae, A. and Fisher, R.M., "High Voltage Electron Metallography—Achievements and Prospects," *Metallography—A Practical Tool for Correlating the Structure and Properties of Materials, ASTM STP 557,* American Society for Testing and Materials, 1974, pp. 169−197.

**ABSTRACT:** Electron metallography in its various forms has now reached the point where it can be used to characterize nearly all of the microstructural features which occur in materials including grain and subgrain size and shape; dislocation density and configuration; precipitate size, shape, and coherency strain; antiphase domains in ordering alloys; and magnetic structure in ferromagnetic alloys, as well as chemical composition changes on a very fine scale. Transmission electron microscopy (TEM) provides the most complete information about internal structures and is especially effective when used in conjunction with scanning microscopy of the same specimen. Development of high voltage instruments capable of operating at 1 mV or more has broadened the scope of application of electron metallography particularly because of the ability to penetrate significantly thicker specimens than with conventional 100 kV instruments. Other important characteristics of high voltage electron metallography (HVEM) such as greater accuracy in selected area diffraction, reduced chromatic aberration of thick specimens, and a unique critical voltage effect are discussed. Typical applications such as studies of recrystallization, deformation, recovery, precipitation, and ordering are described, as well as quantitative three-dimensional (stereo) analysis of dislocation distributions and electron radiation damage.

**KEY WORDS:** metallography, electron probe, microscopy, transmission, high voltage, scanning, stereoscopy, electron diffraction, electron scattering, resolution, penetration, microstructure, gas ionization

Much of what is now known about the microstructures of materials and the way that various features control engineering properties has been derived from a very practical science conveniently referred to as "metallography." Since its founding 75 years ago, the American Society for Testing and Materials (ASTM) has been actively concerned with the development and application of metallographic methods of analysis to improve engineering materials and ensure their effective utilization.

Since the formation of Subcommittee 11 on Electron Microscopy and Diffraction (Committee E-4 on Metallography) exactly 25 years ago, major changes have occurred in the methods and scope of application of electron metallography. For example, the use of replicas has been largely superseded by direct transmission observations or scanning electron microscopy (SEM) of

[1] Associate scientist and manager, Physics/Physical Metallurgy, respectively, Research Laboratory, U.S. Steel Corp., Monroeville, Pa. 15146.

bulk specimens. However, surface replica techniques are still very useful for fractography and extraction replicas are valuable for electron diffraction identification of fine precipitates. Similarly, although X-ray diffraction measurements of lattice parameters to obtain the chemical composition of alloy solid-solutions is still the most precise, the electron microprobe is also used to determine the chemical composition of micro areas or phases which cannot be separated from the bulk material.

Among the various instrumental techniques of metallography, electron microscopy is certainly the most versatile. Transmission electron microscopes still achieve the highest resolution, exceeded only by rather restricted field-ion microscopes. Transmission electron microscopy (TEM) is also the only satisfactory method of examining dislocations and other faults in crystals. Selected area electron diffraction permits identification of crystals and the determination of orientation relationships between features present. It is possible to measure the chemical composition in small areas with the transmission microscope by means of X-ray spectrometer attachments or a "critical voltage" phenomenon to be described in this report. However, scanning electron microscopes equipped for X-ray spectroscopy are generally more useful for measurements of chemical composition. These two primary electron optical instruments should be considered complementary rather than competitive tools.

The wide variety of microstructural features which may occur in steels or other crystalline materials is illustrated schematically in Fig. 1. In addition to

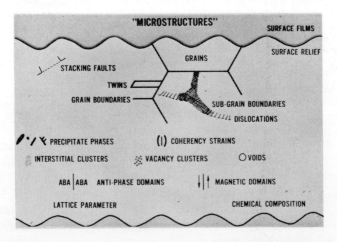

FIG. 1—*Schematic illustration of microstructural features which can exist in or on the surface of crystals.*

revealing the size and shape of these features, TEM can be used to determine crystallographic characteristics such as subboundary angles, Burgers vectors of dislocations and the nature of planar faults. Quantitative measurements of size and distribution of precipitates, density of slip dislocations, total volume of voids, etc., are essential to any interpretation or prediction of the properties of engineering materials.

Although direct TEM of thin metal foils made it possible to observe dislocations and other structures which had never been seen before, severe restrictions on specimen thickness handicapped effective application of the method to many materials of engineering interest. The development of high voltage microscopes capable of operating in 1 mV or more now permits examination of specimens several micrometers in thickness and minimizes difficulties with specimen preparation. The increase in usable specimen thickness greatly reduces any uncertainty about sampling representative areas and eliminates questions about changes in microstructure that may occur during thinning. Stereoscopic methods can be used to determine three-dimensional information about the size, shape, and distribution of precipitate particles, dislocation densities, and other internal structures illustrated in Fig. 1.

## Characteristics of High Voltage Microscopy

The physical basis for increasing the voltage of transmission electron microscopes beyond 100 kV, as illustrated in Fig. 2, is that both electron wavelength and scattering cross section decrease rapidly up to 500 kV and then at a slower rate beyond that voltage. Theoretically, the shorter electron wave-

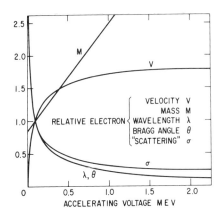

FIG. 2—*Decreasing electron wavelength and scattering with increasing voltage provides the physical basis for the development of high voltage microscopes.*

length should give higher image resolution. Unfortunately, a large relativistic increase in electron mass as well as magnetic saturation of the pole piece results in a longer objective focal length which largely offsets the wavelength effect. When the effects of diffraction and spherical aberration on image resolution are considered, the minimum resolvable distance is approximately

$$d = 0.43 \, C_s^{1/4} \, \lambda^{3/4} \tag{1}$$

where $C_s$ is the spherical aberration of the lens (essentially equal to the focal length, $f$) and $\lambda$ is the electron wavelength; both are proportional to the voltage ($E$) as

$$f \propto \sqrt{E} \tag{2}$$

and

$$\lambda \propto \frac{1}{\sqrt{E}} \tag{3}$$

Substituting in Eq 1 gives

$$d \approx E^{-1/4} \tag{4}$$

This demonstrates that since the minimum resolvable distance ($d$) is essentially proportional to $E^{-1/4}$, the classical limit on resolution is quite insensitive to accelerating voltage.

A more important effect of increasing voltage is reduced scattering of the electrons in the beam by atoms within the specimen which results in greater penetration. As shown in Fig. 3, high energy electrons can penetrate a very thick specimen, but, because of multiple scattering, lose most of their initial energy and cannot be focused into a usable image. In contrast, all electrons

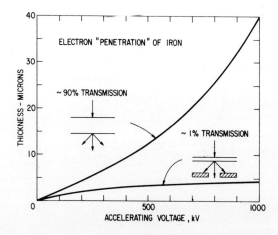

FIG. 3–*Electron penetration of iron as a function of voltage for two quite different criterion. Upper curve–90 percent of the electrons in the beam pass through although a large portion of their energy is lost. Lower curve–100 percent pass through specimens but only 1 percent get through the lens aperture.*

pass through thin specimens corresponding to the lower curve, but only a small fraction (~1 percent) scattered through very small angles pass through the objective aperture and can be used to form an image in the electron microscope. Even in the case of thin specimens, the electron beam transfers some energy to the specimen resulting in "beam heating." Discussion of electron scattering processes is beyond the scope of this review, but the principal energy loss mechanisms are worth noting.

1. Excitation of core electrons resulting in X-ray generation: (relatively unimportant in transmission microscopy).

2. Excitation of lattice phonons: (a) large scattering angle (~1 deg), but energy loss per event very low (~1/40 eV), and (b) contributes to background intensity and lowers contrast.

3. Excitation of conduction electrons: (a) small scattering angle (~0.1 deg) and large energy loss (10 to 25 eV) per event, and (b) causes loss of resolution due to chromatic aberration.

The effects of specimen scattering are shown schematically in Fig. 4. When

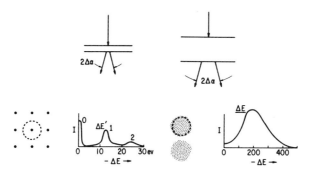

FIG. 4—*Schematic illustration of electron diffraction patterns and energy spectra from thin and thick specimens.*

thick specimens are used the sharp diffraction spots and energy loss spectra (as would be recorded with a velocity analyzer) are spread out considerably so that any fine detail present is lost. The energy loss spectrum gives rise to a series of multiple images in dark field micrographs of small particles with each corresponding to particular energy loss as shown in Fig. 5. The specimen thickness increases across the micrograph, and it may be seen that the images merge into a diffuse streak in the thicker areas.

Chromatic aberration due to inelastic scattering in the specimen has a very marked effect on resolution as illustrated schematically in Fig. 6. The image of a point is smeared by chromatic aberration to a disk of a diameter ($\delta$) given approximately as

$$\delta = 2 \ (\alpha + \Delta\alpha)C_c \frac{\Delta E}{E_o} \qquad (5)$$

where
$\alpha + \Delta\alpha =$  1/2 angle of the electron beam leaving the specimen,
$C_c$     = chromatic aberration of the lens ($\approx f$),
$\Delta E$     = breadth of the energy loss, and

FIG. 5–*Dark field micrograph of beryllium foil showing multiple images corresponding to energy loss spectra. Thickness of foil increases from left to right (100 kV).*

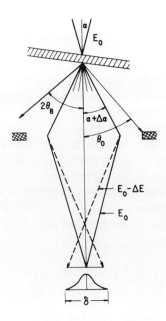

FIG. 6–*Schematic illustration of spread of image point due to chromatic aberration.*

$E_o$ = relativistically corrected accelerating voltage.
The scattering parameters $\Delta\alpha$ and $\Delta E$ are both functions of specimen thickness ($t$) and accelerating voltage, and the lens constants depend on voltage as discussed previously. Substituting rough approximations for the interdependence of $\Delta E$ and $\Delta\alpha$ on $t$ and $E_o$ gives a relationship between thickness and resolution at a particular voltage [1][2] as

$$t \approx \delta^{0.5 \, -0.75} \; E_o^{\, 0.75 \, -1.0} \tag{6}$$

The exact values of the exponents are somewhat uncertain, but this does not markedly affect the general relationship, plotted in Fig. 7, for the central values which show penetration as a function of voltage at several levels of resolution. Surprisingly, very few systematic studies have been carried out

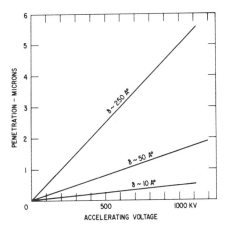

FIG. 7—*Relation between specimen thickness and voltage for high, intermediate, and low resolution in iron foil.*

largely because of difficulty in obtaining a satisfactory criterion for penetration. The results of several observations fall into the central band shown in Fig. 8 relating useful specimen thickness to voltage. These correspond to moderate levels of resolution. In the case of thicker specimens image contrast would decrease very markedly, whereas for thinner specimens the loss in resolution, due to chromatic aberration, is roughly comparable to the capabilities of a typical instrument. The connection between thickness, resolution, and voltage is illustrated in Fig. 9, which shows electron micrographs of the same area in a 0.6-$\mu$m specimen of stainless steel at 100 and 800 kV. The improved contrast and resolution correspond to the changes indicated in Figs. 7 and 8.

---

[2] The italic numbers in brackets refer to the list of references appended to this paper.

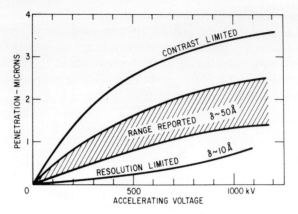

FIG. 8–*Reported useful maximum specimen thickness as a function of accelerating voltage. The resolution is better for thinner specimens and contrast is lost with very thick specimens of iron.*

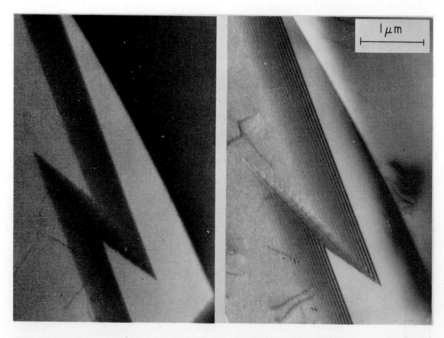

FIG. 9–*Electron micrographs of same area in stainless steel ~0.6 μ m in thickness at* (left) *100 and* (right) *800 kV illustrating improved resolution and contrast.*

Although the preceding discussion of resolution and penetration provides valuable insight into the general relationship between accelerating voltage, and specimen penetration and image resolution, it does not take into account the pronounced effects of coherent scattering, for example, electron diffraction. In the case of crystalline materials, information about structural features of interest, for example, contrast, originates from local variations in diffracted intensity which are related to crystal structure, orientation, composition, etc. The voltage dependence of diffraction contrast is thus rather complex, but the essential features are important to this discussion.

The shorter electron wavelength and correspondingly smaller Bragg angle at high voltage results in the simultaneous excitation of more reflections. In the case of heavy elements such as gold, "many-beam" effects are important at 100 kV, whereas with aluminum they are not pronounced until above 1000 kV [2]. Other elements fall between these values. Examples of 100 and 1000 kV diffraction patterns from copper foil are shown in Fig. 10.

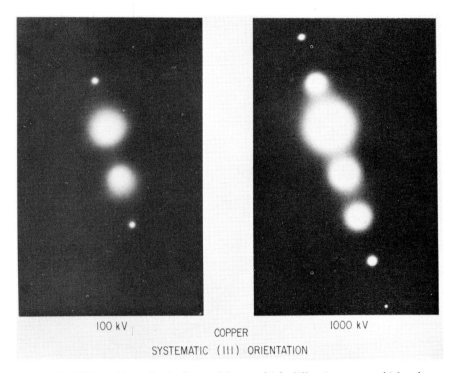

100 kV          COPPER          1000 kV

SYSTEMATIC  (111)  ORIENTATION

FIG. 10–*Diffracted intensity is dispersed into multiple diffraction spots at high voltage because of strong many-beam excitation.*

One important consequence of many-beam interaction at high voltage is a channeling phenomenon which results in greatly enhanced penetration at certain crystallographic orientations, and is characterized by a bright central region in certain extinction contours. An example of the onset of channeling is illustrated in Fig. 11 showing much greater transparency and sharper dislocation images in tungsten at 1000 kV. This region would be essentially opaque at 100 kV. The various orientations have been investigated both theoretically and experimentally for most metals of interest [3]. A summary

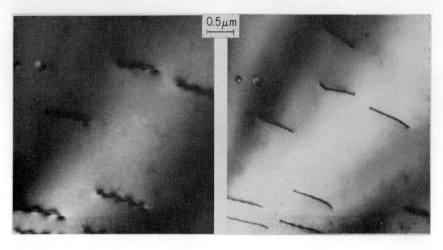

FIG. 11–*Onset of channeling increases penetration and improves contrast in tungsten above 500 kV* (right is 100 kV) *(symmetrical orientation).*

of the orintations for best penetration in bright and dark fields and the maximum useful thickness for several common metals is given in Table 1.

TABLE 1–*Orientation for best penetration.*[a]

|  | Bright Field | Dark Field |
|---|---|---|
| 100 kV – most metal crystals | | |
| (0.1 to 1 $\mu$ m) | + 1st order Bragg position | at Bragg position |
| 1000 kV – light elements | | |
| (Al 6 to 8 $\mu$ m) | + 2nd order Bragg position | at Bragg position |
| 1000 kV – medium elements | | |
| (Fe 3 $\mu$ m) | symmetry position | + 2nd order Bragg position |
| 1000 kV – heavy elements | | |
| (Au 1.5 $\mu$ m) | symmetry position | + 2nd order Bragg position |

[a] Best penetration usually occurs when a low index systematic row is excited.

Another many-beam phenomenon which occurs at high voltage is a "critical voltage" effect where certain second-order image and diffraction characteristics disappear or change at a particular voltage [4]. Figure 12 shows images of bend contours taken above, below, and nearly at the critical voltage ($V_c$). The intensity and symmetry of Kikuchi lines also change and are generally used to measure $V_c$ to within 1/2 percent. Typical values of critical voltages for several metals and the dependence on orientation are listed in Table 2. This critical voltage phenomenon can be used to detect composition changes of alloys on a very fine scale if the basic parameters are known [5].

Another very important consequence of reduced electron wavelength at high voltage is a marked decrease in the size of the region which can be analyzed

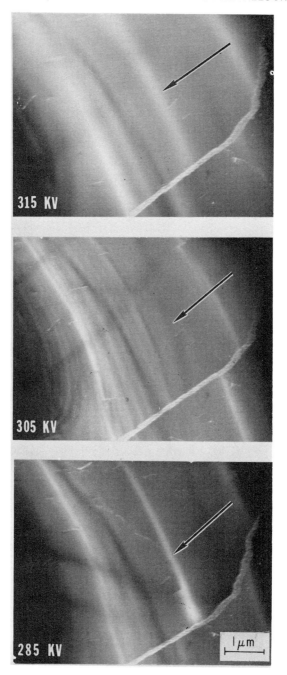

FIG. 12—*Examples of disappearance of second order (220) contours at the critical voltage for a Fe-20Cr alloy.*

TABLE 2–*Some critical voltages of metals.*

| Element | hkl | $V_c$ |
|---|---|---|
| $^{12}$Mg | 002 | 678 kV |
| $^{13}$Al | 200 | 918 |
| $^{24}$Cr | 110 | 265 |
|  | 200 | 1238 |
| $^{26}$Fe | 110 | 305 |
|  | 200 | 1249 |
| $^{29}$Cu | 111 | 310 |
|  | 200 | 600 |
| $^{42}$Mo | 110 | 35 |
|  | 200 | 789 |
| $^{74}$W | 110 | . . . |
|  | 200 | 660 |
| $^{79}$Au | 111 | . . . |
|  | 220 | 108 |

by selected area diffraction (SAD). This improvement, illustrated schematically in Fig. 13, permits diffraction identification of individual precipitate particles in clusters and measurements of differences in crystallographic orientation across subgrain and grain boundaries.

## Effect of Spherical Aberration on SAD.

$$D = D_p + 2C_S(2\theta_B)^3$$

$$D = D_p + 2 C_S\left(\frac{\lambda}{d}\right)^3$$

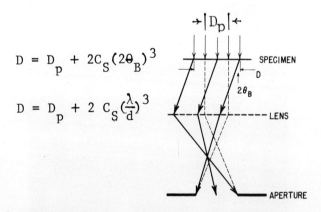

FIG. 13–*Schematic illustration of increased resolution of selected area diffraction at high voltage because of the shorter wavelength.* $D_p$ *represents the projection (dotted line) of the SAD aperture in the specimen plane.*

The diameter (*D*) of the area contributing to the electron diffraction pattern when a transmission microscope is adjusted for SAD is given by

$$D = \frac{D_A}{M_o} + 2\,C_S(2\theta_B)^3 \tag{7}$$

where

$D_A$ = actual diameter of the aperture hole (typically 5 to 100 $\mu$m),
$M_o$ = magnification of the objective lens (typically 25 to X100),
$C_S$ = spherical aberration of the lens (2 to 6 mm), and
$\theta_B$ = Bragg angle of the diffracting crystal plane.

The second term in this expression (Eq 7) represents the displacement, due to spherical aberration, of the region where diffracted rays pass through the SAD aperture. As a result, the size of the area contributing to the diffraction pattern is enlarged especially for very small diffracting angles. Thus, the outer spots in the patterns may not come from material in the area selected. This loss in resolution is much less severe at high voltage because of the marked decrease in wavelength ($\lambda$) and can be evaluated by substituting from Bragg's law

$$n \lambda = 2d \sin \theta \qquad (8)$$

That is, the effective diffracting area $D'$ is given by

$$D' = 2 C_S \left(\frac{\lambda}{d}\right)^3 \qquad (9)$$

For second order reflections of typical metals

$$D' \approx 0.75 \ \mu\text{m at } 100 \text{ kV}$$

and

$$D' \approx 0.015 \ \mu\text{m at } 1000 \text{ kV}$$

Because of difficulties in producing apertures $< {\sim}3 \ \mu$m, the practical lower limit on $D'$ is ${\sim}0.1 \ \mu$m at high voltage.

*Experimental Methods*

Specimen preparation and other experimental methods for high voltage electron metallography (HVEM) are basically the same as those used for conventional transmission microscopy. As discussed previously, greater penetration at high voltage permits the use of much thicker specimens and eases difficulties with specimen thinning, handling, and mounting. In most cases the result of thinning of specimens for transmission microscopy is a tapered rim around a small hole if jet polishing is used, or a straight wedge if cut from the edge of a larger piece polished by the window method. The gain in specimen volume which can be examined at high voltage ensures that the representative areas are available for study. Stereoscopic methods are often necessary to interpret the true three-dimensional arrangement of superimposed microstructural features [6]. This technique is also useful for quantitative measurements of specimen thickness, dislocation density, precipitate size, etc.

Preliminary examination of specimens in the scanning electron microscope at low and intermediate magnification facilitates location of specific areas of interest in the HVEM. Information obtained by X-ray spectrochemical analysis also contributes to the identification of unknown phases. Scanning micrographs of a thinned specimen of free-machining steel mounted for study in the HVEM is shown in Fig. 14, along with a HVEM micrograph and diffraction pattern of the same area.

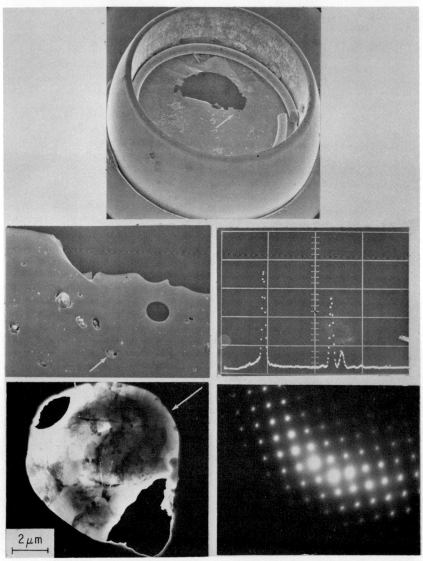

FIG. 14–*Scanning electron micrographs of thin foil sample of free-machining steel in HVEM holder with X-ray spectrum of selected particle. Dark field image and electron diffraction pattern of manganese sulfide particle (1000 kV).*

The development of gas ion milling, illustrated schematically in Fig. 15, now makes it possible to thin nonmetallic materials for transmission microscopy.

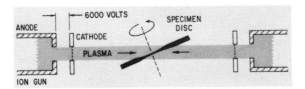

FIG. 15—*Schematic illustration of ion milling to thin nonmetallic specimens for electron microscopy.*

Because such materials are generally very brittle, the greater thickness permitted by HVEM makes them less fragile to handle. The ion beams, shown in Fig. 16, remove material at the rate of about 1 to 2 $\mu$m/h from each surface. This technique is also useful for removing stains which may form on reactive metals during electrolytic or chemical polishing.

FIG. 16—*Photograph of twin argon ion beams directed at specimen in rotating disk holder.*

As an aid to the interpretation of electron diffraction patterns obtained by SAD—especially from complex structures such as minerals—computer methods of generating spot patterns and stereographic projections have been developed. A complete listing of the angles and $d$ spacings up to 333 is also calculated and printed out. Figures 17 and 18 are examples of computer drawn patterns and projections for $Fe_3O_4$ (magnetite) using crystallographic data from the

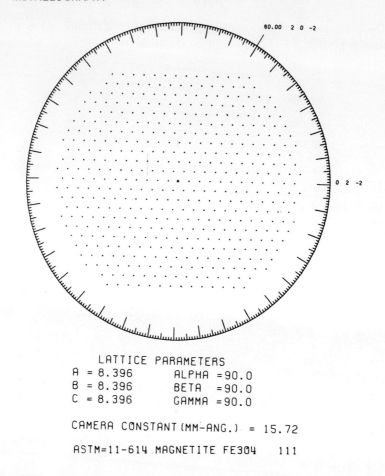

60.00   2  0  -2

0  2  -2

LATTICE PARAMETERS
A = 8.396      ALPHA = 90.0
B = 8.396      BETA  = 90.0
C = 8.396      GAMMA = 90.0

CAMERA CONSTANT (MM-ANG.) = 15.72

ASTM=11-614 MAGNETITE FE3O4   111

FIG. 17–*Computer generated electron diffraction pattern for Fe₃O₄ (magnetite).*

ASTM X-ray card index for a selected orientation. This method has proven to be useful even for a relatively simple and familiar cubic structure, and much greater value results when working with minerals of complex monoclinic and triclinic crystal systems.

### Applications

High voltage electron microscopy has been used to investigate the microstructural aspects of all major metallurgical processes including recrystallization, plastic deformation, fracture, precipitation, phase transformation, corrosion, etc. It is impossible to more than briefly mention some of the major studies carried out in our laboratory [7], the reader is referred to other publications for the details.

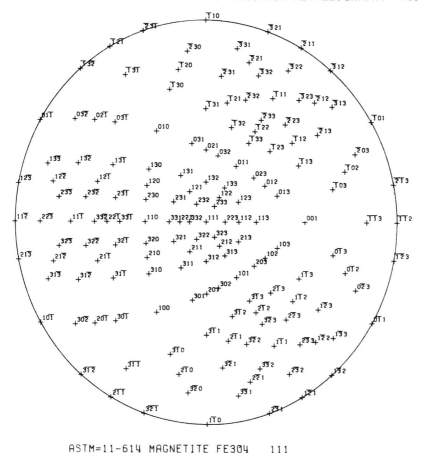

FIG. 18—*Computer generated stereographic projection for* $Fe_3O_4$ *(magnetite).*

## Recrystallization, Recovery, and Grain Growth

Examination of thick specimens by high voltage microscopy has revealed several important characteristics of nucleation and growth of new grains during recrystallization. A low magnification micrograph demonstrating the commonly observed tendency for new grains to nucleate in clusters, particularly in face centered cubic (fcc) metals and alloys, is shown in Fig. 19. A higher magnification image in Fig. 20 reveals the dislocation structure of a mobile boundary in recrystallizing iron, and evidence of substantial recovery in the cold-worked matrix may be seen as clear areas ahead of the moving boundary. In Fig. 21, the results of quantitative measurement of rates of boundary migration in the case of silicon-iron illustrate the tremendous range of growth velocities which can occur [8]. Simultaneous recovery in reducing the driving

FIG. 19–*High voltage electron micrograph illustrating tendency of grains in Ni₃Mn to nucleate in clusters during recrystallization (800 kV).*

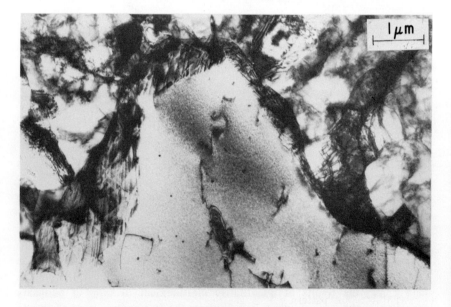

FIG. 20–*HVEM micrograph illustrating partial recovery ahead of mobile boundary in recrystallizing iron (1000 kV).*

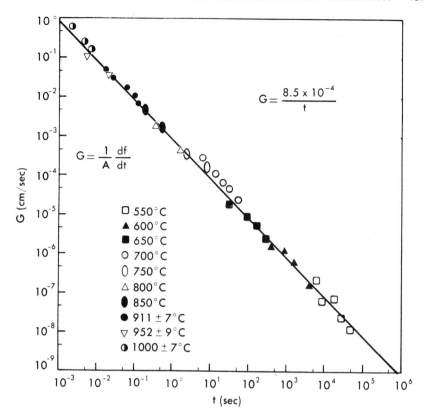

FIG. 21—*Summary of boundary migration rates during recrystallization of 3¼ percent Si iron.*

force for boundary motion lowers the migration rate so that a time dependent effect must be included in theories of recrystallization.

The structure of grain boundaries formed during recrystallization affect the properties of crystalline materials. Figure 22 shows the high density of grain boundary ledges which result from rapid cooling of relatively pure iron from 700°C and causes a greater dependence of yield strength on grain size [9]. The dislocation structure of grain boundaries, and the presence of carbides and other secondary phases, also play an important role in corrosion resistance.

A use of high resolution SAD to identify fine precipitates along prior austenite grain boundaries is illustrated in Fig. 23. The particle enlarged in the lower corner has been identified as boro-cementite from the electron diffraction pattern shown in the upper corner. In a conventional microscope the electron diffraction pattern would come from the whole field of view and a strong pattern from cementite in the pearlite would make it impossible to positively identify boro-cementite, which has a similar crystal structure.

FIG. 22–*Examples of grain boundary ledges formed by quenching* (left) *and furnace cooling of Fe-0.15%Ti (1000 kV).*

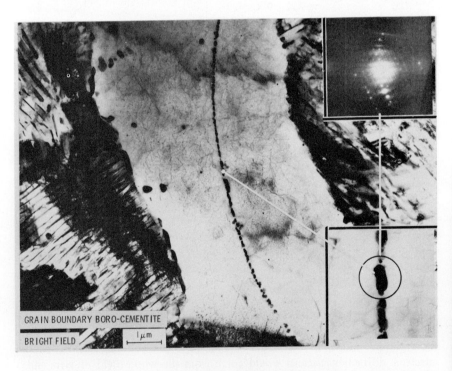

FIG. 23–*Composite electron micrograph showing boro-cementite in prior austenite grain boundaries of type 86B00 boron steel (1000 kV).*

*Precipitation*

The precipitation of secondary phases in ferrous and nonferrous alloys has been the subject of considerable study by electron metallography. High voltage electron microscopy has proven to be useful for extending previous work in certain areas because of greater specimen penetration and accuracy of SAD.

Figure 24 shows an example of precipitation of columbium-carbide at the austenite-ferrite interface during transformation. Stereo viewing of this micro-

FIG. 24—*Walls of columbium carbide formed at ferrite-austenite interface as a result of discontinuous transformation (1000 kV).*

graph reveals that the particles are arranged in parallel walls inclined to the surface. This structure, which results from discontinuous movement of the interface boundary leaving sheets of carbide in the newly formed ferrite, would be difficult to interpret from conventional micrographs of thinner sections. Another type of grain boundary precipitation is shown in Fig. 25. In this case the carbide films which form in 18-8 stainless steel during sensitization by heating at 1200°F have been extracted and mounted for examination. The stainless steel specimen was etched overnight in a methanol $(CH_3OH)$ -10 percent bromine $(Br_2)$ solution to dissolve the ferrite leaving grain-boundary carbide films standing in relief. These flakes are large enough to be picked up with fine tweezers and mounted directly in the high voltage microscope for examination without any thinning. The extensive streaking in the diffraction pattern is due to the presence of a very high density of stacking faults which are formed during growth.

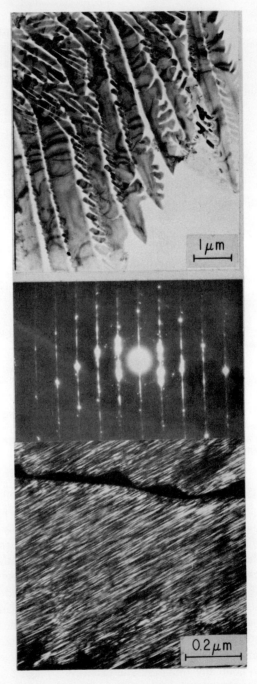

FIG. 25—*Grain boundary film of $Cr_{23}C_6$ carbide removed from sensitized stainless steel. Extensive streaking is due to high density of stacking faults shown in the dark field image (1000 kV).*

*Deformation and Strengthening*

The emphasis now in electron metallographic studies of plastic deformation, strain hardening, and the mechanisms of strengthening of engineering materials is on quantitative measurements of key microstructural components. These include dislocation density, grain size, subgrain misorientation, and precipitate dispersion. Detailed examinations of the nature of barriers to dislocation motion has helped explain strengthening, which can be achieved by reducing grain size or large strain deformation. The results of several investigations in this laboratory are summarized in Fig. 26 to demonstrate the wide range of strength which can be achieved by control of barrier spacing [10]. Research

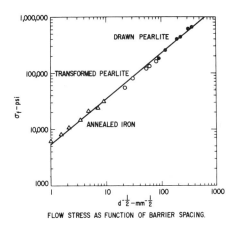

FLOW STRESS AS FUNCTION OF BARRIER SPACING.

FIG. 26–*General effect of barrier spacing on flow stress for pure iron and pearlitic steel.*

investigations related to this subject have provided insight into the deformation of cementite, the change in misorientation of subgrains during deformation [11], the interaction of individual dislocations with precipitates, the effect of dislocation structure on yielding, and changes in the density of dislocations on various slip systems by straining [12].

*Corrosion*

Development of engineering materials with increased corrosion resistance both in the presence or absence of stress is a major research goal. High voltage microscopy has opened a new experimental method of study wherein specimens are corroded after thinning and examined directly in the microscope [13]. This method has revealed that corrosion attack in alloys takes the form of narrow tunnels such as those shown in Fig. 27. The size of the tunnels appears to be related to alloy composition as they are believed to expand until the walls are lined with the more noble alloying element. Attack continues at the base of the pit leading to the type of structure shown in the

FIG. 27—*Corrosion tunnels in electron microscope specimens of alloys exposed to corrosive media (1000 kV). (a) stainless steel, and (b) aluminum-silver alloy.*

micrographs. More work of this type using HVEM controlled environment chambers should provide new insight into the factors controlling corrosion.

Study of the structure of protective coatings on steel and other materials is another important aspect of improving corrosion resistance. Relatively little has been done in this area to date, although the possibility of preparing HVEM specimens comprising substrate and coating appears promising.

## Magnetic and Chemical Ordering

The size, shape, and configuration of magnetic domains and antiphase domains in chemically ordering alloys are important factors affecting the physical, chemical, or mechanical properties of certain materials. HVEM has proven to be a versatile tool for studies of these structures not only because thicker specimens are more representative of bulk samples, but because contrast is increased substantially over 100 kV conditions.

An illustration of the ferromagnetic domain structure in cementite is shown in Fig. 28 of a large spheroidized carbide particle. Antiphase domain boundaries also give good contrast in the HVEM as illustrated in Fig. 29 of an ordered specimen of $Fe_3Al$. This micrograph is half of a stereo pair which clearly reveals the foam-like structure of the domains. In some alloy systems precipitation nucleates on antiphase boundaries of this type. The "boundaries" seen in the micrographs of Figs. 28 and 29 show remarkably high contrast

FIG. 28–*Electron micrograph showing ferromagnetic domains in* $Fe_3C$ *(cementite) (1000 kV).*

considering that they delineate areas with rather subtle differences in character. In the magnetic case electron spin direction is reversed, and in the chemical case the regular array of the two-atom species is out of step. Another seemingly invisible crystal property is the Debye temperature which can now be measured with electron microscope specimens using the critical voltage effect [4].

## Radiation Damage

The nature of radiation damage in crystalline materials has been the subject of considerable study in our laboratory. The threshold for atom displacement by impinging electrons falls between 500 000 and 1 000 000 V for most metals; thus, the electron beam in the HVEM can cause lattice damage. Figure 30 shows small clusters of vacancies and interstitials due to radiation at room temperature [14]. The beam was focused to the central area of this micrograph and the intensity turned up well beyond the normal operating level. After some minutes, the point defects that were produced accumulated into small but visible black spots. At temperatures of 500 to 600°C such defect clusters grow into rather large voids as can be seen in Fig. 31.

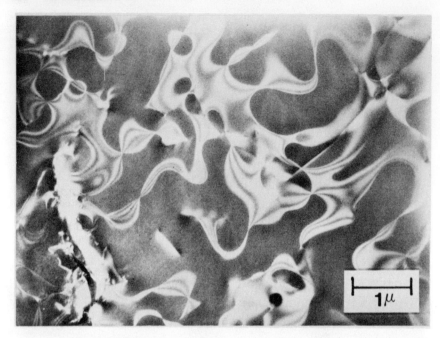

FIG. 29–*High voltage electron micrograph of DO₃ antiphase domains in ordered Fe₃Al (1000 kV).*

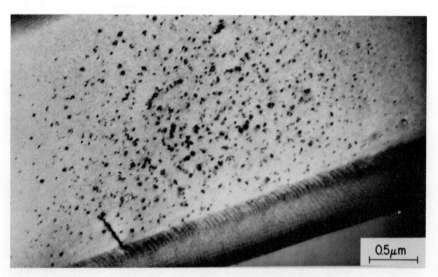

FIG. 30–*Radiation "black-spot" damage formed in stainless steel by electron bombardment in the million volt electron microscope (MVEM) at room temperature (1000 kV).*

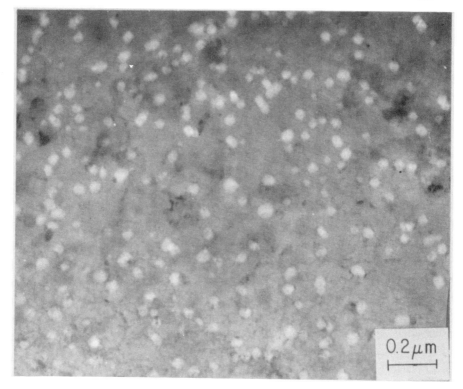

FIG. 31—*Voids formed in stainless steel by electron bombardment in the MVEM at 500°C (1000 kV).*

Radiation damage to structural materials in nuclear reactors, particularly swelling of cladding material of fuel elements due to void formation, is a subject of much concern at the present time. The high voltage microscope is proving to be very useful for studies of this phenomenon since the high beam intensity available in the microscope can cause substantial void formation in just 1h [15]. As much as a year of exposure in a test reactor would be required to produce this amount of void volume.

Stereoscopic analysis of specimens containing voids revealed a depleted zone near the surface, and it is necessary to correct for this when making quantitative comparisons between radiation dose and swelling behavior.

*Minerals*

Methods of HVEM have also proven to be useful for the study of minerals. Usually petrographic thin sections are first prepared by conventional methods for examination in a polarized light optical microscope. These are then thinned for transmission microscopy by milling with ion beams as discussed previously.

The structures observed in minerals are quite analogous to those found in metals; for example, pyroxene decomposes during cooling into two slightly different phases known as augite and pigeonite, generating a microstructure reminiscent of pearlite. Chemical ordering occurs in many minerals and the resulting antiphase boundaries can readily be studied and analyzed. Dislocation and stacking faults also occur in minerals and affect properties much like those in the case of metals.

## Future Developments

Predicting things to come is always hazardous, but the general trend of future developments in high voltage microscopy is already apparent.

The greater penetrating power of high voltage microscopy and the larger space available in the objective lens makes it possible to carry out direct observation of chemical reactions by means of controlled environment chambers. This technique combined with video recording will be used more extensively to study the role of microstructures in oxidation and reduction and other types of gas-solid reactions as well as sintering.

Another certain development is the construction of more and larger high voltage electron microscopes in this country and abroad. The availability of high voltage facilities to scientists in the United States is already behind Europe and Japan, and because of delivery schedules the trend during the next few years will be to increase the microscope gap. Overseas million volt electron microscope (MVEM) facilities include two 3-mV microscopes, one in France and one in Japan. In addition, plans to build an 8-mV microscope in Japan were announced several years ago. The full value of microscopes operating above 2 mV is not thoroughly established, but it is likely that there will eventually be at least one in this country. As for additional 1 to 2-mV facilities, it is probable that there will be at least eight distributed throughout the country by 1980.

During the past several years the perfection of (1) reliable instrumentation, (2) convenient specimen preparation techniques, and (3) quantitative image interpretation methods have established a sound basis for exploitation of the advantages of HVEM for research on materials. This can also be said for scanning microscopy, although image interpretation is not so fully developed. Thus it can be said with some assurance that future ASTM symposia on metallography will include reviews of important new information to be generated by electron optical methods during the coming several years.

*Acknowledgments*

A number of people have played an active part in the development and application of the U.S. Steel Million Volt Electron Microscope including J.S. Lally, L.E. Thomas, W.R. Duff, S. Lentz, G.P. Wray, P.R. Swann, and C.J. Humphreys.

# References

[1]    Fisher, R.M., *Proceedings,* Electron Microscopy Society of America, Vol. 2, 1968, pp. 324-325.

[2]    Metherell, A.J.F., Fisher, R.M., and Duff, W.R., *Proceedings,* Electron Microscopy Society of America, Vol. 2, 1968, pp. 328-329.

[3]    Humphreys, C.J., Thomas, L.E., Lally, J.S., and Fisher, R.M., *Philosophical Magazine,* Vol. 23, No. 181, Jan. 1971, pp. 87-115.

[4]    Lally, J.S., Humphreys, C.J., Metherell, A.J.F., and Fisher, R.M., *Philosophical Magazine,* Vol. 25, No. 2, Feb. 1972, pp. 321-343.

[5]    Thomas, L.E., Shirley, C.G., Lally, J.S., and Fisher, R.M., "The Critical Voltage Effect and Its Applications" in *Proceedings,* 3rd International Conference on High Voltage Metallography, Royal Microscopic Society, Oxford, England, 27-30 Aug. 1973, in press, 1974.

[6]    Thomas, L.E., *Proceedings,* Electron Microscopy Society of America, Vol. 6, 1972, pp. 46-61.

[7]    Fisher, R.M. in *Proceedings,* 5th International Materials Symposium, Berkeley, Calif., Eds., G. Thomas, R.M. Fulbrath, R.M. Fisher, University of California Press, Sept. 1971, pp. 60-84.

[8]    Speich, G.R. and Fisher, R.M. in *Proceedings, Recrystallization, Grain Growth and Textures,* American Society for Metals Seminar, 16-17 Oct. 1965, Detroit, Mich., 1966, Chapter 13, p. 563.

[9]    Bernstein, I.M. and Rath, B.B., *Metallurgical Transactions,* Vol. 4, 1973, pp. 1545-1551.

[10]   Embury, J.D., Keh, A.S., and Fisher, R.M., *Transactions,* Metallurgical Society of AIME, Vol. 236, 1966, pp. 1252-1260.

[11]   Langford, G. and Cohen, M., "Microstructural Analysis of Severely Drawn Iron Wires by HV Electron Diffraction," *Metallurgical Transactions,* in press, 1974.

[12]   Spitzig, W.A. and Thomas, L.E., *Philosophical Magazine,* Vol. 25, No. 5, 1972, pp. 1041-1052.

[13]   Swann, P.R. and Duff, W.R., *Metallurgical Transactions,* Vol. 1, 1970, pp. 69-73.

[14]   Thomas, L.E., *Radiation Effects,* Vol. 5, 1970, pp. 183-194.

[15]   Thomas, L.E. and Fisher, R.M., "HVEM Studies of Radiation Swelling of Reactor Steels" in *Proceedings,* International Conference on Physical Metallurgy of Reactor Fuel Elements, Berkeley Nuclear Labs., Berkeley, England, 2-7 Sept. 1973, in press, 1974.

D.R. Muzyka[1] and G.N. Maniar[1]

# Microstructure Approach to Property Optimization in Wrought Superalloys

REFERENCE: Muzyka, D.R. and Maniar, G.N., "Microstructure Approach to Property Optimization in Wrought Superalloys," *Metallography—A Practical Tool for Correlating the Structure and Properties of Materials, ASTM STP 557,* American Society for Testing and Materials, 1974, pp. 198–219.

ABSTRACT: The effects of structure control available from the precipitating phases in wrought superalloys were demonstrated in a recent review. It was shown that criteria for selection of superalloys should be reviewed periodically to establish that they reflect the state of the art. For example, expensive materials may have been specified where lower cost alloys could do a job equally well. This is especially true for superalloys in applications where properties up to about 1200°F are critical.

This paper reviews some results of the continuing study by superalloy metallurgists to reveal means of "retrograding" elevated temperature requirements to lower cost compositions that, combined with proper processing, will meet property requirements. It is shown that microstructure studies, combined with knowledge of phase relationships, prove to be an invaluable tool. Recent examples of improved hot-work behavior, heat-treat response, and property development are reviewed. Effects of thermomechanical processing are also discussed.

KEY WORDS: heat resistant alloys, microscopy, tensile properties, X-ray diffraction, precipitation hardening, microstructure

The wrought austenitic nickel- and nickel-iron-base alloys are characterized by relatively simple structures when examined via the light microscope. Typically, they show only austenite grains and some MC-type carbides. In fact, until the recent advances in electron metallographic techniques relating to this type of alloy, superalloy metallurgists were often in a quandary to explain the success or failure of a particular alloy in a particular application on the basis of microstructure. It is only within the past 10 to 15 years that some measure of success could be claimed for a correlation of microstructures and properties for these alloys.

This paper will be concerned with the relationships between microstructures and properties of the wrought superalloys. Particular attention will be paid to characterization of microstructure as a tool to maximize the process and property capability of two types of these alloys. It is not intended to present a complete literature review on the relationship of microstructures and properties of wrought superalloys, but rather to review some recent practical applica-

---

[1] Manager, Alloy Research and Development, and manager, Physical Metallurgy Research and Development, respectively, Carpenter Technology Corp., Research and Development Center, Reading, Pa. 19603.

tions where this approach has been successfully applied in the maximization of properties of an alloy leading to real or implied commercial success.

## Alloys

The group of alloys known as superalloys includes the austenitic iron-, nickel-, nickel-iron-, and cobalt-base alloys intended for use above about 1000°F. Most of the cobalt-base superalloys and many of the nickel-base superalloys are utilized only in the cast condition. The present paper will be concerned with the wrought superalloys where numerous processing parameters can be invoked to control microstructures and properties.

The wrought superalloys can be further subdivided into a group of alloys that derive their strength capabilities primarily from precipitation hardening and ones which are not precipitation strengthened. The choice here will be limited to the precipitation hardening alloys since many of these alloys are widely used and involve complex metallurgical reactions. Nominal compositions of some contemporary wrought superalloys are listed in Table 1.

An earlier review [1][2] discussed the advantages for classifying the wrought superalloys into two general types as follows:

Type I: Alloys with $\gamma'$ as the major precipitating phase useful for structure control.

Type II: Alloys with a second precipitating phase such as $\eta$ or $\delta$ or both (in addition to $\gamma'$ or $\gamma''$) available for structure control.

Those not familiar with the physical metallurgy of superalloys are referred to Refs 1 and 2 for a detailed description of these phases. They will be discussed briefly later in this paper.

Table 1 divides the various wrought superalloys into one of the two types and indicates the appropriate structure control phases [1]. Comparative "equilibrium" diagrams for typical Type I and Type II alloys, which will be useful later in this discussion, are shown in Fig. 1.

The inherent cost advantage of the iron- and nickel-iron-base superalloys should make substitution of these for the nickel-base superalloys desirable, provided that properties equivalent or nearly equivalent to the nickel-base alloys can be achieved. In many cases, especially for applications below about 1400°F, successful substitutions have been and will continue to be made. Furthermore, design advantages can be realized if properties of "bill-of-material" alloys are improved, whether they are iron, nickel-iron, or nickel base. This is especially true if no cost disadvantage occurs, that is, due to the need for an expensive processing step.

It is the aim of this review to describe how, through microstructure characterization, optimum benefits in processes and properties might be realized in many wrought precipitation-hardened superalloys. Examples will be given for both the nickel- (Type I) and nickel-iron-base (Type II) alloy groups.

---

[2] The italic numbers in brackets refer to the list of references appended to this paper.

TABLE 1–*Composition of wrought superalloys.*

| Alloy | Type | Structure Control Phase(s) | C | Ni | Co | Fe | Ti | Al | Cr | Mo+W | B | Other |
|---|---|---|---|---|---|---|---|---|---|---|---|---|
| Ni-Base | | | | | | | | | | | | |
| Waspaloy | I | $\gamma'$ | 0.05 | 58.5 | 13.5 | ... | 3.0 | 1.3 | 19.5 | 4.3 | 0.005 | 0.05 Zr |
| Astroloy | I | $\gamma'$ | 0.05 | 57.0 | 15.0 | ... | 3.5 | 4.4 | 15.0 | 5.25 | 0.030 | 0.05 Zr |
| IN 100 | I | $\gamma'$ | 0.18 | 60.5 | 15.0 | ... | 5.0 | 5.5 | 10.0 | 3.0 | 0.015 | 1.0 V, 0.05 Zr |
| René 95 | I | $\gamma'$ | 0.15 | 61.5 | 8.0 | ... | 2.5 | 3.5 | 14.0 | 7.0 | 0.010 | 3.5 Cb, 0.05 Zr |
| Fe-Base | | | | | | | | | | | | |
| A286 | II | $\gamma' + \eta$ | 0.05 | 26.0 | ... | 55.5 | 2.0 | 0.20 | 15.0 | 1.25 | 0.005 | 0.30 V |
| V-57 | II | $\gamma + \eta$ | 0.05 | 25.5 | ... | 55.0 | 3.0 | 0.25 | 15.0 | 1.25 | 0.005 | 0.30 V |
| Ni-Fe-Base | | | | | | | | | | | | |
| 901 | II | $\gamma' + \eta$ | 0.05 | 42.5 | ... | 36.0 | 2.5 | 0.25 | 13.5 | 6.1 | 0.015 | ... |
| Pyromet 860 | II | $\gamma' + \eta$ | 0.05 | 42.5 | 4.0 | 30.0 | 3.0 | 1.25 | 14.0 | 6.0 | 0.010 | ... |
| 718 | II | $\gamma' + \delta$ | 0.04 | 52.5 | ... | 19.5 | 0.90 | 0.50 | 19.0 | 3.0 | 0.005 | 5.30 Cb |
| 706 | II | $\gamma' + \eta + \delta$ | 0.02 | 40.0 | ... | 39.0 | 1.70 | 0.30 | 16.0 | ... | 0.004 | 2.75 Cb |

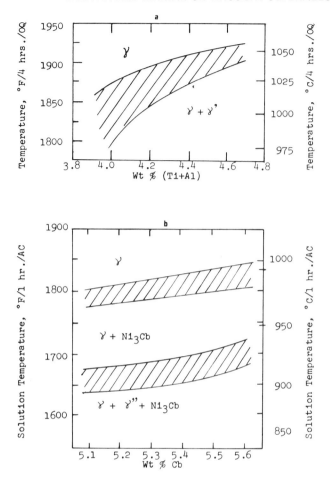

FIG. 1–*"Equilibrium" diagrams for superalloys.* (a) *Typical Type I alloy − Waspaloy (Refs 1,3) and* (b) *typical Type II alloy − 718 (Ref 2).*

## Primary Manufacturing Steps

Most wrought superalloys require special melting which includes either electric-arc, air-induction, or vacuum-induction techniques. Most often the alloys are remelted either by vacuum arc remelting (VAR) or electroslag remelting (ESR).

The superalloy ingot is then heated and forged or cogged into a billet or bloom. Macro- and microstructure examinations are used to ascertain if the hot work has "broken up" the cast ingot structure into a desirable equiaxed fine-grained structure (finer than about ASTM 3). The final structure, of course, is governed by starting ingot structure, thermal history, and deformation sequence. Figure 2 shows the degree of homogenization which may be achieved by a proper practice.

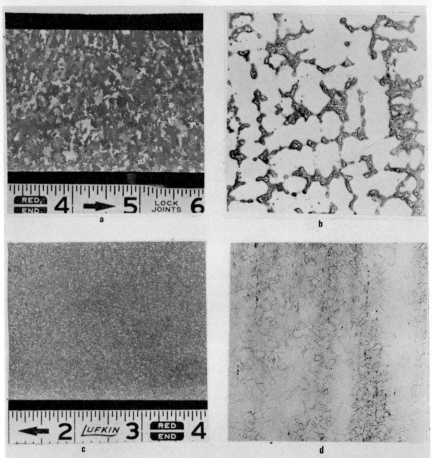

FIG. 2–*Structure improvement in 718 alloy due to hot working.* (a) *As-cast 9 in. ingot (X0.68), etchant: HCl + $H_2O_2$.* (b) *As-cast 9 in. ingot (X68), etchant: glyceregia.* (c) *Four inch square billet (X0.68), etchant: HCl + $H_2O_2$.* (d) *Four inch square billet (X68), etchant: glyceregia.*

Some of the high $\gamma'$ solvus temperature wrought nickel-base superalloys such as IN 100 and René 95 are difficult to remelt into sound, useful size ingots. For these alloys, the prealloyed powder metallurgy approach is evolving as a useful alternative to the remelted ingot/cogged billet approach. A billet, similar in form to one produced by cogging a remelted ingot, or a preform for direct forging, will result. Figure 3 shows that the powder product has a more homogeneous microstructure, indicated by a fine as-cast grain size, lack of large primary carbides, and a very uniform distribution of precipitated phases, as compared to the conventional ingot-billet product.

Once a wrought superalloy is formed into a billet or bloom, it can be subsequently processed into a more useful form such as a turbine disk, shaft, bar, wire, sheet, or strip. Microstructure, again, is a useful tool to monitor these procedures and to predict the properties.

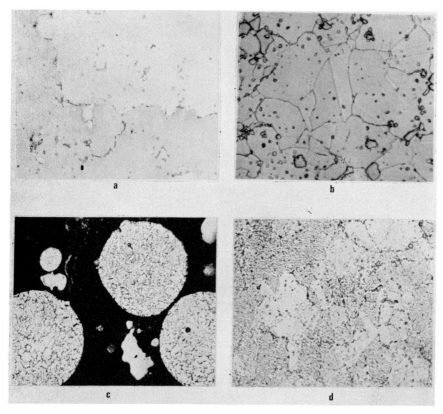

FIG. 3—*Comparative microstructures of conventionally and powder processed René 95 — all etched in Kalling's reagent — No $H_2O$.* (a) *Conventional — 12 in. diameter ingot (X71).* (b) *Conventional — 7 in. square billet (X355).* (c) *Atomized powder particles (X176).* (d) *Isostatic pressed powder (X355).*

## Phases in Wrought Superalloys and Metallographic Techniques

Optical microstructural examination of wrought superalloys generally reveals only MC carbides in an austenite matrix. Austenite grain size and MC distribution can often be related to mechanical properties. For example, fine grains (ASTM 7-10) produce good strength and ductility to about 1200°F; coarse grains (ASTM 3 or coarser) produce good strength above about 1400°F; and intermediate grain sizes (ASTM 4-6) are best in the 1200 to 1400°F range. Duplex microstructures have sometimes been associated with the poorer attributes of each component grain size, but in René 95 [4] a duplex structure is aim.

The phases available to control the grain size of superalloys vary with alloy composition and history. These phases can be studied by optical and electron microscopy as well as X-ray techniques. ASTM Methods for Microetching Metals and Alloys (E 407-70), lists etchants and etching techniques for superalloy microscopy. Thin foil transmission electron microscopy (TEM) [5], optical and replica electron microstructures, and phase extraction and analysis techniques [6], are detailed in several recent papers.

Figure 4 demonstrates useful grain size control ranges for various phases in the two types of wrought superalloys. The primary carbides, usually of MC

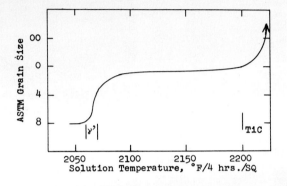

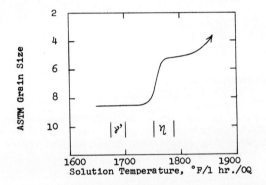

FIG. 4–*Grain size response in wrought superalloys.* (a) *Typical Type I alloy –* Astroloy, *and* (b) *typical Type II alloy – 901 (Ref 1).*

type, appear to be the controlling factor for the coarser grain sizes. For the finer grain sizes, precipitating phases such as γ′ control the microstructure.

The main strengthening phases in superalloys are γ′ and γ″. The γ′ has an ordered face centered cubic (fcc) structure and a composition based on $Ni_3Al$. The γ″ has a metastable body centered tetragonal (BCT) structure and an $Ni_3Cb$ composition. The other phases include η, which has a hexagonal closed packed (HCP) structure and $Ni_3Ti$ stoichiometry, and δ, which has an orthorhombic structure and $Ni_3Cb$ chemistry.

The η phase can exist as intragranular platelets and a cellular grain boundary form. The δ phase occurs only in a globular or platelet form in commercial superalloys. The intragranular η and δ can be used for structure and property control, see Fig. 4b. Similarly, nickel-base superalloys with a capability to form large volume fractions of $\gamma'$ (for example, Astroloy, IN 100, and René 95) lend themselves to grain size control via large $\gamma'$, see Fig. 5.

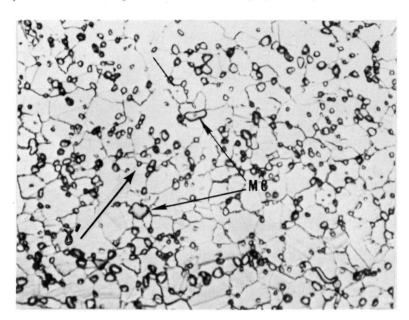

FIG. 5—*Micrograin structure in René 95. Etchant: Kalling's without $H_2O$ (X1000).*

## Microstructures and Properties

In early turbine engine designs, tensile yield strength and stress-rupture strength properties were considered to be critical. It was established that fine grain structures gave best properties at the lower temperatures (less than about 1200°F), and coarser grain sizes gave best properties at the higher temperatures. Current turbine engine designs and performance requirements, however, cause other limiting materials characteristics, such as ultimate tensile (burst) strength, high cycle and low cycle fatigue strength, and toughness or crack propagating characteristics. Creep strength has remained an important parameter. The relationship of several of these materials parameters with microstructure is not well established. Thus, the relationship of engine performance to mechanical property to microstructure becomes a complex matter.

For the alloys used above about 1200°F, the usual manufacturing steps include a final heat treatment which annihilates the prior thermomechanical history. Experience shows that if this is not done, potentially mobile dislocations may remain which will drastically reduce creep/rupture strength. Strength improvements in this temperature range, for wrought alloys, have been almost entirely confined to composition changes which raise solvus temperatures and the heat treatments themselves. As an example of this, one might note the progressive development of the alloys: Waspaloy ($\gamma'$ solvus $\simeq$ 1875°F), Astroloy ($\gamma'$ solvus $\simeq$ 2050°F), and IN 100 ($\gamma'$ solvus $\simeq$ 2150°F). In their wrought forms, these alloys find increasing usage in this same order as temperature/strength requirements increase.

## Recent Developments

The more interesting recent process developments for the wrought super-alloys have occurred for applications with aim use temperatures below about 1200°F. Some of these include:

1. Micrograin processing.
2. Structure-control heat treating.
3. Minigrain[3] processing.
4. Thermomechanical processing.

It is intended that this list be only representative of the recent wrought alloy developments. All significant recent developments cannot be reviewed due to space limitations.

The balance of this paper will review these four developments from the point of view of the microstructural characteristics which appear to have helped to reveal or aid these developments. In some cases, economic advantages will be discussed.

## Micrograin Processing

A historical review of the forgeability of superalloys will reveal that as $\gamma'$ solvus temperatures of new alloys increased, forgeability decreased. For the nickel-base superalloys, it was found that the maximum hardener (aluminum + titanium) content, consistent with even marginal forgeability, was about 6 weight percent. Of course, that was the case where forging was begun above the $\gamma'$ solvus and discontinued slightly below the $\gamma'$ solvus. However, there was a need for forging the alloys with hardener contents above 6 weight percent, such as Astroloy (7.5 weight percent), and through meticulous study, the forgers learned that improved ductilities in forging could be achieved by confining the entire forging operation to temperatures below the $\gamma'$ solvus. For the Type I alloy in Fig. 1a, this amounts to a lowering of the temperature at which forging was started from the single phase field to the two phase $\gamma$ + $\gamma'$ field.

Microstructurally, it was observed that finer grain sizes were created and maintained during the forging operations, for example, ASTM 6/8 versus ASTM 2/3. However, forgers still experienced many cracked forgings causing high prices for the successful parts. The search for a more reliable way to make forgings continued.

Moore et al [7] recognized a practical extension of this approach. By using carefully controlled initial deformation conditions, that is, by 6:1 extrusion

---

[3] Trademark of United Aircraft Corporation.

from a furnace temperature about 200°F below the γ′ solvus of alloys such as Astroloy and IN 100, they were able to achieve microstructures of the type shown in Fig. 5. They had achieved a micrograin structure with austenite grains of 5 to 10 μm diameter pinned by γ′ particles 1 to 2 μm in diameter. It appears that they then speculated and confirmed the capability of this structure to demonstrate superplastic behavior.

Two examples of the superplastic capability of a properly preprocessed superalloy are shown in Fig. 6. Figure 5 shows the typical starting structure

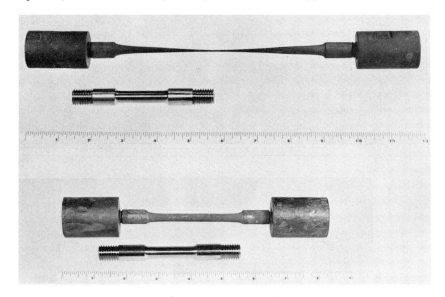

FIG. 6–Superplasticity in René 95 alloy. (a) 1700°F (927°C), 0.005 in./min (0.13 mm/min), 360 percent elongation. (b) 1800°F (982°C), 0.010 in./min (0.254 mm/min), 113 percent elongation.

for both of these specimens. The finishing microstructure of each was nearly identical. It is believed that the coarse γ′ particles acted as a structure controlling phase to maintain the micrograin austenite structure throughout the processes. Others have achieved close tolerance superalloy forgings by employing similar conditions on specially designed forging equipment. Dies heated to the forging temperature are necessary if superplastic conditions are to be realized.

The extension of micrograin practices to many Type I alloys is possible. However, it is believed that this will be more readily achieved in Type I alloys capable of forming large volume fractions of γ′. Also, alloys with high γ′ solvus temperatures are more amenable to this practice so that higher process temperatures can be used in commercial practices–to minimize die wear, etc. The potential economic advantage for this approach is primarily through improved materials utilization and is still under development.

## Structure Control Heat Treating

During 1970, the International Nickel Company announced a new precipitation-hardened nickel-iron-base alloy designated as Alloy 706. Early studies indicated that the recommended, commercial heat treatment for the alloy provided limited 1200°F/100 ksi stress-rupture ductility. Typical data are given in Table 2a. An extensive program was conducted to remedy this situation [8,9].

TABLE 2—Typical properties of Alloy 706 (Ref. 9).

| | Tensile | | | | | 1200°F/100 ksi Stress-Rupture | |
|---|---|---|---|---|---|---|---|
| deg F | Ultimate Tensile Strength, ksi | 0.2% Yield Strength, ksi | Elongation % | Reduction in Area, % | Life, h | Elongation, (%) | Reduction in Area, (%) |
| | | | Commercial Heat Treatment[a] | | | | |
| 70 | 190 | 148 | 21 | 40 | 200 | 6 | 10 |
| 1200 | 148 | 127 | 23 | 56 | | | |
| | | | Structure Control Heat Treatment[b] | | | | |
| 70 | 199 | 170 | 17 | 35 | 220 | 16 | 46 |
| 1200 | 154 | 144 | 19 | 59 | | | |

[a] 1800°F/1 h/air cooled + 1550°F/3 h/air cooled + 1325°F/8 h/cool 100°F/h to 1150°F/8 h/air cooled.
[b] 1650°F/1 h/air cooled + 1325°F/8 h/cool 100°F/h to 1150°F/8 h/air cooled.

Microstructure studies revealed that the alloy with the commercial heat treatment had typically a grain size of about ASTM 6, Fig. 7a. Electron metallography, Fig. 7b, revealed extensive precipitation of cellular and needle-like constituents at or near the grain boundaries. A duplex $\gamma''$ size was noted with denuded zones around the grain boundaries and coarse platelets. Detailed microstructure studies showed that the grain boundary constituents included both HCP $\eta$ ($Ni_3Ti$) and orthorhombic $\delta$ ($Ni_3Cb$). It was speculated that the properties of the alloy could be optimized if an improved morphology could be developed for these phases. The preferred microstructure would have these phases in a more globular form.

Since Alloy 706 forms $\eta$ and $\delta$, in addition to a strengthening precipitate, $\gamma''$, it is a Type II alloy. Referring to Fig. 1b, it was deemed necessary to reveal the phase relationships for Alloy 706. This was done, and the results are reported elsewhere [4]. Basically, the studies showed (depending upon exact heat composition) a $\gamma''$ solvus of about 1625°F and an $\eta/\delta$ solvus of about 1750°F.

Studies revealed that the $\eta$ and $\delta$ phases could be precipitated in the preferred globular to plate-like form by a combined procedure of completing

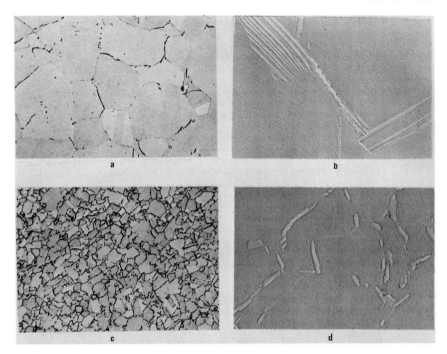

FIG. 7–*Effect of heat treatment on the microstructure of 706 alloy (Ref 8).* (a) *"Commercial" heat treatment, etchant: glyceregia (X315).* (b) *"Commercial" heat treatment structural replica micrograph X(4851).* (c) *"Structure control" heat treatment, etchant: glyceregia (X315).* (d) *"Structure control" heat treatment, structural replica micrograph (X4851).*

hot working below the $\eta/\delta$ solvus temperature, followed by a solution-treating practice between the $\eta/\delta$ solvus temperature and the $\gamma''$ solvus temperature. Preferably, a microstructure of the type shown in Fig. 7c and d would be formed. These micrographs show a relatively fine-grained equiaxed structure formed by a forging practice including a final reduction of about 65 percent from 2000°F, finishing below 1750°F. The desired globular to plate-like $\eta$ and $\delta$ can be seen in the grain boundaries. Transmission electron micrographs representative of the commercial and structure control heat treatments are shown in Fig. 8. Property advantages for the structure control heat treatment can be noted in Table 2.

Alloy 706 with the improved hot work/heat treatment is very close in property capability to Alloy 718. Table 1 shows that Alloy 706 contains considerably less nickel than Alloy 718. Also, 706 has been shown [10] to be easier to machine than 718. The potential economic advantage in substitution of wrought 706 over wrought 718 becomes quite obvious.

It is believed that the structure control type of heat treatment, which includes a "solution-treating" practice at a temperature between the $\gamma'$ or $\gamma''$ and the $\eta/\delta$ solvus ranges, can lead to useful property advantages for any commercial Type II alloy capable of forming $\eta$ and $\delta$.

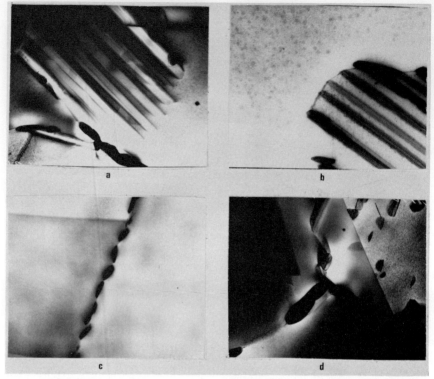

FIG. 8—*Transmission electron micrographs from thin foils of 706 alloy.* (a) *"Commercial" heat treatment (X9100).* (b) *"Commercial" heat treatment (X24 500).* (c) *"Structure control" heat treatment (X9100).* (d) *"Structure control" heat treatment (X13 090).*

## Minigrain Processing

Below about 1400°F, deformation of fcc austenitic superalloys is characterized by relatively easy planar slip. Thus, when coarse-grained materials experience a crack initiation at a structural heterogeneity such as a carbide or other brittle phase, long crystallographic fractures can readily occur. This leads to relatively low fatigue lives for these alloys and, in consequence, low endurance limit/yield strength ratios. An ideal way to improve endurance limit in these alloys would be to improve the distribution and morphology of brittle phases and at the same time, to reduce grain size.

The discussion just completed on structure control processing reveals an approach to grain refinement in Type II alloys. The $\eta/\delta$ phases were used to pin grain boundaries and inhibit grain growth during solution heat treatment. The work of Brown et al [11] presents an interesting extension of that approach, that is, the use of the $\eta$ or $\delta$ to inhibit grain growth during forging and provide even further grain refinement.

Most Type II alloys are capable of forming a Widmanstätten array of $\eta$ or $\delta$ or both. Figure 9a shows such a structure in Alloy 718. Spacings between these platelets are on the order of 4 to 10 $\mu$m. If a structure such as the one

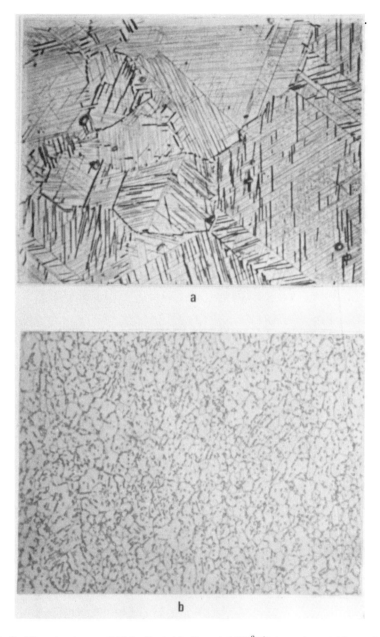

FIG. 9—*Microstructures of 718 alloy.* (a) *Heated 1650°F/8 h to form Widmanstätten array of δ (X500) (Ref 11).* (b) *Minigrain processed (X1000) Ref 11).*

shown in Fig. 9a can be developed and warm-worked at a temperature below the solvus temperature of the platelet phase, it may be possible to disperse the potentially brittle δ platelets and achieve a fine grain size, since the platelets might inhibit grain growth.

Brown et al [11] reveal that this process indeed works in Alloys 901 and 718. For Alloy 718, as Fig. 1b shows, the δ solvus is about 1825°F. Kinetic studies have shown that depending upon initial conditioning, δ can be precipitated in Alloy 718 in varying amounts. Brown et al found that after hot extruding Alloy 718 4:1 at 1900°F, an 8-h soak at 1650°F produced a desirable Widmanstätten array of δ. The alloy was then extruded 4:1 from 1800°F, which Fig. 1b indicates is below the δ solvus temperature. It is desired to finish this type of warm-working operation only slightly below the $\gamma''$, solvus temperature of the alloy so the alloy does not become too stiff for deformation to proceed.

After the warm working at 1800°F, the alloy was recrystallized at 1775°F, again below the δ solvus. Final aging is the conventional treatment at 1325°F/8 h/cool 100°F/h to 1150°F/8 h/air cooled. Figure 9b shows the ASTM 12/13 Minigrain microstructure thus achieved. Properties for this and the coarser-grained processed Alloy 718 are compared in Table 3. Note the unprecedented increase from 0.33 to 0.59 in 850°F endurance limit/ultimate tensile strength (UTS) ratio for these structure changes in Alloy 718. Brown et al [11] also show a similar property increase in Alloy 901.

It is believed that Minigrain processing can be extended to other Type II alloys. Alloys with high η or δ or both solvus temperatures, a propensity to form large volume fraction of η or δ or both, and wide temperature separation between η or δ and $\gamma'$ or $\gamma''$ solvus temperatures, will permit the most flexible and economic processing.

### Thermomechanical Processing

The recently renewed interest in thermomechanical processing for high temperature alloys was caused by a realization that alloying alone will not provide the strengths required for projected jet engine designs. In a sense, all forge/heat treat sequences are a form of thermomechanical processing. For this paper, however, let us confine the term "thermomechanical" processing to those situations where the express intent is to use the strain energy from the forming process to provide strength to the finished forged and heat-treated part. The term "conventional" processing is then used to describe the cases where microstructure control is performed primarily to equalize the structural and property characteristics of a forging, such as in the three recent process developments just described.

Most recent thermomechanical studies on superalloys have been empirical in nature. Lowered processing temperatures have been combined with rather unconventional heat-treat approaches. Some unexpectedly good balances of strength and ductility have been achieved. As an example, some recent data developed in the authors' laboratory are cited.

TABLE 3—*Grain size effects on the properties of Alloy 718* (Ref 12).

| | 1000°F Tensile | | | |
|---|---|---|---|---|
| Grain Size ASTM | Ultimate Tensile Strength, ksi | 0.2% Yield Strength, ksi | Elongation, % | Reduction in Area, % |
| 2 | 166 | 126 | 20 | 44 |
| 5 | 172 | 145 | 21 | 43 |
| 12 | 192 | 155 | 14 | 36 |

| 850°F Low Cycle Fatigue | | |
|---|---|---|
| Grain Size ASTM | Stress, ksi | Cycles to Failure Average of 8 Tests |
| 2 | $40 \pm 80$ | 14 000 |
| 5 | $40 \pm 80$ | 24 000 |
| 12 | $40 \pm 80$ | 53 000 |

| 850°F High Cycle Fatigue at $K_t = 1$ | | |
|---|---|---|
| Grain Size ASTM | Runout Stress $10^7$ Cycles, ksi | Fatigue Ratio FS/UTS |
| 2 | 55 | 0.33 |
| 5 | 80 | 0.45 |
| 12 | 115 | 0.59 |

A 1-in.-square bar, processed from an ~ 4–5/8 in. diameter, 100-lb VAR ingot of René 95, was used for this study. This bar, processed using a combination forging and rolling sequence (all at 2000°F furnace temperature), had a grain size of about 5 μm. The bar was air cooled after the final hot rolling. Specimen 0-1 was held as-rolled. Initially, specimens of this material were further processed under the conditions indicated by codes 0-2 through 0-7 in Table 4. Specimens 0-2 through 0-5 were flattened from about 1 in. thick to about 5/8 in. thick using a 500 ton press and were air cooled after forging. Specimen 0-6 was made by heating for 1 h and upsetting the 1-in. thickness to 7/8 in. thick, reheating for 30 min and upsetting to 5/8 in. thick, air cool. Specimen 0-7 was made by heating for 1 h and rolling about 10 percent and reheating 30 min, a total of eight times, and rolling to 5/8 in. thick, followed by air cool. Test blanks were cut from this material, aged 1400°F/16 h/air cooled, and tested. Test data for 1200°F tension tests and 1200°F stress/rupture tests are given in Table 5. A comparison of these properties with conventionally processed and heat-treated, hot-rolled René 95 bar shows the improved strength, particularly the ductility, obtained in the thermomechanically processed (TMP) René 95. It is also seen that thermo-mechanically working in the vicinity of the γ′ solvus (specimen 0-5) appears

TABLE 4—*Thermomechanical processes used on Rene' 95 bar.*

| Code No. | Pretreatment | Forging Temperature, deg F | Quench |
|---|---|---|---|
| | *Initial Studies* | | |
| 0-1 | as-rolled | . . . | . . . |
| 0-2 | as-rolled | 1700 | AC$^a$ |
| 0-3 | as-rolled | 1800 | AC |
| 0-4 | as-rolled | 1900 | AC |
| 0-5 | as-rolled | 2000 | AC |
| 0-6 | as-rolled | 1800 | AC |
| 0-7 | as-rolled | 1800 | AC |
| | *Secondary Studies* | | |
| I-B | as-rolled | 1800 | WQ$^b$ |
| I-C | as-rolled | 1900 | WQ |
| I-D | as-rolled | 2000 | WQ |
| I-E | as-rolled | 2100 | WQ |
| II-B | 1650°F/24 h/AC + 2000°F/1 h/OQ | 1800 | WQ |
| II-C | 1650°F/24 h/AC + 2000°F/1 h/OQ | 1900 | WQ |
| II-D | 1650°F/24 h/AC + 2000°F/1 h/OQ | 2000 | WQ |
| III-B | 1650°F/24 h/AC + 2000°F/1 h/OQ + 1400°F/16 h/AC | 1800 | WQ |
| III-C | 1650°F/24 h/AC + 2000°F/1 h/OQ + 1400°F/16 h/AC | 1900 | WQ |
| III-D | 1650°F/24 h/AC + 2000°F/1 h/OQ + 1400°F/16 h/AC | 2000 | WQ |
| IV-B | 2090°F/1 h/AC | 1800 | WQ |
| IV-C | 2090°F/1 h/AC | 1900 | WQ |
| IV-D | 2090°F/1 h/AC | 2000 | WQ |
| V | 1650°F/24 h/AC + 2000°F/1 h/OQ | 2050 | OQ$^c$ |
| VI | 1650°F/24 h/AC + 2000°F/1 h/OQ | 1950 | OQ |
| VII | 1650°F/24 h/AC + 2000°F/1 h/OQ | 2000 | OQ |
| VIII | 1650°F/24 h/AC + 2000°F/1 h/OQ | 2000 | OQ |

$^a$ Air cooled.
$^b$ Water quench.
$^c$ Oil quench.

to give the best combination of properties. The $\gamma'$ solvus for the heat involved was estimated to be in the vicinity of 2075°F for a 1-h treatment. The material TMP at 2000°F gave the best properties.

The optical microstructures of some of these specimens are shown in Fig. 10. The grain size of the bar processed at 2000°F is ~ 3 to 4 $\mu$m (ASTM 13). The 1900°F bar has a slightly finer grain size. It also appears that the 2000°F exposure has dissolved some coarse $\gamma'$ particles, compared to the 1900°F exposure.

Representative replica electron micrographs are also shown in Fig. 10 for specimens 0-4 and 0-5. Three types of $\gamma'$ precipitates are evident: (1) residual,

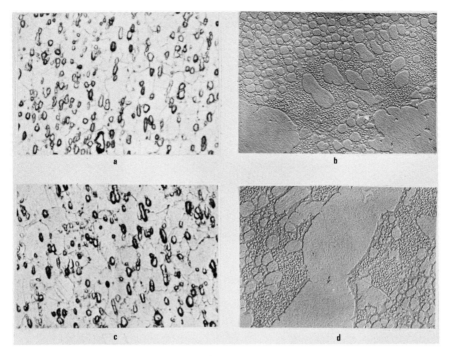

FIG. 10—*Microstructures of TMP René 95.* (a) *Specimen 0-4 (X620), etchant: Kalling's without $H_2O$.* (b) *Specimen 0-4 (X10 850), structural replica micrograph.* (c) *Specimen 0-5 (X620), etchant: Kalling's without $H_2O$.* (d) *Specimen 0-5 (X10 850), structural replica micrograph.*

or coarse $\gamma'$, (2) medium $\gamma'$, and (3) fine or aging $\gamma'$. The coarse $\gamma'$ particles appear to be slightly fewer in number and larger in size for the 2000°F temperature. The medium $\gamma'$ also show some significant differences. In specimen 0-4, these appear to be of nearly cuboidal morphology, whereas, in specimen 0-5 due to the higher forging temperature used, this $\gamma'$ becomes of irregular morphology. Forging temperature also affects the dispersion of fine $\gamma'$ obtained after aging. It is more uniform and slightly larger in size in specimen 0-5 as compared to specimen 0-4. This may be responsible for the slight decrease in strength in specimen 0-5. The cuboidal $\gamma'$ in specimen 0-4 may have lowered the tensile ductility.

Creep/rupture properties are equally important for superalloys such as René 95. Even though thermomechanical processes gave the alloy very high ductilities, the rupture lives were very low. A second TMP study was designed to improve the creep properties as well. The TMP procedures are listed in Table 4*b*.

New variables introduced included pretreatments as listed in Table 4 and water or oil quenching after forging. The pretreatments, including a 1650°F/24-h exposure, were selected based on background knowledge of the processing of conventional René 95 for best creep/rupture properties [*12*].

The effects of a 1650°F/24-h preexposure of René 95, although investigated in the authors' laboratory, remain unknown. The 2090°F pretreatment was included since it is slightly above the γ′ solvus of René 95. Both the 2090°F pretreatment and the quench treatments after forging were designed to maintain as much γ′ as possible in solution for the controlled aging reaction.

The tensile and stress-rupture data for the second TMP study are given in Table 5, while creep curves are shown in Fig. 11.

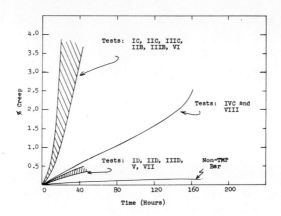

FIG. 11—*Summary of 1200°F/150 ksi creep data on TMP René 95.*

An analysis of these data indicates the following:

(*a*) Forging at 2000°F, that is, in the vicinity of the γ′ solvus (especially when followed by a rapid quench) appears to give the best overall properties.

(*b*) Process conditions leading to best 1200°F creep/rupture properties often cause cracking during forging or quenching after forging.

(*c*) A rapid quench, compared to an air cool, appeared to improve creep properties. This is attributed to precipitation of very fine γ′ during final aging. Oil quenching is preferred over water quenching to inhibit cracking.

(*d*) A pretreatment of 1650°F/24 h/air cooled + 2000°F/1 h/air cooled helped improve creep life and ductility.

A comparison of the data for 2000°F forgings from the second TMP series with the first (specimen 0-5) reveals significantly improved creep/rupture strength for the second TMP series specimens. This is attributed to a larger quantity of fine γ′ precipitated during the aging of the Series II specimens which were quenched after forging.

The authors speculate that thermomechanical processing of René 95 and possibly other Type I superalloys, provides improved strength and ductility via creation of idealized dislocation–γ′ interactions. Careful TEM studies would be necessary to reveal these interactions. Certainly, the improvement of creep life via the quench treatments after forging supports such a theory.

Increased emphasis on understanding the nature of strength improvement in superalloys via thermomechanical processes is recommended. Only then will the full impact of the potential of thermomechanical processing for improving the properties of wrought superalloys be felt.

## Summary

Many useful property improvements have been achieved in wrought super-alloys. Most of these have been accompanied by relatively complete micro-structural understanding. Microstructure studies of problem situations have often revealed the approach to property improvement.

After developing the state of the art of understanding the microstructure of the wrought superalloys, especially related to processing, several recent process developments were reviewed. In three of these—micrograin processing, structure control heat treating, and Minigrain processing—microstructure studies lead the way in the development of improved processes or properties or both. In the fourth case (thermomechanical processing), empirical approaches have dominated most contemporary work and understanding through microstructure study is just beginning.

## References

[1]    Muzyka, D.R., *Metals Engineering Quarterly,* Vol. 11, No. 4, Nov. 1971, pp. 12-20.
[2]    Muzyka, D.R. in *The Superalloys,* C.T. Sims and W.C. Hagel, Eds., Wiley, New York, 1972, Chapter 4.
[3]    Rehrer, W.P., Muzyka, D.R., and Heydt, G.B., *Journal of Metals,* Vol. 22, No. 2, Feb. 1970, pp. 32-38.
[4]    Couts, W.H., Jr. and Coyne, J.E. in *Proceedings,* Second International Conference on Superalloys, Processing, Report MCIC-72-10, Battelle Columbus Labs., Columbus, Ohio, Sept. 1972, pp. K1-K20.
[5]    Kotval, P.S., *Metallography,* Vol. 1, Nos. 3 and 4, Jan. 1969, pp. 251-285.
[6]    Donachie, M.J., Jr. and Kriege, O.H., *Journal of Materials,* Vol. 7, No. 3, Sept. 1972, pp. 269-278.
[7]    Moore, J.B. and Athey, R.L., "Fabrication Method for the High Temperature Alloys," *U.S. Patent 3,519,503,* 7 July 1970.
[8]    Moll, J.H., Maniar, G.N., and Muzyka, D.R., *Metallurgical Transactions,* Vol. 2, No. 8, Aug. 1971, pp. 2143-2151.
[9]    Moll, J.H., Maniar, G.N., and Muzyka, D.R., *Metallurgical Transactions,* Vol. 2, No. 8, Aug. 1971, pp. 2153-2160.
[10]   Eiselstein, H.L., *Metals Engineering Quarterly,* Vol. 11, No. 4, Nov. 1971, pp. 20-25.
[11]   Brown, E.E., Boettner, R.C., and Ruckle, D.L. in *Proceedings,* Second International Conference on Superalloys, Processing, Report MCIC-72-10, Battelle Columbus Labs., Columbus, Ohio, Sept. 1972, pp. L1-L12.
[12]   Wukusick, C.S. and Smashy, R.W., "Ultra High Strength Superalloys," Technical Report AFML-TR-68-214, Oct. 1968.

TABLE 5 – *Properties of thermomechanically processed Rene' 95.*

| Sample Code | 1200°F Tensile | | | | 1200°F/150 ksi, Creep/Rupture | | |
|---|---|---|---|---|---|---|---|
| | Ultimate Tensile Strength, ksi | 0.2% Yield Strength, ksi | Elongation, % | Reduction in Area, % | Life, h | Elongation, % | Reduction in Area, % |
| *Initial Studies* | | | | | | | |
| 0-1 | 222 | 188 | 9.4 | 10.3 | 11.6 | 23.1 | 30.9 |
| 0-2 | 246 | 206 | 10.7 | 14.4 | 10.1 | 16.9 | 24.4 |
| 0-3 | 250 | 216 | 9.6 | 16.6 | ... | ... | ... |
| 0-4 | 248 | 215 | 7.2 | 10.3 | 10.9 | 24.5 | 38.6 |
| 0-5 | 234 | 207 | 14.4 | 21.4 | 6.5 | 25.5 | 37.4 |
| 0-6 | 245 | 213 | 11.2 | 18.5 | 12.3 | 19.9 | 25.8 |
| 0-7 | 224 | 192 | 8.7 | 13.5 | ... | ... | ... |
| Non-TMP[a] Bar Stock | 224 | 187 | 7.8 | 9.6 | 333.0 | 1.8 | 6.3 |
| *Secondary Studies* | | | | | | | |
| I-B | 242 | 212 | 13.7 | 24.7 | 14.7 | 23.0 | 34.9 |
| I-C | 229 | 213 | 11.4 | 13.8 | 23.6 | 12.0 | 21.3 |
| I-D | no test – specimen cracked[b] | | | | 86.1 | 4.5 | 7.6 |
| I-E | no test – specimen cracked[b] | | | | no test – specimen cracked[b] | | |
| II-B | 242 | 212 | 11.4 | 17.6 | 37.0 | 11.8 | 37.0 |
| II-C | 231 | 205 | 8.0 | 11.5 | 36.2 | 16.9 | 36.2 |
| II-D | no test – specimen cracked[b] | | | | 89.0 | 0.8 | 4.4 |

| | | | | | | |
|---|---|---|---|---|---|---|
| III-B | 241 | 200 | 6.5 | 9.4 | 34.0 | 15.4 | 27.3 |
| III-C | 230 | 196[b] | 11.6 | 15.2 | 26.1 | 14.0 | 14.0 |
| III-D | no test – specimen cracked[b] | | | | 135.4 | 3.6 | 3.0 |
| IV-B | >201 | 198 | fractured in threads | | no test – Specimen cracked[b] | | |
| IV-C | specimen accidentally overheated | | | | 175.6 | 4.1 | 7.6 |
| IV-D | no test – specimen cracked[b] | | | | no test – specimen cracked[b] | | |
| V | no test – insufficient material | | | | 20.1 | 0.6 | 0 |
| VI | no test – insufficient material | | | | 30.6 | 9.4 | 11.5 |
| VII | no test – insufficient material | | | | 80.5 | 3.9 | 3.2 |
| VIII | no test – insufficient material | | | | 176.3 | 5.1 | 3.2 |

[a] Conventionally heat treated: 1650°F/24 h/AC + 2000°F/1 h/OQ + 1400°F/16 h/AC, all others aged only 1400°F/16 h/AC after the TMP in Table 4.
[b] Cracked during forging/quenching operation.

O.H. Kriege[1]

# Phase Separation as a Technique for the Characterization of Superalloys

REFERENCE: Kriege, O.H., "Phase Separation as a Technique for the Characterization of Superalloys," *Metallography—A Practical Tool for Correlating the Structure and Properties of Materials, ASTM STP 557*, American Society for Testing and Materials, 1974, pp. 220–234.

ABSTRACT: Specific anodic dissolution procedures are detailed for the quantitative separation of carbides, topologically close-packed (TCP) phases, and $\gamma'$ from high temperature nickel-base superalloys. Reagents are suggested for the isolation of phases from mixed anodic deposits through selective dissolution techniques. Methods for the chemical analysis of separated phases are discussed. The application of phase separation to specific metallurgical studies is described in detail.

KEY WORDS: heat resistant alloys, X-ray diffraction, carbides, borides, nickel alloys, sigma phase, separation, chemical analysis, dissolving

Nickel-, cobalt- and iron-base alloys hardened by geometrically close-packed phases such as gamma prime ($\gamma'$) and eta ($\eta$), as well as by carbides such as MC, $M_{23}C_6$, and $M_6C$, are commonly called superalloys. These high temperature alloys achieve their strength from an appropriate dispersion of the foregoing phases plus solid solution strengthening. Other phases such as nitrides and topologically close-packed (TCP) phases of the $\mu$, $\sigma$ and Laves type may also be present and adversely affect strength. Knowledge of the type, amount, and physical parameters of all of the preceding phases is vital for achievement of optimum properties in superalloys. Microstructural analysis by metallography, X-ray diffraction, and electron microscopy, and *in situ* chemical composition studies with an electron microprobe have long been recognized as techniques for determining some of the necessary phase information. However, for precise chemical analysis, quantitative measurement of the amounts of phases, and lattice parameter studies, the separation of phases has considerable value [1].[2]

Utilizing techniques developed in the analysis of steels [2], much of the early work on nickel-base alloys was devoted to procedures for the separation of carbides, nitrides, borides, carbonitrides, carbosulfides, $\mu$, $\sigma$, and Laves. In general, the system for separation was based either on chemical techniques

---

[1] Technical supervisor, Materials Engineering and Research Laboratory, Pratt and Whitney Aircraft, East Hartford, Conn. 06108.

[2] The italic numbers in brackets refer to the list of references appended to this paper.

involving organic solvents and strong oxidizing agents such as bromine ($Br_2$), or on anodic dissolution methods utilizing electrolytes such as hydrochloric acid (HCl) (about 10 percent) in a miscible solvent such as methanol ($CH_3OH$). Recently, emphasis has been placed on the development of techniques for the separation of both major and minor constituents in high temperature alloys through the careful control of electrode potentials in complex electrolyte systems. Much of the work has been coordinated in this country through ASTM Committee E-04.91 Task Group (Phase Identification in Superalloys). A summary of the committee's work has been recently published [3]. Extensive studies of techniques for phase separation have also been done in Russia, and a comprehensive survey of this work was recently made by Lashko and coworkers [4].

The major purpose for the separation of phases is to concentrate them free of matrix contamination and permit their more accurate identification and chemical analysis. Currently, work is in progress in several laboratories both in the United States and in Russia to develop techniques for the isolation of phases separated by general procedures. For example, the separation of MC, $M_{23}C_6$, and $M_6C$ carbides or the separation of carbides from TCP phases with which they are isolated by anodic dissolution using HCl and $CH_3OH$. Recent advances in analytical instrumentation have permitted the development of precise methods for the quantitative analysis of extremely small amounts of specimens. This paper will summarize suggested procedures for the separation of phases from complex high temperature alloys, discuss techniques for the analysis of separated material, and indicate areas of application for this type of information.

## Specific Techniques for Phase Separation

Equipment required for phase separation is quite inexpensive and is frequently assembled from components already available in a particular laboratory, rather than by purchase of an integrated unit. Furthermore, there has been a comparative lack of knowledge by many of the experimenters in this country of the extensive programs of phase separation being done by chemists and metallurgists in Russia. As a result, a wide range of techniques have been developed, many of which give similar results for a particular alloy. Without trying to detail all possible satisfactory parameters, a summary of methods which have proven reliable in our laboratory will be given next. All techniques are, of course, influenced by the size and chemical composition of phases in the specimens studied.

### Preparation of Specimen

A convenient specimen for electrolytic dissolution weighs 5 to 10 g. The specimen is polished until it has smooth surfaces and then is given an initial extraction for 15 min at a current of 150 mA in 10 percent HCl-$CH_3OH$ to remove any strain-induced phases from the abraded surfaces. Cast alloys and parts operated at high temperature frequently have a high concentration of oxides and nitrides near the surface. A preliminary electrolytic extraction will usually remove surface areas of the specimen which contain these phases. If it is desired to include surface oxide and nitride phases in the separated material, then no preliminary or surface preparation extraction is done on the alloy specimen selected for analysis. Following surface preparation, or initial extraction, the specimen is weighed.

*Separation of Carbides and TCP Phases*

The most satisfactory general procedure for the separation of carbides along with TCP phases is an anodic dissolution of the $\gamma$ and $\gamma'$ components of the superalloy in a solution consisting of 10 percent HCl and $CH_3OH$. The concentration of HCl has been varied from as little as 2.5 percent to as much as 15 percent with comparatively minor effects on phase recoveries. The rate of matrix dissolution is slower in lower HCl concentrations, while there is more tendency for TCP phase dissolution in higher concentrations of acid. Most experimenters prefer working with an electrolyte consisting of 10 percent HCl and $CH_3OH$, although comparable results are found in ethanol ($C_2H_5OH$) or water mixtures with HCl [4].

A d-c power supply is used to stabilize the current during electrolysis. While stainless steel or other metal electrodes have been used, most work is done with platinum or tantalum electrodes. The specimen, connected by a platinum wire, serves as the anode, while a 40-$cm^2$ section of platinum foil may be used as the cathode. The specimen may be attached to the platinum wire by wrapping in platinum wire mesh which is attached to the electrode. Alternately, a hole may be drilled through the specimen and the platinum wire passed through it. The electrolyte (200 ml) is contained in a beaker of convenient size (250 to 400 ml) and stirred during electrolysis. Electrolysis is performed usually at current densities of 20 to 100 $mA/cm^2$ and is frequently continued from 4 to 8 h to collect sufficient material to permit accurate chemical analysis. Recent unpublished work by members of ASTM Committee E-04.91 Task Group has shown that it is sometimes necessary to cool the electrolyte to 40°F in order to obtain quantitative recoveries of $\gamma'$.

Following electrolysis, adhering material is removed from the specimen with a rubber policeman. The specimen and electrodes are carefully washed with $CH_3OH$, and the specimen is reweighed. Insoluble material is separated from the electrolyte by collection on a solvent-resistant filtration pad, or by centrifuging of the solution. In order that a truly quantitative measure can be made of the concentration of carbide and TCP phases in a specimen, it is essential that careful techniques be followed to collect all insoluble material from the specimen, anode, electrolyte, and electrolytic vessel. In addition, the separation of insoluble material from the electrolyte should be accomplished without extended delay to avoid dissolution of fine particles. Ultrasonic techniques have been found to be useful for removing insoluble material from the surfaces of some specimens.

If phase separation by size is desired, the insoluble material may be stirred actively in the electrolyte for 30 s and allowed to settle for varying periods of time. The upper portion of electrolyte will contain the finer particles, while the lower portion will be richest in coarse particles. In some alloys, certain of the platelets of $\sigma$ or $\mu$ settle very slowly from stirred solutions and may be separated from the more cubical carbide phases.

Contamination of extraction residues by the oxides of columbium, tantalum, or tungsten can be controlled by the addition of 1 percent (by weight) of tartaric acid to the electrolyte. Matrix or $\gamma'$ contamination of the residue is more difficult to eliminate and is apparently affected by specific conditions of electrolysis including current density, volume of electrolyte, temperature of the cell, and surface area of the electrodes. It is particularly important that a practical compromise be reached between slow dissolution rates (low current densities) and high matrix contamination (high current densities). Certain alloy specimens are much more subject to matrix contamination of carbides and TCP phases than are others. This may be influenced by the distribution of carbides and TCP phases within the specimen. Another possible factor in matrix contamination is the relative chemical composition of phases which affects polarization during electrolysis. Attempts to selectively dissolve matrix contamination from extracted carbides and TCP phases prove very difficult without dissolution of some of the TCP phases.

Separation of MC carbides from superalloys may also be accomplished through the dissolution of matrix and $\gamma'$ with a mixture of $Br_2$ and $CH_3OH$. Mu, Laves, $M_{23}C_6$, and $\sigma$ are also dissolved in this mixture which permits the isolation of MC carbides free of TCP phases. This technique has enjoyed less popularity because of the unpleasantness of working with this reagent mixture, the difficulty of quantitative recovery of carbides from the reaction products, the slowness of reaction, and also, because of the fact that TCP phases are dissolved.

*Separation of Gamma Prime ($\gamma'$)*

Two general types of electrolytes have been considered for the anodic dissolution separation of $\gamma'$ from nickel-base superalloys. Phosphoric acid (usually 20 percent in water) was frequently used in this country for the separation of $\gamma'$, while Russian experimenters [5] suggested an aqueous solution containing 1 percent ammonium sulfate and 1 percent citric or tartaric acid. Published work in this country [6,7], as well as studies by members of the Phase Identification in Superalloys Task Group (ASTM E-04.91), have demonstrated that $\gamma'$ recoveries from a variety of superalloys, using the ammonium sulfate-citric acid (or tartaric acid) electrolyte are more quantitative than those using phosphoric acid. The difference in yield is probably caused by the significantly higher dissolution rate of fine $\gamma'$ particles in phosphoric acid than in the less acidic electrolyte. Comparative results for $\gamma'$ recoveries (corrected for carbide contamination) from 15 typical nickel-base superalloys are shown in Table 1 [7]. It should be emphasized that the

TABLE 1 – *Comparison of gamma prime recoveries for various electrolytes* (Ref 7).

| Alloy | wt.% $\gamma'$, With A[a] | wt.% $\gamma'$, With B[b] | wt.% $\gamma'$, With C[c] | wt.% $\gamma'$, With D[d] |
|---|---|---|---|---|
| IN 100 | 64.0 | 63.9 | 53.5 | 55.4 |
| TRW 1900 | 63.3 | 63.0 | 56.6 | 22 |
| B-1900 | 61.6 | 61.6 | 49 | 5 |
| Nicrotung | 57.2 | 57.4 | 51 | 11 |
| Mar-M200 | 55.8 | 53.9 | 26 | 13 |
| Inconel 713C | 48.5 | 50.0 | 39 | 27 |
| Nimonic 115 | 47.0 | 46.7 | 40.0 | 40.9 |
| Udimet 700 | 35.0 | 35.4 | 28 | 28 |
| Udimet 500 | 33.4 | 31.8 | 28.4 | 30.2 |
| Inconel 700 | 25.9 | 25.8 | 21.4 | 22.2 |
| René 41 | 23.9 | 22.4 | 7 | 16.1 |
| Waspaloy | 22.1 | 21.5 | 15 | 17.9 |
| GMR 235 | 21.4 | 21.3 | 19.2 | 20.1 |
| Unitemp AF 1753 | 19.7 | 18.6 | 14.6 | 15.0 |
| Inconel X-750 | 14.5 | 13.9 | 8 | 10.6 |

[a] Electrolyte A–1% ammonium sulfate, 1% tartaric acid in water.
[b] Electrolyte B–1% ammonium sulfate, 1% citric acid in water.
[c] Electrolyte C–20% phosphoric acid in water.
[d] Electrolyte D–5% sulfuric acid, 0.01% potassium thiocyanate in water.

amount of $\gamma'$ reported for a particular alloy is valid only for the specific specimen tested and is affected by exact chemical composition and thermal history of the alloy.

Experimental parameters for the separation of $\gamma'$ in an electrolyte consisting of an aqueous solution containing 1 percent ammonium sulfate and 1 percent citric (or tartaric) acid are similar to those used for the separation of carbides and TCP phases in 10 percent $HCl$-$CH_3OH$ with the following exceptions: current density is maintained at 10 to 80 mA/cm$^2$, the potential of the anode is 1.1 to 1.4 V versus a saturated calomel electrode, and time of electrolysis is usually limited to 3 to 4 h. The major portion of the $\gamma'$ is retained on the surface of the specimen in a rather compact form and frequently cannot be completely removed with a rubber policeman. A satisfactory procedure for quantitative removal of adhering $\gamma'$ from the undissolved specimen is to briefly rinse the specimen with water, dry it under a heat lamp, and remove most of the $\gamma'$ from the specimen using a scalpel. The removed material plus any solids in the electrolyte are reserved for analysis. The last traces of particularly adherent $\gamma'$ are removed from the specimen with a wire brush before reweighing to determine the amount of specimen dissolved.

Matrix contamination is not a problem for the alloys investigated; however, carbides do separate with the $\gamma'$, and this must be taken into consideration in any analysis of the separated $\gamma'$. The separation of $\gamma'$ from specimens containing significant concentrations of TCP phases presents a particular problem. There does not appear to be appreciable contamination of the extracted

$\gamma'$ by TCP phases; however, recovery of $\gamma'$ is incomplete using the conventional procedure. The problem of quantitative recovery of $\gamma'$ from superalloys containing appreciable amounts of TCP phases has not been satisfactorily resolved, although work is continuing in this area by members of Task Group E-04.91.

The presence of chromium in the matrix of the alloy evidently has a significant effect on the polarizability (and, hence, the extractability) of $\gamma'$ [8]. Unpublished data on nickel-aluminum-molybdenum, nickel-aluminum-tungsten, and nickel-aluminum-columbium alloys show that it is not possible to quantitatively separate $\gamma'$ from these ternary systems using anodic dissolution at room temperature in a 1 percent ammonium sulfate, 1 percent citric (or tartaric) acid electrolyte. Two examples of this effect on low chromium alloys have also been noted [9]. Since most nickel-base superalloys contain appreciable amounts of chromium, $\gamma'$ can be separated from these alloys without difficulty. Recent work by members of Task Group E-04.91 indicated that separation of $\gamma'$ from NX-188 (Ni-18Mo-8Al) can be made in the 1 percent ammonium sulfate, 1 percent citric acid electrolyte provided the electrolytic cell is kept at a very low temperature (40°F). The adherence of $\gamma'$ to the specimen is extremely strong for NX-188 specimens and very rigorous scraping must be used to remove $\gamma'$ from the remaining specimen.

*Selective Dissolution of Phases Isolated by Anodic Dissolution*

Extensive studies have been made of techniques for the selective dissolution of phases isolated by anodic dissolution. While it is possible in many cases to individually separate various phases from complex superalloys by careful adjustment of electrolyte composition and electrode potentials, a more convenient technique is to separate TCP and carbide phases using a 10 percent HCl-CH$_3$OH electrolyte and then chemically separate the phases by selective dissolution. Lashko and coworkers [4] have assembled much information on the selective solubility of phases, and excerpts from this work are included in Table 2. It should be emphasized that the quantitative separation of a mixture of phases is significantly dependent upon the size, chemical composition, shape, and relative abundance of the phases. For example, the rate of dissolution of $\mu$ having a composition of Fe$_7$W$_6$ will differ significantly from that composed of Co$_7$W$_6$ or (Cr,Ni)$_7$(W,Mo)$_6$. A phase having a thin plate-like configuration with high surface area will be much more easily dissolved than the same phase in a more blocky shape. The data in Table 2 should be used only as a guide, and optimum experimental conditions should be determined for the specific phases found in the alloys analyzed.

**Analysis of Separated Phases**

Recently, there has been significant improvement in techniques for the quantitative analysis of small amounts of material. The development of the atomic absorption spectrophotometer has provided an instrument which can

TABLE 2—*Selective dissolution of phases from anodic deposits* (Ref 4).

| Phases Present | Reagents | Period of Heating | Insoluble Residue |
|---|---|---|---|
| CbC, VC, $M_{23}C_6$, $Fe_2$(W,Mo) | 20% HCl | 3 h | VC, CbC, $Fe_2$(W,Mo) |
| $Fe_2$Mo, TiC, TiN | 37%HCl+10% $H_2SO_4$ | 2 h | TiC, TiN |
| TiC, $TiB_2$, $Fe_2$Ti | 5 to 10% $H_2SO_4$ | 1 to 1½ h | TiC |
| $Ni_3$(Ti,Al), TiC, TiN, NiAl | 5% $H_2SO_4$ | 1 to 2 h | TiC, TiN |
| CbC, $Fe_2$Cb | 40% HF | ½ h | CbC |
| $Fe_2$W, σ | $HNO_3$ + oxalic + citric acid | ¼ to 1 h | σ |
| $Fe_2$W, CrN | HCl + $H_2O_2$ + $H_2O$ | 1 h | CrN |
| $M_6$C, $M_{23}C_6$, $Fe_2$(Mo,W) | HCl + $C_2H_5OH$ | 3 to 4 h | $M_6$C, $Fe_2$(Mo,W) |
| $Fe_2$W, σ | HCl + $C_2H_5OH$ | 1/3 h | $Fe_2$W |
| CbC, $M_{23}C_6$ | tartaric acid + $H_2O_2$ | 2 h at 50°C | $M_{23}C_6$ |
| $M_{23}C_6$, TiC, γ, σ | 5% $HgCl_2$ + 5% HCl | 2 h | $M_{23}C_6$, TiC |

be used to determine chromium, aluminum, molybdenum, cobalt, titanium, iron, and vanadium in a 50-mg specimen of extracted $\gamma'$ (plus carbides) with an accuracy of ±5 percent. Basic techniques are those which were reported for the determination of these elements in nickel-base alloys [10]. By using similar atomic absorption procedures to determine the composition of the matrix which has dissolved in the ammonium sulfate-citric (or tartaric) acid electrolyte, a material balance can be obtained which will aid in an evaluation of the reliability of the analytical results. Alternate procedures which may be used to accurately determine the composition of extracted phases are solution X-ray fluorescence techniques [11] and emission spectrographic methods utilizing the vacuum cup technique [12]. Columbium, tantalum, tungsten, and hafnium are not determined with great sensitivity by atomic absorption procedures; however, these metals are particularly applicable to determination by solution X-ray fluorescence or vacuum cup methods. The composition of the carbides contaminating the $\gamma'$ is determined (using spectrographic methods) on a separate portion of the specimen extracted with $HCl$-$CH_3OH$ and the composition of $\gamma'$ plus carbides corrected accordingly.

Sometimes there is insufficient material extracted to permit analysis by atomic absorption, vacuum cup, or solution X-ray fluorescence procedures. This is frequently the case for carbide and TCP extractions. In that case, less precise elemental analysis may be done using conventional spectrographic methods. The extracted material is ignited to form oxides, mixed with a specific ratio of lithium carbonate and graphite, excited by conventional arcing techniques, and compared with known oxide mixtures prepared in the same way. Average error of results obtained in this way is approximately 20 percent of the value reported.

Since two other papers at this symposium are devoted to a detailed study of X-ray diffraction procedures,[3] no extensive discussion of this technique will be offered at this time. However, it should be readily apparent that the quantitative separation of minor phases from the matrix and $\gamma'$ significantly increases the ease of detection of these minor crystalline materials by X-ray diffraction techniques. Combining precise chemical analysis of extracted phases with careful X-ray diffraction is an accurate technique for minor phase characterization in high temperature alloys.

## Application of Phase Separation to Metallurgical Studies

### Comparison and Interrelation with Other Analyses

The utilization of selective separation and specific dissolution techniques permits a more precise chemical analysis of a particular phase than that possible using an electron microprobe. The size of very small particles prevents their analysis by the electron microprobe, in addition to which, the accuracy

[3] See pp. 4 and 23.

of chemical analyses of major phases (where 50 mg or more of material is separated) is considerably better than that possible with a microprobe.

X-ray diffraction results are certainly more reliable when contaminating phases are separated from the specimen to be analyzed. This is particularly valuable for the determination of trace constituents. In a study of X-ray diffraction of $\gamma'$ separated by anodic dissolution in an electrolyte consisting of 1 percent ammonium sulfate and 1 percent citric (or tartaric) acid it was noted there was a significant difference in the intensity of superlattice lines [13]. A careful chemical analysis of the extracted $\gamma'$ demonstrated the effect of alloying elements on the intensity of superlattice lines. Selected values are given in Table 3 and show the relationship between the empirical formula of the $\gamma'$ (based on analyzed composition), thermal history of the alloy, and the intensity of the superlattice lines. Such studies are an aid to an understanding of substitution mechanisms in phases of complex alloys.

It should be stressed that the optimum use of phase separation for the characterization of superalloys is not as a tool by itself but, in conjunction with a variety of techniques such as electron microscopy, scanning electron microscopy, and optical metallography which provide information on the distribution of phases within an alloy. It is important that all available techniques be utilized to obtain the best possible determination of the phase distribution and phase composition in complex systems.

*Alloy Phase Equilibria*

One application in which phase separation is particularly valuable is in a study of alloy phase equilibria. Information relating the affect of the chemical composition of an alloy to the amount and composition of the phases is valuable in predicting the properties of experimental alloys. Because $\gamma$ and $\gamma'$ constitute the major phases of nickel-base superalloys, it is especially important to accurately measure their composition and quantity. Analytical schemes such as that assumed when employing PHACOMP [13] have been used with some success to predict deleterious phases; however, approximations have been made concerning the composition of $\gamma$ and $\gamma'$ which are not precisely correct. By experimentally determining the compositions and quantities of the major phases, prediction schemes of increased accuracy can be developed [9].

Using the procedures detailed earlier, $\gamma'$ was quantitatively extracted from 15 typical high temperature nickel-base alloys [7]. The composition of $\gamma'$ is given in Table 4. It should be emphasized that there will be a variation in the amount and composition of the $\gamma'$ as a function of the melt chemistry and the thermal history of the specimen examined; however, results given in Table 4 are typical of those found in other heats of the same alloys. In a similar manner the compositions of the $\gamma$ phase in the same specimens were determined and are shown in Table 5. The partitioning of elements between the $\gamma$ and $\gamma'$ phases is given in Table 6. While there is significant variation in the distribution of elements in various alloys, certain trends are observed. It is evident that aluminum and titanium are not completely present as $\gamma'$, but a

TABLE 3—Superlattice line intensity of gamma prime extracted from various alloys (Ref 13).

| Alloy | Thermal History | Empirical Formula for $\gamma'$ | $I_{(100)}/I_{(200)}$ |
|---|---|---|---|
| B-1900 | as-cast | $Ni_{2.76}Co_{0.24}Cr_{0.09}(Al_{0.73}Ti_{0.07}Mo_{0.089}Ta_{0.073}Cr_{0.04})$ | 0.041 |
|  | 1230°C/4 h + 870°C/100 h | $Ni_{2.61}Co_{0.31}Cr_{0.08}(Al_{0.69}Ti_{0.07}Mo_{0.114}Ta_{0.072}Cr_{0.05})$ | 0.029 |
| Mar-M200 | as-cast | $Ni_{2.69}Co_{0.26}Cr_{0.05}(Al_{0.64}Ti_{0.13}Cb_{0.028}W_{0.136}Cr_{0.07})$ | 0.017 |
|  | 1230°C/4 h + 870°C/100 h | $Ni_{2.68}Co_{0.25}Cr_{0.07}(Al_{0.67}Ti_{0.12}Cb_{0.020}W_{0.151}Cr_{0.04})$ | 0.014 |
| Nicrotung | as-cast | $Ni_{2.75}Co_{0.22}Cr_{0.03}(Al_{0.54}Ti_{0.28}W_{0.083}Cr_{0.10})$ | 0.042 |
|  | 1230°C/100 h + 870°C/100 h | $Ni_{2.80}Co_{0.20}(Al_{0.53}Ti_{0.27}W_{0.088}Cr_{0.11})$ | 0.032 |
| Udimet 700 | as-cast | $Ni_{2.67}Co_{0.27}Cr_{0.06}(Al_{0.58}Ti_{0.29}Mo_{0.047}Cr_{0.08})$ | 0.092 |
|  | 1230°C/100 h + 870°C/100 h | $Ni_{2.52}Co_{0.38}Cr_{0.10}(Al_{0.63}Ti_{0.27}Mo_{0.043}Cr_{0.06})$ | 0.078 |

TABLE 4–Composition of gamma prime in nickel-base alloys (Ref 7).

| Alloy | w/o[a] Ni | w/o Cr | w/o Co | w/o Al | w/o W | w/o Mo | w/o Ti | w/o Cb | w/o V | w/o Fe | w/o Ta |
|---|---|---|---|---|---|---|---|---|---|---|---|
| B-1900 | 71.2 | 2.8 | 6.1 | 8.3 | ... | 3.9 | 1.6 | ... | ... | ... | 6.1 |
| GMR 235 | 78.7 | 2.3 | ... | 9.0 | ... | 2.6 | 4.6 | ... | ... | 2.8 | ... |
| Inconel 700 | 67.7 | 4.1 | 13.0 | 6.8 | ... | 2.2 | 6.0 | ... | ... | 0.2 | ... |
| Inconel 713C | 80.4 | 3.4 | ... | 9.7 | ... | 2.7 | 1.2 | 2.6 | ... | ... | ... |
| Inconel X-750 | 77.0 | 2.1 | ... | 3.3 | ... | ... | 11.0 | 4.7 | ... | 1.9 | ... |
| IN 100 | 68.6 | 3.3 | 10.7 | 7.1 | ... | 1.3 | 7.7 | ... | 1.3 | ... | ... |
| Mar-M200 | 65.8 | 2.7 | 7.5 | 6.8 | 12.5 | ... | 3.0 | 1.7 | ... | ... | ... |
| Nicrotung | 69.1 | 3.1 | 6.6 | 7.2 | 7.5 | 1.1 | 6.5 | ... | ... | ... | ... |
| Nimonic 115 | 72.0 | 4.0 | 8.4 | 8.0 | ... | 2.3 | 6.5 | ... | ... | ... | ... |
| René 41 | 77.9 | 3.3 | 2.5 | 4.5 | ... | ... | 9.5 | ... | ... | ... | ... |
| TRW 1900 | 69.6 | 3.6 | 6.8 | 8.3 | 8.5 | ... | 1.2 | 2.0 | ... | ... | ... |
| Udimet 500 | 75.6 | 2.8 | 6.0 | 6.8 | ... | 1.8 | 7.0 | ... | ... | ... | ... |
| Udimet 700 | 72.8 | 2.6 | 8.8 | 7.0 | ... | 1.6 | 7.2 | ... | ... | ... | ... |
| Unitemp AF 1753 | 72.1 | 1.2 | 2.9 | 5.6 | 5.9 | 0.5 | 9.9 | ... | ... | 1.9 | ... |
| Waspaloy | 77.8 | 2.3 | 3.0 | 4.7 | ... | 1.2 | 11.0 | ... | ... | ... | ... |

[a] w/o = wt.%

TABLE 5 – *Composition of gamma in nickel-base alloys* (Ref 7).

| Alloy | w/o[a] Ni | w/o Cr | w/o Co | w/o Al | w/o W | w/o Mo | w/o Ti | w/o Fe |
|---|---|---|---|---|---|---|---|---|
| B-1900 | 55.8 | 16.4 | 16.4 | 2.4 | ... | 9.0 | ... | ... |
| GMR 235 | 61.4 | 18.8 | ... | 1.8 | ... | 5.4 | 0.5 | 12.1 |
| Inconel 700 | 41.6 | 17.7 | 33.3 | 1.9 | ... | 4.0 | 0.8 | 0.7 |
| Inconel 713C | 66.8 | 22.6 | ... | 3.9 | ... | 6.6 | 0.1 | ... |
| Inconel X-750 | 74.9 | 16.3 | ... | 0.3 | ... | ... | 1.0 | 7.5 |
| IN 100 | 46.0 | 22.0 | 24.0 | 2.3 | ... | 5.3 | 0.4 | ... |
| Mar-M200 | 56.4 | 17.3 | 12.9 | 1.4 | 12.0 | ... | ... | ... |
| Nicrotung | 52.6 | 22.5 | 14.9 | 0.4 | 8.8 | ... | 0.8 | ... |
| Nimonic 115 | 47.5 | 24.4 | 20.5 | 2.2 | ... | 4.9 | 0.5 | ... |
| René 41 | 51.0 | 23.6 | 12.8 | 0.6 | ... | 11.4 | 0.6 | ... |
| TRW 1900 | 49.8 | 21.5 | 15.5 | 3.5 | 9.4 | ... | 0.3 | ... |
| Udimet 500 | 41.5 | 26.0 | 25.9 | 1.1 | ... | 5.0 | 0.5 | ... |
| Udimet 700 | 42.9 | 22.3 | 24.4 | 2.5 | ... | 6.6 | 1.3 | ... |
| Unitemp AF 1753 | 48.4 | 19.6 | 8.8 | 1.1 | 8.3 | 1.7 | 0.9 | 11.2 |
| Waspaloy | 54.7 | 22.5 | 16.4 | 0.5 | ... | 5.3 | 0.6 | ... |

[a] w/o = wt.%

TABLE 6—Partitioning of elements between gamma prime and gamma[a] (Ref 7).

| Alloy | Al | Ti | Cb | Co | Cr | Mo | W | V | Fe | Ta |
|---|---|---|---|---|---|---|---|---|---|---|
| B-1900 | 1:0.29 | 1:<0.05 | ... | 0.37:1 | 0.17:1 | 0.43:1 | ... | ... | ... | 1:<0.05 |
| GMR 235 | 1:0.20 | 1:0.11 | ... | ... | 0.12:1 | 0.48:1 | ... | ... | 0.23:1 | ... |
| Inconel 700 | 1:0.28 | 1:0.13 | ... | 0.39:1 | 0.23:1 | 0.55:1 | ... | ... | 0.29:1 | ... |
| Inconel 713C | 1:0.40 | 1:0.08 | 1:<0.05 | ... | 0.15:1 | 0.41:1 | ... | ... | ... | ... |
| Inconel X-750 | 1:0.09 | 1:0.09 | 1:<0.05 | ... | 0.13:1 | ... | ... | ... | 0.25:1 | ... |
| IN 100 | 1:0.32 | 1:0.05 | ... | 0.45:1 | 0.15:1 | 0.25:1 | ... | 1:<0.05 | ... | ... |
| Mar-M200 | 1:0.21 | 1:<0.05 | 1:<0.05 | 0.58:1 | 0.16:1 | ... | 1.04:1 | ... | ... | ... |
| Nicrotung | 1:0.06 | 1:0.12 | ... | 0.44:1 | 0.14:1 | ... | 0.85:1 | ... | ... | ... |
| Nimonic 115 | 1:0.27 | 1:0.08 | ... | 0.41:1 | 0.16:1 | 0.22:1 | ... | ... | ... | ... |
| René 41 | 1:0.13 | 1:0.06 | ... | 0.20:1 | 0.14:1 | 0.20:1 | ... | ... | ... | ... |
| TRW 1900 | 1:0.42 | 1:0.25 | 1:<0.05 | 0.44:1 | 0.17:1 | ... | 0.90:1 | ... | ... | ... |
| Udimet 500 | 1:0.16 | 1:0.07 | ... | 0.23:1 | 0.11:1 | 0.36:1 | ... | ... | ... | ... |
| Udimet 700 | 1:0.45 | 1:0.18 | ... | 0.36:1 | 0.12:1 | 0.24:1 | ... | ... | ... | ... |
| Unitemp AF 1753 | 1:0.20 | 1:0.09 | ... | 0.33:1 | 0.06:1 | 0.29:1 | 0.71:1 | ... | 0.17:1 | ... |
| Waspaloy | 1:0.11 | 1:0.05 | ... | 0.18:1 | 0.10:1 | 0.23:1 | ... | ... | ... | ... |

[a] Concentration of an element in the γ' compared to that in the γ.

significant fraction remains in the $\gamma$ phase. This is particularly important in alloy design where techniques for the formation of large amounts of the major hardening phase, $\gamma'$, are of special concern in the development of alloys with commercial potential. While general conclusions may be drawn (using data like that given in Tables 4, 5, and 6) with regard to the composition of phases in superalloys, the only way to truly determine the precise compositions of these phases is to extract them from specimens specifically of interest.

*Study of Thermal History Processes*

Another application of phase separation techniques is to the study of thermal history processes. In a recent program involving Udimet 700, the following relationships were measured: (1) effect of aging time at various temperatures on the volume fraction of $\gamma'$, (2) effect of aging time at 1800°F on the composition of the $\gamma'$ phase, and (3) composition of $\gamma'$ as a function of temperature after aging for 16 h [15]. Of particular interest was the determination of the volume fraction of $\gamma'$ as a function of temperatures between 1300 and 2070°F. These data are presented in Table 7. In obtaining these data, it is imperative that specimen quenching be extremely rapid to prevent the formation of fine $\gamma'$ on cooling.

TABLE 7 – *Volume fraction of $\gamma'$ in Udimet 700 as a function of temperature (Ref 15).*

| Deg F | Volume Fraction $\gamma'$ |
| --- | --- |
| 1300 | 37.4 |
| 1550 | 37.4 |
| 1600 | 37.6 |
| 1650 | 39.5 |
| 1700 | 37.2 |
| 1750 | 35.0 |
| 1800 | 33.2 |
| 1850 | 29.8 |
| 1900 | 26.0 |
| 1950 | 21.5 |
| 2000 | 13.6 |
| 2070 | 0 |

**Summary**

The separation of phases from superalloys is a powerful tool for the characterization of high temperature nickel-base alloys. Following their quantitative separation, the precise composition of the phases, as well as their abundance, may be determined using conventional analytical techniques. This information has proven useful in a study of phase equilibria, substitution mechanisms in phases, and in the design of new superalloys.

*Acknowledgment*

I wish to thank M.J. Donachie, Jr. for his careful reading of this paper and his constructive criticism. In addition, I wish to thank members of ASTM E-04.91 for their contributions to a knowledge of phase separation, both through experimental studies and, also, through many stimulating discussions.

## References

[1]   Lund, C.H. and Wagner, H.J., "Identification of Microconstituents in Super-alloys," DMIC Memorandum 160, 15 Nov. 1962.

[2]   *Determination of Nonmetallic Compounds in Steel, ASTM STP 393,* American Society for Testing and Materials, June 1965.

[3]   Donachie, M.J., Jr. and Kriege, O.H., *Journal of Materials,* Vol. 7, 1972, pp. 269-278.

[4]   Lashko, N.F., Zaslavskaya, L.V., Kozlova, M.N., Morozova, G.I., Sorokina, K.P., Khakhlova, N.V., and Yakovleva, Y.F., Physicochemical Phase Analysis Methods for Steels and Alloys, *Metallurgy Publishing House, Moscow, 1970. An English* Translation of Chapters 6 and 10 is available as Report JPRS 55369, 7 March 1972, and an English translation of Chapters 3, 7, 8, 12, and 16 is available as Report JPRS 56746, 11 Aug. 1972, Joint Publications Research Service, 1000 North Glebe Road, Arlington, Va.

[5]   Golubtsova, R.B., *Phase Analysis of Nickel Alloys,* Izd-vo Nauka, Moscow, 1969; translation FTD-MT-24-261-70, 4 Jan. 1971, U.S. Government Clearing House.

[6]   Kriege, O.H. and Sullivan, C.P., *Transactions of American Society for Metals,* Vol. 61, 1968, pp. 278-282.

[7]   Kriege, O.H. and Baris, J.M. *Transactions of American Society for Metals,* Vol. 62, 1969, pp. 195-200.

[8]   Feller, H.G. and Borggräffe, P., *Corrosion Science,* Vol. 8, 1968, pp. 41-47.

[9]   Dreshfield, R.L. and Wallace, J.F., *Metallurgical Transactions,* Vol. 5, 1974, pp. 71-78.

[10]  Welcher, G.G. and Kriege, O.H., *Atomic Absorption Newsletter,* Vol. 8, 1969, pp. 97-101.

[11]  Bertin, E.P. in *Advances in X-ray Analysis,* Plenum Press, New York, 1968, Vol. 11, pp. 1-22.

[12]  Leao, E.C., Hobart, E.W., and Fornwalt, D.E., *Applied Spectroscopy,* Vol. 20, 1966, pp. 400-403.

[13]  Karg, A.V., Fornwalt, D.E., and Kriege, O.H., *Journal of the Institute of Metals,* Vol. 99, 1971, pp. 301-305.

[14]  Woodyatt, L.R., Sims, C.T., and Beattie, H.J., Jr., *Transactions of the American Institute of Mining, Metallurgical, and Petroleum Engineers,* Vol. 236, 1966, pp. 519-527.

[15]  Van Der Molen, E.H., Oblak, J.M., and Kriege, O.H., *Metallurgical Transactions,* Vol. 2, 1971, pp. 1627-1633.

Metallography, a practical tool for
    correlating the structure and
    properties of materials : a symposium
    presented at the seventy-sixth annual
    meeting, American Society for Testing
    and Materials, Philadelphia, Pa., 25-
    26 June 1973 / Halle Abrams and G. N.
    Maniar, symposium cochairmen ;
    [Committee E-4 on Metallography
    sponsored the symposium]. --
    Philadelphia : The Society, 1974.
        234 p. : ill. ; 24 cm. -- (ASTM
    special technical publication ; 557)
        Includes bibliographies.
        ISBN 0-455-70002-8

(Cont. on next card)